D0597172

Theories of Electrons in Molecules

WILLIAM T. SIMPSON

Professor of Chemistry
University of Washington

PRENTICE-HALL, INC.

Theories of Electrons in Molecules

Englewood Cliffs, New Jersey, 1962

PRENTICE-HALL INTERNATIONAL
London · Tokyo · Sydney · Paris
PRENTICE-HALL OF CANADA, LTD.
PRENTICE-HALL DE MÉXICO, S.A.

PRENTICE-HALL INTERNATIONAL SERIES IN CHEMISTRY

Simpson, **Theories of Electrons in Molecules**

Printed in the United States of America. Library of Congress Catalog Card No.: 62-19680

91318-C

Preface

This book is intended to fill in the gap between what is found in quantum chemistry books and what is found in the journals. There is an introductory chapter, mainly on atoms, then three chapters on molecular problems. Of the three, two deal with the time-honored molecular orbital and valence bond methods, and the last with the independent systems approach for molecular crystals and weakly interacting parts of a single molecule.

The ligand field theory is only touched on, because the coverage is quite frankly along the lines of the author's research interests. If the scope is thus narrowed, perhaps a compensating feature is a sort of cohesiveness and continuity between the parts of the book. At least, this is the plan. As to the level of the treatment, the aim is more in the direction of rigor than of intuitive understanding. Among other things, it is hoped that this approach may help to bring research in theoretical solid state physics and molecular electronic quantum mechanics into a little better relationship.

Although the bracket notation can be downright repugnant, it is used liberally here because it is part of the apparatus of transformation theory—which in turn is vital for quantum mechanical insight.

I especially want to thank my wife Dr. Carmen Tschudi Simpson for reading, with me, the entire manuscript, and for helping in many other ways. Then, I would like to thank my graduate students and post-doctorates for their help in finding mistakes, and for their suggestions. Thanks are also due my quantum mechanics students at the University of Washington, and participants in the lecture series at the University of California on the valence bond method, all of whom suffered exposure to earlier versions.

Thanks go to Mrs. Marilyn Hornbeck, who typed a part of the book, and to Mrs. Susan Johnston, who typed indefatigably and otherwise shepherded the project through. I am truly glad to acknowledge contractual support from the Air Force Office of Scientific Research.

Finally, I want to thank my colleagues and teachers (including those not known to me personally, whose books are in my library). Particular thanks here are due my teacher and research supervisor for the Ph.D., Dr. Kenneth S. Pitzer.

WILLIAM T. SIMPSON

Contents

2

The Molecular Orbital Method

3

The Valence Bond Method

4

The Independent Systems Approach

Index

CHAPTER 1

Introduction: Atoms

The Hamiltonian for a system of light and heavy particles has kinetic and potential energy terms referring to both kinds of particles, and interaction terms. We shall assume that the systems being considered have low nuclear charges so that magnetic* and relativistic† terms may be reserved as being the ultimate perturbations (LS-coupling), with the consequence that the first Hamiltonian has only the coulombic interactions. The eigenvalues and eigenfunctions of this Hamiltonian may usually be calculated using the Born-Oppenheimer approximation (see Appendix); that is, provided that the electronic

* See, for example, D. S. McClure, *J. Chem. Phys.*, **20** (1952), 682; M. Karplus, *Revs. Mod. Phys.*, **32** (1960), 455.

† A. Fröman, *Revs. Mod. Phys.*, **32** (1960), 317.

state differences turn out to be bigger than the vibrational increments. The many-electron Hamiltonian is then

$$H = \sum \left[T_\nu + e^2 \left(-\frac{Z_i}{r_{\nu i}} + \frac{Z_i Z_j}{r_{ij}} + \frac{1}{r_{\mu\nu}} \right) \right]$$

where T is the kinetic energy of the electrons, the Greek subscripts refer to electrons and the ordinary subscripts to atomic nuclei. Our first aim is a general orientation, starting with a treatment of single atoms.* Since an atom has only one nucleus, we can leave out the corresponding subscripts. In the course of the work with atoms, a bracket notation will be gradually introduced.

1.1 CLOSED-SHELL MATRIX ELEMENTS

The various approximate methods that have proved to be valuable have in common the use of matrix elements over the many-electron Hamiltonian. We shall therefore review the computation of two representative types of matrix elements, restricting ourselves at this stage to the simple case of a wave function that is a single Slater determinant involving orbitals, each doubly filled. Moreover, it will be convenient to consider an example: four electrons in two orbitals, though the treatment may be easily generalized for any closed-shell† configuration.

The spinorbitals will be named in various ways

$$|a\ \nu)\ |\ \alpha\ \nu) \equiv |a\alpha\nu) \equiv a\alpha_\nu \equiv a_\nu\ \alpha_\nu$$

where a is an orbital designation, α the spin label, and ν the electron number. The Slater determinant corresponding to the configuration $a^2\ b^2$ may thus be written‡

$$|\psi\rangle = \frac{1}{\sqrt{4!}} \begin{vmatrix} a\alpha_1 & a\beta_1 & b\alpha_1 & b\beta_1 \\ a\alpha_2 & a\beta_2 & b\alpha_2 & b\beta_2 \\ a\alpha_3 & a\beta_3 & b\alpha_3 & b\beta_3 \\ a\alpha_4 & a\beta_4 & b\alpha_4 & b\beta_4 \end{vmatrix}$$

$$= \frac{1}{\sqrt{4!}} \sum_P (-1)^P\, P\, a\alpha_1\, a\beta_2\, b\alpha_3\, b\beta_4$$

where P is an operator which permutes the electron coordinate labels, the numbers.

* For a comprehensive and authoritative treatment see J. C. Slater, *Quantum Theory of Atomic Structure*, Vols. I and II (New York: McGraw-Hill Book Company, Inc., 1960–1961).

† *Closed-shell* means doubly filled orbitals and the absence of spatial degeneracy.

‡ We use new Dirac brackets for many-electron functions.

The first and simpler representative type of matrix element involves a sum of operators each referring to a single electron (for example the many-electron Hamiltonian without the interelectronic interaction). For the time being, we shall consider the one-electron operator not a function of spin variables

$$U \equiv \sum_{\nu=1}^{4} U_\nu \equiv U_1 + U_2 + U_3 + U_4$$

and calculate the matrix element

$$\int \psi \sum_{\nu=1}^{4} U_\nu \psi \, d\tau \equiv \langle \psi \mid U \mid \psi \rangle$$

This is

$$\frac{1}{4!} \int \sum_P (-1)^P P \, a\alpha_1 \, a\beta_2 \, b\alpha_3 \, b\beta_4 \sum_{\nu=1}^{4} U_\nu \sum_P (-1)^P P \, a\alpha_1 \, a\beta_2 \, b\alpha_3 \, b\beta_4 \, d\tau$$

which simplifies to

$$4! \left[\frac{1}{4!} \int a\alpha_1 \, a\beta_2 \, b\alpha_3 \, b\beta_4 \sum_{\nu=1}^{4} U_\nu \sum_P (-1)^P P \, a\alpha_1 \, a\beta_2 \, b\alpha_3 \, b\beta_4 \, d\tau \right]$$

where on the left only the leading term of the determinant is used. The reason is that any complete integral based on another term on the left turns out to be precisely the same, all sign changes brought in by a permutation occurring in pairs. (Note that the nature of the operator U is not relevant here.) It remains to consider each of the 24 terms coming from the expansion of the determinant on the right. The first of these terms gives

$$\begin{aligned} \int a\alpha_1 \, a\beta_2 \, b\alpha_3 \, b\beta_4 \\ [U_1 + U_2 + U_3 + U_4] \, a\alpha_1 \, a\beta_2 \, b\alpha_3 \, b\beta_4 d\tau_1 \, d\tau_2 \, d\tau_3 \, d\tau_4 \\ = 2(a\nu \mid U_\nu \mid a\nu) + 2(b\nu \mid U_\nu \mid b\nu) \end{aligned} \tag{1.1}$$

where, for example,

$$\begin{aligned} (a\nu \mid U_\nu \mid a\nu) &= \int a\alpha_\nu \, U_\nu \, a\alpha_\nu \, d\tau_\nu \\ &= \int a_\nu \, U_\nu \, a_\nu \, dx_\nu \, dy_\nu \, dz_\nu \end{aligned}$$

(integration over the spin gives unity).

None of the remaining 23 terms makes a contribution, because of the spin orthogonality and an assumed orbital orthogonality

$$\int a_\nu \, b_\nu \, dx_\nu \, dy_\nu \, dz_\nu = 0$$

Consider for example, an integral in which electron numbers have changed but so as to prevent spin orthogonality from appearing (electrons one and three for example)

$$-\int a\alpha_1\, a\beta_2\, b\alpha_3\, b\beta_4\, [U_1 + U_2 + U_3 + U_4]\, a\alpha_3\, a\beta_2\, b\alpha_1\, b\beta_4\, d\tau$$

This integral has four parts; the first over U for electron one is zero

$$\int a\alpha_1\, a\beta_2\, b\alpha_3\, b\beta_4\, U_1\, a\alpha_3\, a\beta_2\, b\alpha_1\, b\beta_4\, d\tau_1\, d\tau_2\, d\tau_3\, d\tau_4 = 0$$

because of the orbital orthogonality in the integration over $d\tau_3$. A similar result occurs in the U_3 part after integration over $d\tau_1$, and emphatically for U_2 and U_4.

The final result for the diagonal matrix element of a one-electron operator for a closed-shell configuration is the sum of the one-electron matrix elements—in the present case, the result Eq. (1.1) for the leading term on the right

$$\langle\psi \mid U \mid \psi\rangle = 2(a\nu \mid U_\nu \mid a\nu) + 2(b\nu \mid U_\nu \mid b\nu) \tag{1.2}$$

The second representative type of matrix element involves a two-electron operator, for example, the interelectronic interaction. We shall use Q for such an operator, which, for four electrons, is

$$Q \equiv \sum_{\mu<\nu} Q_{\mu\nu} = Q_{12} + Q_{13} + Q_{14} + Q_{23} + Q_{24} + Q_{34}$$

The matrix element is $\langle\psi \mid Q \mid \psi\rangle$ which immediately simplifies to

$$\int a\alpha_1\, a\beta_2\, b\alpha_3\, b\beta_4 \sum_{\mu<\nu} Q_{\mu\nu} \sum_P (-1)^P P\, a\alpha_1\, a\beta_2\, b\alpha_3\, b\beta_4\, d\tau$$

In this case, the leading term of the determinant on the right contributes most but not all of the terms

$$\begin{aligned}\int a\alpha_1\, a\beta_2\, b\alpha_3\, b\beta_4 \\ (Q_{12} + Q_{13} + Q_{14} + Q_{23} + Q_{24} + Q_{34})\, a\alpha_1\, a\beta_2\, b\alpha_3\, b\beta_4\, d\tau_1\, d\tau_2\, d\tau_3\, d\tau_4 \\ = (a\mu \mid (a\nu \mid Q_{\mu\nu} \mid a\mu) \mid a\nu) + 4(a\mu \mid (b\nu \mid Q_{\mu\nu} \mid a\mu) \mid b\nu) \\ + (b\mu \mid (b\nu \mid Q_{\mu\nu} \mid b\mu) \mid b\nu)\end{aligned} \tag{1.3}$$

where*

$$(i\mu \mid (j\nu \mid Q_{\mu\nu} \mid k\mu) \mid l\nu) = \int i_\mu\, j_\nu\, Q_{\mu\nu}\, k_\mu\, l_\nu\, d\tau_\mu\, d\tau_\nu$$

Additional non-vanishing terms are the integrals between electrons having the same spin, that is, 1 and 3 and 2 and 4. One finds a contribution from, for example,

* Here we use $d\tau_\mu$ for $dx_\mu\, dy_\mu\, dz_\mu$, without the spin "volume element."

$$- \int a\alpha_1\, a\beta_2\, b\alpha_3\, b\beta_4\, Q_{13}\, a\alpha_3\, a\beta_2\, b\alpha_1\, b\beta_4\, d\tau$$
$$= - \int a_1\, b_3\, Q_{13}\, a_3\, b_1\, d\tau_1\, d\tau_3$$
$$= - (a\mu \mid (b\nu \mid Q_{\mu\nu} \mid b\mu) \mid a\nu)$$

These integrals are different from the ones brought in by the leading term of the determinant and are the exchange integrals.

Multiple exchanges give no contribution because of the orbital orthogonality, and of course, exchanges following which a single electron has a mixed spin give no contribution. The net effect of considering all terms other than the leading one is to bring in only single exchanges between electrons having the same spin, in the present example the 1-3 and 2-4 exchanges, giving

$$-2(a\mu \mid (b\nu \mid Q_{\mu\nu} \mid b\mu \mid a\nu)$$

All together, the matrix element for the two-electron operator is

$$\langle \psi \mid Q \mid \psi \rangle = (a\mu \mid (a\nu \mid Q_{\mu\nu} \mid a\mu) \mid a\nu) + 4(a\mu \mid (b\nu \mid Q_{\mu\nu} \mid a\mu) \mid b\nu) + (b\mu \mid (b\nu \mid Q_{\mu\nu} \mid b\mu) \mid b\nu) - 2(a\mu \mid (b\nu \mid Q_{\mu\nu} \mid b\mu) \mid a\nu) \qquad (1.4)$$

We next use the formulas for matrix elements of one- and two-electron operators in connection with the problem of selecting the shapes of the orbitals a and b so as to be optimal.

1.2 BEST CLOSED-SHELL FUNCTION*

The expectation value of the many-electron Hamiltonian is a minimum with respect to arbitrary (subject to the antisymmetry requirement) variations in the function when the function is the true first eigenfunction. Even with present-day high-speed computing techniques, it is not usually feasible to work with the most general antisymmetric many-electron function. Accordingly, it becomes a matter of interest to find conditional minima and hence best functions in a restricted sense, but with the compensating feature of simplicity. Because of the ease with which one can think about orbitals and products of orbitals, and for historical reasons, the single closed-shell Slater determinant occupies a preeminent position in this regard.

We shall now study the selection of a best Slater determinant. The one-electron functions (orbitals), which are such a key part, were at one time taken as eigenfunctions of a νth part of an unperturbed Hamiltonian

* D. Hartree, *The Calculation of Atomic Structures* (New York: John Wiley & Sons, Inc., 1957).

$$\sum_{\nu} \left(T_\nu - \frac{Z}{r_\nu} \right)$$

obtained from the full Hamiltonian by leaving out the interelectronic interaction (here we put $e^2 = 1$). This proves to be too narrow an approach, but the idea of defining the orbitals by means of a one-electron eigenvalue equation will be retained. In preparation for this, the full Hamiltonian is partitioned so as to contain an unperturbed part which is a sum of one-electron operators, that is,

$$H = H^0 + V \tag{1.5a}$$

where

$$H^0 = \sum_{\nu} (T_\nu + U_\nu) \tag{1.5b}$$

In consequence, the perturbation becomes

$$V = \sum_{\nu} \left(-\frac{Z}{r_\nu} - U_\nu \right) + \sum_{\mu<\nu} \frac{1}{r_{\mu\nu}} \tag{1.5c}$$

The one-electron operator, U_ν, has the attraction part, and in some average way brings in the interaction with all the other electrons. At this stage, however, we leave the form of U_ν unspecified.

Our strategy for selecting the best Slater determinant is to begin by passing over the notion of minimizing the energy expectation value and taking up what turns out to be a related problem—the choice of U_ν so as to make the first-order perturbation vanish

$$\langle \psi \mid V \mid \psi \rangle = 0$$

At first sight, even this looks questionable, because V contains both a one-electron operator and a two-electron operator. We shall find, however, that it is possible to make $\langle \psi \mid V \mid \psi \rangle$ vanish for any well-behaved orbital functions, so that for any choice of orbitals, a U_ν is determined. In spite of this not particularly deterministic result, we shall then quickly be able to find the best Slater determinant (to do so will bring us back to the one-electron eigenvalue equation).

Now we go on to calculate an expression for U_ν which makes $\langle \psi \mid V \mid \psi \rangle$ vanish, given certain orbitals. We shall abbreviate

$$-\frac{Z}{r_\nu} - U_\nu = -X_\nu \tag{1.6}$$

in which case, the vanishing of the perturbation implies, Eq. (1.5c)

$$\langle \psi \mid \sum_{\nu} X_\nu \mid \psi \rangle = \langle \psi \mid \sum_{\mu<\nu} \frac{1}{r_{\mu\nu}} \mid \psi \rangle \tag{1.7}$$

We shall continue to use four electrons in the two orbitals, a and b, as an example. The above relation, in consideration of our study of one- and two-electron operators, Eq. (1.2) and Eq (1.4), then becomes

$$\begin{aligned}2(a\nu \mid X_\nu \mid a\nu) &+ 2(b\nu \mid X_\nu \mid b\nu)\\ &= (a\mu \mid (a\nu \mid \frac{1}{r_{\mu\nu}} \mid a\mu) \mid a\nu) + (b\mu \mid (b\nu \mid \frac{1}{r_{\mu\nu}} \mid b\mu) \mid b\nu) \\ &+ 4\,(a\mu \mid (b\nu \mid \frac{1}{r_{\mu\nu}} \mid a\mu) \mid b\nu) - 2\,(a\mu \mid (b\nu \mid \frac{1}{r_{\mu\nu}} \mid b\mu) \mid a\nu)\end{aligned} \tag{1.8}$$

We shall use a general (non-diagonal) form for the operator X_ν and shall then be able to satisfy this relation. With such a general form for X_ν the left-hand side becomes

$$2 \int_{dr'} a(r') \int_{dr} X(r'r)\, a(r) + 2 \int_{dr'} b(r') \int_{dr} X(r'r)\, b(r)$$

where r and r' refer to points in different three-dimensional spaces, and $dr = dx\,dy\,dz$, $dr' = dx'\,dy'\,dz'$. It is helpful to regard these expressions as analogous to the matrix triple product: row vector $\times$ square matrix $\times$ column vector, and it is for this reason that the definite integrals are written with the variable of integration appearing as a dummy index in a summation.

We shall be almost successful in having $\langle \psi \mid V \mid \psi \rangle$ vanish if we use for X_ν an integral

$$X^{(1)}\,(r'r) = \int_{dr''} \frac{\delta(r' - r)}{|r'' - r'|} [a^2\,(r'') + b^2\,(r'')] \tag{1.9}$$

The δ function makes $X^{(1)}$ a diagonal operator. The first part of the matrix element over orbital a

$$\int_{dr'} a(r') \int_{dr} \int_{dr''} \frac{\delta(r' - r)}{|r'' - r'|}\, a^2\,(r'')\, a(r)$$

is computed by integrating over dr before integrating over dr'', giving

$$\int_{dr'} a(r') \int_{dr''} \frac{a^2\,(r'')\, a(r')}{|r'' - r'|} = (a\mu \mid (a\nu \mid \frac{1}{r_{\mu\nu}} \mid a\mu) \mid a\nu)$$

Similarly, the second part

$$\int_{dr'} a(r') \int_{dr} \int_{dr''} \frac{\delta(r' - r)}{|r'' - r'|}\, b^2\,(r'')\, a(r)$$

becomes

$$(a\mu \mid (b\nu \mid \frac{1}{r_{\mu\nu}} \mid a\mu) \mid b\nu)$$

The b matrix element is calculated in the same way, giving for the full matrix element of $X^{(1)}$ over $|\psi\rangle$

$$2(a\nu \mid X^{(1)} \mid a\nu) + 2(b\nu \mid X^{(1)} \mid b\nu)$$

$$= 2\,(a\mu \mid (a\nu \mid \frac{1}{r_{\mu\nu}} \mid a\mu) \mid a\nu) + 4\,(a\mu \mid (b\nu \mid \frac{1}{r_{\mu\nu}} \mid a\mu) \mid b\nu)$$

$$+ 2\,(b\mu \mid (b\nu \mid \frac{1}{r_{\mu\nu}} \mid b\mu) \mid b\nu)$$

This result has the interaction of an electron with all the others as well as itself and fails to reflect a diminution in repulsion brought about by using an antisymmetric function. Fortunately, the faults can be simultaneously corrected—by the addition of a non-diagonal operator

$$X^{(2)}\,(r'r) = -\frac{1}{2\mid r' - r\mid}\,[a(r')\,a(r) + b(r')\,b(r)] \qquad (1.10)$$

as we shall now see. Again starting with the a expectation value, we find

$$-\frac{1}{2}\Big[\int_{dr'} a(r') \int_{dr} a(r')\,\frac{1}{|r' - r|}\,a(r)\,a(r)$$

$$+ \int_{dr'} a(r') \int_{dr} b(r')\,\frac{1}{|r' - r|}\,b(r)\,a(r)\Big]$$

$$= -\frac{1}{2}\,(a\mu \mid (a\nu \mid \frac{1}{r_{\mu\nu}} \mid a\mu) \mid a\nu) - \frac{1}{2}\,(a\mu \mid (b\nu \mid \frac{1}{r_{\mu\nu}} \mid b\mu) \mid a\nu)$$

Bringing in the b part gives us all together

$$2(a\nu \mid X_\nu^{(2)} \mid a\nu) + 2(b\nu \mid X_\nu^{(2)} \mid b\nu)$$

$$= -\,(a\mu \mid (a\nu \mid \frac{1}{r_{\mu\nu}} \mid a\mu) \mid a\nu) - (b\mu \mid (b\nu \mid \frac{1}{r_{\mu\nu}} \mid b\mu) \mid b\nu)$$

$$- 2\,(a\mu \mid (b\nu \mid \frac{1}{r_{\mu\nu}} \mid b\mu) \mid a\nu)$$

Finally, therefore, putting

$$X = X^{(1)} + X^{(2)}$$

we duplicate the result Eq. (1.4) for the matrix element

$$\langle\psi \mid \sum \frac{1}{r_{\mu\nu}} \mid \psi\rangle$$

which was required by Eq. (1.7). We have satisfied Eq. (1.8), showing that indeed

$$\langle\psi \mid V \mid \psi\rangle = 0 \qquad (1.11)$$

with a suitable choice for X_ν and hence, by Eq. (1.6), for U_ν in the unperturbed part. All of this satisfies the tenets of perturbation theory in that not only is the resulting perturbation in a sense small, but the unperturbed part is "simple" (a sum of identical one-electron parts). The one-electron effective potential in Eq. (1.5) is Eq. (1.6), Eq. (1.9), Eq. (1.10)

$$U_\nu = U(r'r) = \frac{\delta(r' - r)Z}{r} + \int_{dr''} \frac{\delta(r' - r)}{|r'' - r'|} [a^2(r'') + b^2(r'')]$$
$$- \frac{1}{2 \mid r' - r \mid} [a(r')\, a(r) + b(r')\, b(r)] \tag{1.12}$$

Strangely enough, this gives $\langle \psi \mid V \mid \psi \rangle = 0$ for any well-behaved a and b.

We are now in a position to find the best Slater determinant. If we wish to minimize the variational integral with respect to variations in the orbitals,

$$\delta\langle \psi \mid H \mid \psi \rangle = 0 \tag{1.13}$$

we have only to minimize the integral over the unperturbed part, because the variations in a and b are accompanied by a continuously changing partition Eq. (1.5) of H into H^0 and V such that at all times

$$\langle \psi \mid V \mid \psi \rangle = \text{const}$$

(in fact, const = 0) whence also

$$\delta\langle \psi \mid V \mid \psi \rangle = 0 \tag{1.13a}$$

We now need only ask how to find an a and b which minimize the expectation value of H^0. In the case of just one independent variable, it is well known that the application of the calculus of variations to the variational integral leads to the condition on a wave function that it be an eigenfunction of H. In the present case, the many-electron function will be an eigenfunction of H^0 if it is a product of orbitals, each an eigenfunction of one of the independent (equal) parts of H^0. If

$$(T_\nu + U_\nu)a_\nu = \lambda_a\, a_\nu$$
$$(T_\nu + U_\nu)b_\nu = \lambda_b\, b_\nu$$

then any one of the spinless functions

$$Pa_1\, a_2\, b_3\, b_4$$

(where P is a coordinate permutation) will be an eigenfunction belonging to the eigenvalue $2\lambda_a + 2\lambda_b$. Moreover, any linear combination of these four-electron functions will also be an eigenfunction.

This leads us to conclude that our original Slater determinant will satisfy Eq. (1.13)

$$\delta\langle\psi \mid H^0 \mid \psi\rangle = \delta\langle\psi \mid H \mid \psi\rangle = 0$$

if its constituent orbitals are eigenfunctions of the one-electron Hamiltonian $T_\nu + U_\nu$.

For the actual computation of a and b, one must use a stepwise process, because a and b occur in U. Thus one assumes trial orbitals $a^{(1)}$ and $b^{(1)}$ leading to a trial Hamiltonian, $(T_\nu + U_\nu)^{(1)}$. The eigenfunctions of this Hamiltonian are called $a^{(2)}$ and $b^{(2)}$ and lead to a new U_ν, $U_\nu^{(2)}$. The process is repeated until the output orbitals agree as closely as desired with the input orbitals, at which point the Slater determinant can be constructed if desired. The expectation value of the energy throughout the process is just the expectation value of the unperturbed part, H^0, which in turn is the sum of the orbital energies, $2\lambda_a + 2\lambda_b$. The final energy is the best value obtainable with a variation function that consists of a single Slater determinant.

The foregoing process is an adaptation of the Hartree-Fock method, which itself leads to the same result. The present scheme is not identical in form, however; a somewhat different partition of H having been used.* (In the conventional Hartree-Fock scheme the partition used gives a result such that the energy is not the sum of the λ's, but the λ's can be easily interpreted as ionization potentials.)†

The Hartree-Fock energies are accurate to within a per cent or so for atoms. For example, for helium the calculated energy is -2.862 a.u., whereas the observed energy is -2.9037 a.u. Again, for beryllium, calculated is -14.58 a.u. and observed is -14.67 a.u. In general, the discrepancy between calculated and observed may well be too much for the method to be really useful in chemistry (recall that one atomic unit is ~ 600 kcal/mole). In this circumstance, it is necessary to go to the second order in perturbation theory (or to use some equivalent procedure). If the calculation is to be carried beyond the Hartree-Fock stage there is no longer a strong reason for having the absolute best single Slater determinant. Thus it might prove satisfactory to base V on orbitals which are reasonable, if not optimal in the full Hartree-Fock sense, but retaining the condition Eq. (1.11)

$$\langle\psi \mid V \mid \psi\rangle = 0$$

* W. Tobocman, *Phys. Rev.*, **107** (1957), 203.

† See, for example, J. C. Slater, *Phys. Rev.*, **98** (1955), 1039.

1.3 SYSTEMATIC APPROACH

Whatever specific method is used for making accurate energy eigenvalue calculations, there is the fundamental problem of having available functions which span the space of well-behaved many-electron functions. The fundamental theorem in this connection says that one can construct a complete set of many-electron functions by using all possible products of one-electron functions. The situation is, of course, complicated by spin, but we shall see how this may be incorporated into the theorem. First, without spin, we have that given any complete set of orbitals: $|a)$, $|b)$, $|c)$, . . . we can span the space of ν-electron functions using all possible products

$$| a\zeta) \, | b\eta) \, | c\theta) \ldots | n\nu)$$

where every orbital is employed for electron ζ, and also for electron η, and so on.

An intuitive understanding of this expansion theorem may be obtained using the delta function. Let us consider only two electrons and let the physical space be one-dimensional. By the completeness of the one-electron (orbital) functions, we have for electron ν

$$\delta(x_\nu - \bar{x}) = \sum_i k_{\bar{x}i} \, i(x_\nu)$$

where the i's are the orbitals. This gives a function sharply peaked at $\bar{x}$ (Fig. 1.1). Considering just the one dimension, if we can manufacture a delta function at an arbitrary point $\bar{x}$, we can manufacture an arbitrary function (linear combination of delta functions). Now let us consider the

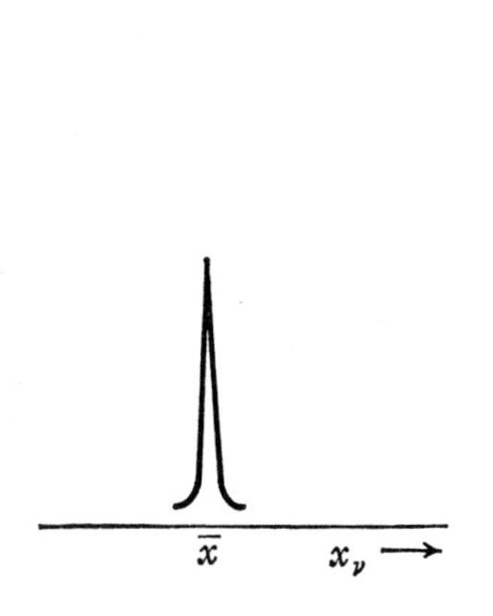

Figure 1.1

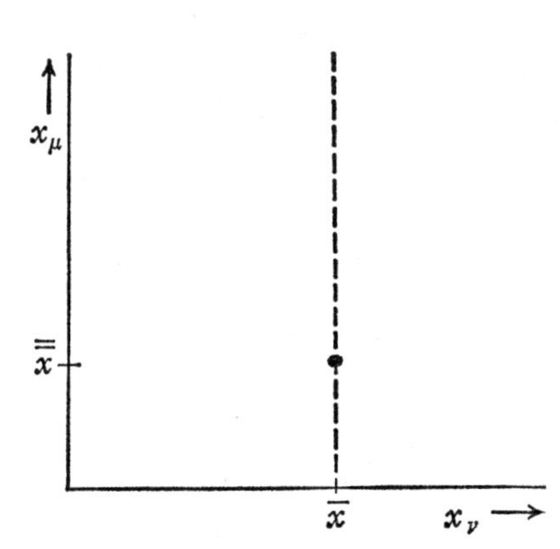

Figure 1.2

$x_\mu x_\nu$ plane, the space of two electrons (Fig. 1.2). The point in the diagram represents a two-dimensional delta function, and we wish to see how this function can be constructed using products of orbitals. A "paper-thin" function at $\bar{x}$ (dotted line in Fig. 1.2) having the shape of a single μ-orbital, $j(x_\mu)$, is obtained from the product

$$j(x_\mu)\,\delta(x_\nu - \bar{x})$$

and a linear combination of these functions will be the two-dimensional delta function

$$\begin{aligned}\delta(x_\mu - \bar{\bar{x}})\,\delta(x_\nu - \bar{x}) &= \sum_j k_{\bar{\bar{x}}j}\,j(x_\mu)\,\delta(x_\nu - \bar{x})\\ &= \sum_{ji} k_{\bar{\bar{x}}j}\,k_{\bar{x}i}\,j(x_\mu)\,i(x_\nu)\end{aligned}$$

Since the two-dimensional delta function is a linear combination of products, an arbitrary function (linear combination of delta functions) is likewise a linear combination of products.

The space for electrons has to involve products not of orbital functions but of spinorbital functions

$$|a\alpha),\ |a\beta),\ |b\alpha),\ |b\beta),\ \ldots$$

where $|a)$, $|b)$, . . . are the ordinary orbitals. Moreover, the most general many-electron function in this slightly complicated space turns out to be too general. The most general many-electron function may be represented as a linear combination of functions which are themselves general within a given *symmetry species* of the permutation group. For example, for two electrons, the most general function may be represented as a linear combination of two kinds of two-electron functions: one which is symmetric and one which is antisymmetric under the operation P_{12} (permutation of electron numbers in the function). Only the antisymmetric is found in nature.

A theorem discussed in the Appendix to Chapter 2 (Section 2.11) tells us that we can operate on a combination of functions, each belonging to a single symmetry species, to wash out all but a given species. The operator used is called the *character operator* for the species. In order to span the subspace of functions belonging to the "Fermi representation" (all operations which may be expressed as a product of an odd number of pairwise interchanges have characters of -1, otherwise $+1$), we use the following character operator, also called the *determinantal operator*, or the *antisymmetrizer*

$$\sum_P (-1)^p P \equiv A$$

Finally if we let $|1)$, $|2)$, $|3)$, . . . refer to spin orbitals, we can redefine our complete set of one-electron functions

$$|1) \equiv |a\alpha)$$
$$|2) \equiv |a\beta)$$
$$|3) \equiv |b\alpha), \text{ and so on}$$

Now we can specify the nature of a complete set of many-electron functions which span the subspace found in nature for electrons. The set may be symbolized

$$\left\{\sum_P (-1)^p P \mid 1\zeta) \mid 2\eta) \mid 3\theta) \ldots |n\nu)\right\}$$

the set of all Slater determinants which can be built up out of the complete set of spinorbitals.

In order to put the theorem to practical use, we need a convenient set of ordinary orbitals. The hydrogen-like orbitals are less than satisfactory because they do not form a complete set unless wave functions corresponding to states of the continuum are employed. Consider the $1s$ function displaced by an amount δ from the origin as expanded in terms of discrete hydrogen-like functions, $|i)$, centered at the origin

$$|1s, \delta) = \sum k_i \mid i)$$

The sum of the squares of the coefficients in the expansion turns out to be only 0.605 δ, showing for this example, anyway, how really important the continuum states are. To correct this difficulty, it has been pointed out that functions which are hydrogen-like in the angular coordinates but special in the r part form a complete orthonormal set and are always discrete. The special r part, apart from normalization, is

$$r^l L_{\nu+l+1}^{2l+2} (r)e^{-r/2}$$

where r is a reduced radius and the L are so-called associated Laguerre polynomials of degree $\nu + l$ and order $2l + 2$ (l is the angular momentum quantum number and ν is the index of the radial part of the one-electron function). These functions differ from the hydrogen-like functions in not having the principal quantum number occur in the exponent. This is often advantageous, because the ordinary hydrogen-like functions spread out rapidly as the principal quantum number goes up, making them not suitable for expansion of a function whose main variations occur within a few Bohr radii from the origin (as for almost any atom in its ground state). There has been considerable research on the use of the discrete Laguerre functions (recently by Shull and Löwdin)* and it could well turn out that they will be accepted as indispensable for many-electron calculations. Nevertheless, they have the drawback of not being eigenfunctions of a one-electron Hamiltonian. This causes difficulty when one attempts to use perturbation theory, for example, because the usual form of perturbation theory is based on functions which are eigenfunctions of the part that is simple, H^0.

We shall see next how to adapt perturbation theory to the circumstance that the many-electron functions are made up from the fully discrete orbital functions having the aforementioned limitation. We start with the energy eigenvalue relation for the true many-electron function for a given state,

$$H \mid \psi\rangle = E \mid \psi\rangle \tag{1.14}$$

and we assume a set of orthonormal many-electron functions

$$|\psi_0\rangle, |\psi_1\rangle, |\psi_2\rangle, \ldots$$

the zeroth being an approximation to $|\psi\rangle$. If $|\psi\rangle$ is normalized, not to unity, but so that

$$\langle\psi_0 \mid \psi\rangle = 1$$

then we may expand

$$|\psi\rangle = |\psi_0\rangle + \sum_{j=1}^{\infty} a_j \mid \psi_j\rangle$$

and Eq. (1.14) becomes

$$H(|\psi_0\rangle + \sum_{j=1}^{\infty} a_j \mid \psi_j\rangle) = E(|\psi_0\rangle + \sum_{j=1}^{\infty} a_j \mid \psi_j\rangle) \tag{1.15}$$

Multiplying by $\langle\psi_0|$ gives

$$E = \langle\psi_0 \mid H \mid \psi_0\rangle + \sum_{j=1}^{\infty} a_j\langle\psi_0 \mid H \mid \psi_j\rangle$$

The term on the far right may be written as involving a row vector times a column vector and will be called ΔE

$$\Delta E \equiv E - \langle\psi_0 \mid H \mid \psi_0\rangle = \langle\psi_0 \mid H \mid \boldsymbol{\Psi}\rangle\, \mathbf{a} \tag{1.16}$$

Multiplying Eq. (1.15) by some function other than the first gives

$$\langle\psi_i \mid H \mid \psi_0\rangle + \sum_{j=1}^{\infty} a_j\langle\psi_i \mid H \mid \psi_j\rangle = E\, a_i$$

* H. Shull and P. O. Löwdin, *J. Chem. Phys.*, **23** (1955), 1362.

or

$$\langle \psi_i \mid H \mid \psi_0 \rangle = \sum_{j=1}^{\infty} \langle \psi_i \mid E - H \mid \psi_j \rangle \, a_j$$

which may be written as

$$\langle \boldsymbol{\Psi} \mid H \mid \psi_0 \rangle = (\mathbf{E} - \mathbf{H}) \, \mathbf{a}$$

and solved for **a**

$$(\mathbf{E} - \mathbf{H})^{-1} \langle \boldsymbol{\Psi} \mid H \mid \psi_0 \rangle = \mathbf{a}$$

Substituting this expression for **a** into Eq. (1.16) for ΔE gives

$$\Delta E = \langle \psi_0 \mid H \mid \boldsymbol{\Psi} \rangle \, (\mathbf{E} - \mathbf{H})^{-1} \langle \boldsymbol{\Psi} \mid H \mid \psi_0 \rangle \tag{1.17}$$

This is an exact remainder formula

$$E = \langle \psi_0 \mid H \mid \psi_0 \rangle + \Delta E$$

but is quite closely related to the regular second-order perturbation formula. To see the resemblance let us assume that the first function is in fact an eigenfunction of a part of the Hamiltonian, H^0. (This might be the case, for example, if we had used the effective Hamiltonian Eq. (1.5) and Eq. (1.12) and approximated the eigenfunctions as closely as desired, using an expansion in terms of the discrete Laguerre functions.)

$$H^0 \mid \psi_0 \rangle = E_0 \mid \psi_0 \rangle$$

$$H = H^0 + V$$

Then

$$\langle \psi_0 \mid H \mid \psi_0 \rangle = E_0 + \langle \psi_0 \mid V \mid \psi_0 \rangle$$

(or in the modified Hartree-Fock case $= E_0$). The central part of (1.17) is

$$\begin{aligned} (\mathbf{E} - \mathbf{H}^0 - \mathbf{V})^{-1} &= \{[\mathbf{I} - \mathbf{V}(\mathbf{E} - \mathbf{H}^0)^{-1}] \, (\mathbf{E} - \mathbf{H}^0)\}^{-1} \\ &= (\mathbf{E} - \mathbf{H}^0)^{-1} \, [\mathbf{I} - \mathbf{V}(\mathbf{E} - \mathbf{H}^0)^{-1}]^{-1} \\ &= (\mathbf{E} - \mathbf{H}^0)^{-1} \, [\mathbf{I} + \mathbf{V}(\mathbf{E} - \mathbf{H}^0)^{-1} + \ldots] \end{aligned} \tag{1.18}$$

The "wings" of the ΔE expression, Eq. (1.17), may be simplified

$$\langle \psi_0 \mid H \mid \boldsymbol{\Psi} \rangle = \langle \psi_0 \mid H^0 + V \mid \boldsymbol{\Psi} \rangle = \langle \psi_0 \mid V \mid \boldsymbol{\Psi} \rangle \tag{1.19}$$

on account of $\langle \psi_0 \mid H^0 = E_0 \langle \psi_0 |$ and the assumed orthonormality of the $\langle \psi_i |$'s.

The formula Eq. (1.17) with Eq. (1.18) and Eq. (1.19) thus becomes

$$\Delta E = \langle \psi_0 \mid V \mid \boldsymbol{\Psi} \rangle \, (\mathbf{E} - \mathbf{H}^0)^{-1} \langle \boldsymbol{\Psi} \mid V \mid \psi_0 \rangle + \ldots$$

the leading term of which closely resembles the second-order perturbation formula,

$$\sum_{j=1}^{\infty} \frac{\langle \psi_0^0 \mid V \mid \psi_j^0 \rangle \langle \psi_j^0 \mid V \mid \psi_0^0 \rangle}{E - \langle \psi_j^0 \mid H^0 \mid \psi_j^0 \rangle}$$

Having to use a matrix in the central part in effect allows interactions between the $|\psi_j\rangle$'s to make up for the fact that they are not taken to be eigenfunctions of H^0. (Only $|\psi^0\rangle$ is.) Having the true energy, E, in the remainder formula poses a problem, but it turns out that it is a very close approximation to use $E^0 = \langle\psi_0 | H^0 | \psi_0\rangle$ for the true energy to calculate a $\Delta E^{(1)}$, then in a second step to use $E_0 + \Delta E^{(1)}$ for E.

A particularly simple application of this perturbation approach has been made by Shull for helium using

$$H^0 = T_1 + T_2 - \frac{1.6875}{r_1} - \frac{1.6875}{r_2}$$

$$V = -\frac{0.3125}{r_1} - \frac{0.3125}{r_2} + \frac{1}{r_{12}}$$

The function ψ_0 is hydrogen-like

$$\psi_0 = \text{const}\, e^{-Zr_1/2}\, e^{-Zr_2/2}$$

where $Z = 1.6875$, and is an eigenfunction of H^0. Using this partition of H one finds

$$\langle\psi_0 | V | \psi_0\rangle = 0$$

although the orbitals are not optimal in the Hartree-Fock sense.

The energy is

$$E_0 = \langle\psi_0 | H^0 | \psi_0\rangle = -2.8475 \text{ a.u.}$$

and

$$E + \Delta E = -2.9053 \text{ a.u.}$$

(Recall the experimental energy is -2.9037 a.u.) The perturbation approach has the advantage that matrix elements of the perturbation, which are comparatively difficult to compute, are used only between the various $|\psi_i\rangle$'s and $|\psi_0\rangle$ rather than between, say, $|\psi_i\rangle$ and $|\psi_j\rangle$. It has the disadvantage of obligating one to take enough terms so as to ensure convergence.

There is a widely used approach for energy eigenvalue calculations, which is simply to carry out a linear variation calculation using many-electron basis functions ordered according to estimated energy expectation values. The discrete Laguerre functions again are appropriate as orbital functions, though other functions may be employed. A straight variation calculation using, say, m many-electron basis functions is first carried out. Then the number of basis functions is increased by an appreciable fraction of m and a new and larger secular equation solved. In time, it will be found that, as this process is continued, the energy eigenvalue which is being sought does not change much (consideration being given to the degree of accuracy desired). At this point, the calculation is considered to have been completed. This method has the advantage that no study has to be made of the partitioning of the Hamiltonian between H^0 and V, and that the eigenvalue obtained is the true one. (Apparent convergence to a false eigenvalue is theoretically possible if the ordering of the configurations is such that certain essential ones are relegated to the "last" part of the series.) The method is therefore equivalent to a calculation of $E_0 + \Delta E$ using the exact formula Eq. (1.17) and indeed use of this formula as an aid in solving a large secular equation is a useful practice.

The variation approach for He using the discrete Laguerre functions has been carried out using only functions with no orbital angular momentum, with a result -2.88 a.u., and bringing in some angular momentum (20 basis functions all together) with a result -2.90 a.u.* More elaborate variation calculations have, of course, also been made, with as much accuracy as desired. Once a fairly large-sized secular equation has been set up for a linear variation calculation, the information is at hand to allow the calculation of energies of not one but several levels. This stems from the fact that matrix elements connecting one excited basis function with another have been computed over the full Hamiltonian, which perhaps is less efficient than with the perturbation method if all that is required is the energy of a particular state. As remarked earlier, in the perturbation method, matrix elements over the full Hamiltonian are needed only between an unperturbed function and excited functions.

1.4 CONFIGURATION INTERACTION

Whether variation or perturbation methods are used, going along with an approximate energy eigenvalue one finds a function consisting of linear combinations of Slater determinants

$$\sum_i c_i \mid \psi_i\rangle$$

Since each $|\psi_i\rangle$ contains an antisymmetrized product of orbitals, it may be represented by a configuration symbol.† The essence of the systematic approach may therefore be called *configuration interaction.* As we have seen, the best orbital approach (single configuration only) for some purposes is not unsatisfactory, so that one may well wonder whether also for molecules an orbital approach would prove reasonably satisfactory, or whether configuration interaction is necessary. Before considering this ques-

* H. Shull and P. O. Löwdin, *J. Chem. Phys.*, **30** (1959), 617; see also A. W. Weiss, *Phys. Rev.*, **122** (1961), 1826.

† For example, for helium: $1s^2$, $1s\ 2s$, $1s\ 2p_x$, . . .

tion, we shall look more closely into configuration interaction for atoms.

In order to determine the probability of several independent events, the rule is to use the product of the independent probabilities. Much the same rule obtains in interpreting the wave functions, though the situation is more complicated because a wave function has to be squared to give a probability. Even so, we may take a simple product of orbitals, each referring to a numbered electron, as epitomizing uncorrelated behavior and, at the same time, as being the purest form of a single-configuration function. Already when we form a sum of such products designed to be antisymmetric (as in a single Slater determinant!), we are departing from a pure single configuration function in the present sense: we are introducing configuration interaction and we are introducing an inevitable concomitant, correlation.

As an example, the triplet function for the $1s\ 2s$ configuration of helium already has some configuration interaction and shows its effect (correlation). Two terms occur, owing to what is called the *permutation degeneracy.* Since the electrons may have the same spin, the function must be orbitally antisymmetric. Apart from spin, the function is

$$2^{-1/2}\,(1s_1\,2s_2 - 1s_2\,2s_1)$$

with square

$$\tfrac{1}{2}\,[(1s_1\,2s_2)^2 + (1s_2\,2s_1)^2 - 2(1s_1\,2s_1\,1s_2\,2s_2)]$$

The probability contains squared terms which, considered alone, give a distribution in which one electron is in a $1s$ orbital while the other is in a $2s$ orbital, the two entirely independent. The cross term modulates this independent-systems probability. When electron one is in a region of the overlap distribution function $(1s\ 2s)_1$ with a certain sign the probability is decreased if also electron two is in a region with the same sign (in particular if electrons one and two are in the same region). If electron one is in a region where $(1s\ 2s)_1$ is positive but electron two is in a region where $(1s\ 2s)_2$ is negative, the effect of the cross term is to add probability over and above what is given by the squared terms, or independent-systems part. The sum of all the additions to, and subtractions from, the independent-systems part is zero. Indeed even if we fix electron one, say, arbitrarily at r_1, this sum is zero

$$\int 1s(r_1)\,2s(r_1)\,1s(r_2)\,2s(r_2)\,d\tau_2 = 0$$

Whereas the average effect of the modulating term is zero, the local effects are strong, a fact which is associated with the equality of the coefficients of the participating pure configurations in the wave function. The modulating effect is of this nature: the numbered electrons are spatially correlated, and the correlation in the present example may be called *essential*. This corresponds to the zero-order configuration interaction, "zero-order" because of the equal coefficients of the participating pure configurations.

By contrast, consider the following approximate function for the ground state (as found after the fragmentary application of first-order perturbation theory):

$$1s_1\, 1s_2 - \frac{\langle 1s^2 \mid V \mid 2s^2 \rangle}{\Delta W}\, 2s_1\, 2s_2 + \ldots$$

Assuming $\langle 1s^2 \mid V \mid 2s^2 \rangle / \Delta W$ is a small quantity of the first order, which we call ϵ, the wave function is normalized ($\epsilon^2 = 0$)

$$\int [(1s_1\, 1s_2)^2 - 2\epsilon 1s_1\, 1s_2\, 2s_1\, 2s_2]\, d\tau_1\, d\tau_2 = 1$$

The probability distribution now has the same modulating term as before, but with a factor of -2ϵ, associated with the $-\epsilon$ in the function. The correlating effect may be considerable but it is not what has been called essential, and in fact may be called *first order*.

A certain amount of zero order configuration interaction occurs, going hand in hand with essential correlation, in almost all approximate atomic eigenfunctions. Sometimes it occurs as in the preceding example for the $1s\, 2s$ configuration because of the permutation degeneracy. Sometimes it occurs because of the spatial degeneracy. (Literally speaking, it is always present between electrons having the same spin, an effect which is built right in the Slater determinants.) Notwithstanding all this, in the case of atoms, what is usually meant by correlation is the non-essential kind associated with first-order corrections to the wave function. In this case, one has the picture of the shape of the wave function as being determined almost entirely by the dominant positive charge of the nucleus. The electron distribution deforms so as to keep individual electrons apart, but not at the expense of too big a change in the orbitals.

The situation is different for molecules, because in a sense, a molecule is an atom with parts of the nucleus dispersed. A dominating central field may no longer be the governing factor so that an orbital approach might be a poor approximation—or to put it another way, for molecules there might be more configuration interaction. To see a first example of this, we shall study the emergence of the Heitler-London function for H_2 as a result of configuration interaction. We shall then recognize essential correlation in the Heitler-London function and shall see its connection with a form of permutation degeneracy peculiar to molecules.

We shall build up functions for H_2 which become correct when the protons are quite far apart. The corresponding one-electron functions (bonding and antibonding molecular orbitals for H_2^+) are linear combinations of atomic orbitals a and b

$$\frac{1}{\sqrt{2 \pm 2s}}\,(a \pm b)$$

where

$$s = \int ab\,d\tau$$

Filling up the bonding orbital with two electrons gives a singlet (apart from normalization)

$$|1\rangle = (a + b)_1\,(a + b)_2\,(\alpha_1\,\beta_2 - \alpha_2\,\beta_1) \tag{1.20a}$$

The antibonding orbitals are approximately degenerate with the bonding ones when the atoms are distant; hence one is automatically obliged to consider also the following singlet function

$$|B\rangle = [(a + b)_1\,(a - b)_2 + (a + b)_2\,(a - b)_1]\,(\alpha_1\,\beta_2 - \alpha_2\,\beta_1)$$

and finally

$$|2\rangle = (a - b)_1\,(a - b)_2\,(\alpha_1\,\beta_2 - \alpha_2\,\beta_1) \tag{1.20b}$$

The state $|B\rangle$ does not interact over any totally symmetric operator (such as the Hamiltonian for H_2) with $|1\rangle$ and $|2\rangle$—because the wave functions for $|1\rangle$ and $|2\rangle$ are symmetric when the function (for electrons one and two simultaneously) is inverted, whereas $|B\rangle$ is antisymmetric. The interaction between configurations $|1\rangle$ and $|2\rangle$ produces mixing with equal coefficients in the limit where each function has the same unperturbed energy, so that one obtains

$$|1\rangle \pm |2\rangle$$

as the correct zero-order functions for the separated atoms. The difference-state, apart from spin, is the Heitler-London function, as may be seen using the expanded form of the functions Eq. (1.20)

$$\begin{array}{r} a_1\,a_2 + b_1\,b_2 + a_1\,b_2 + a_2\,b_1 \\ -(a_1\,a_2 + b_1\,b_2 - a_1\,b_2 - a_2\,b_1) \\ \hline 2(a_1\,b_2 + a_2\,b_1) \end{array}$$

The square of the Heitler-London function has essential correlation in the most elementary sense in the squared terms

$$(a_1\,b_2)^2 + (a_2\,b_1)^2$$

in that when one electron is on proton a the other is on proton b. This may be looked upon as a consequence of the mixing between $|1\rangle$ and $|2\rangle$—

configuration interaction. There is additional correlation given by the modulating term

$$2a_1 b_2 a_2 b_1 \equiv 2(ab)_1 (ab)_2$$

namely, when electron one is in the overlap region ($ab \neq 0$) between the protons, the over-all probability is enhanced, provided that electron two is in the same region—at the same time so to speak. This modulation effect accounts for the chemical bond (the triplet function brings in the same modulation term with opposite sign and is a repulsive state for the system of two atoms).*

The form of the Heitler-London function in general terms is one half-filled orbital per atom, as modified by the accompanying permutation degeneracy. We shall consider the general problem when there are more than two atoms in Chapter 3.

1.5 DIRECTED VALENCE

The subject of directed valence underlies many of the applications in later chapters. Appropriately for this chapter, the subject may be considered largely as involving the electronic states of but a single atom. When one thinks of directed valence, he thinks of the tetrahedral carbon atom, the cornerstone of the marvelously successful structural theory of organic chemistry. Yet tetrahedral angles may not exemplify the essence of directed valence because four objects placed on the surface of a hard sphere and repelling one another naturally take up positions at the corners of a regular tetrahedron. The same argument when applied to the water molecule, considered as a collection of the three ions: $2H^+$, $O^=$ leads to the conclusion that the HOH angle should be 180°. In fact, the angle is 105°, less than the tetrahedral angle and greater than the angle between the axes of two $2p$ orbitals, 90°. We may therefore regard water as exemplifying the directed valence phenomenon, and we shall consider the water molecule from two points of view which, apparently, are not closely related.

The first point of view is *polarized ionic*. Empirical–intuitive evidence indicates that the ionic model for water: $2H^+$, $O^=$ may be worthwhile, and even for this simple model we shall be able to see how a bond angle close to 90° could arise.

The wave function for the oxide ion is approximated as a closed-shell Slater determinant based on the configuration $1s^2\, 2s^2\, 2p^6$. The electron

* For a systematic analysis of hydrogen molecule wave functions using *natural spin-orbitals* see H. Shull, *J. Chem. Phys.*, **30** (1959), 1405.

density is spherically symmetric, by Unsold's theorem.* Any closed-shell Slater determinant based on new orbitals obtained from the old ones by a unitary transformation is found upon expansion to be the same Slater determinant and, again, leads to an electron density for the oxygen ion which is spherically symmetrical. In particular, one can just as well use hybrid orbitals, tetrahedral ones: $t_1\, t_2\, t_3\, t_4 = T\, 2s\, 2p_x\, 2p_y\, 2p_z$ (where T symbolizes a unitary transformation). It would appear that we must guard against too superficial an approach.

When a proton comes up to a spherically symmetrical oxide ion, it polarizes the electron distribution. This is described by using first-order perturbation theory for the wave function. Looking at the problem from an orbital point of view, and calling the proton-oxygen line the z axis, we have a polarized $2p_z$ orbital

$$\sigma_z = 2p_z - \frac{(2p_z \mid V \mid 3s)}{E_{3s} - E_{2p}}\, 3s + \dots$$

$$= 2p_z + \epsilon 3s + \dots$$

where V is the potential energy of the interaction and the denominator contains the $3s$, $2p$ unperturbed energy difference, and ϵ stands for the coefficient. Adding a spherically symmetrical function like $3s$ to $2p_z$ has the effect of adding to the probability amplitude on one side of the plane of symmetry and on the outside of the atom, and correspondingly of taking away from the probability amplitude on the opposite side of the plane (see Fig. 1.3). The probability distribution is modified in that more

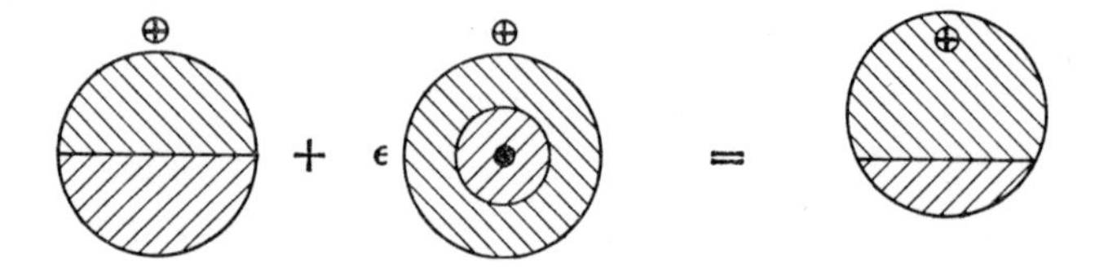

Figure 1.3

* An example of this theorem is afforded by the orbitally symmetric three-electron function based on $2p_x\, 2p_y\, 2p_z$

$$6^{-1/2} \sum_P P x_1\, e^{-r_1}\, y_2\, e^{-r_2}\, z_3\, e^{-r_3}$$

The square of this function integrated over $d\tau_2\, d\tau_3$ gives the probability distribution function for one of the three electrons with the non-trivial part

$$(x_1^2 + y_1^2 + z_1^2)\, e^{-2r_1} = \text{const}\; r_1^2\, e^{-2r_1}$$

negative electricity comes in the vicinity of the proton, and the second-order energy gives a stabilization. (The second-order energy is the expectation value of the perturbation over the normalized first-order perturbed function.)

When a second proton comes up, it finds as a necessary feature accompanying the polarization to accommodate the first proton, a region of diminished electron density in the zone on the side of the z axis opposite the first proton. It therefore goes more or less into the equatorial region depending on the relative magnitudes of the proton-proton repulsion and the stabilization arising from the polarization. The second proton can achieve a stabilization corresponding to the original stabilization by going in anywhere in the equatorial plane. The wave function for the second proton is, say,

$$\sigma_y = 2p_y + \epsilon 3s + \cdots$$

which (to the first order in ϵ) is normalized and orthogonal to σ_z.

The reason for mentioning transformations of the basis set in the preliminary discussion above was to make it clear that wave functions outside the closed shell set (for example, $3s$) have to be brought in. Hybridization does not change the energy of the closed-shell configuration, because it does not change the function. Correspondingly, it can introduce no polarization.

When the central ion has an open-shell configuration, the situation is different. The NH_2 radical furnishes a convenient example. We assume an ionic model as before, in which case the central anion is $N^=$ with a configuration

$$2s^2\, 2p^5$$

The protons here may be considered as perturbing the $2p$ orbitals. If the plane containing the three ions is taken as the xy plane and if the bond angle is less than 180°, then the resulting splitting of the nitrogen orbitals mainly involves the lowering of the $2p_x$ and $2p_y$. The lowest energy configuration is thus $2s^2\, 2p_x^2\, 2p_y^2\, 2p_z^1$. Further splitting involving interaction

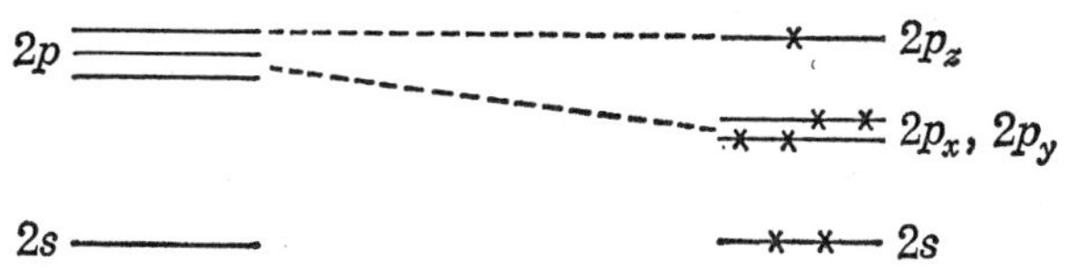

2p
2s
$2p_z$
$2p_x, 2p_y$
2s

among the $2p_x\, 2p_y$ and $2s$ orbitals to make hybrid orbitals again may be disregarded because now, in a sense, the configuration $2s^2\, 2p_x^2\, 2p_y^2$ is a closed-shell configuration for the "inner shell" underlying the single $2p_z$ electron. The doubly filled $2p_x$ and $2p_y$ orbitals give a cylindrically symmetric charge distribution about the z axis. Carrying this reasoning based on an ionic model further, one sees that without the effect of polarization the $H^+ N^= H^+$ angle would be determined purely by proton-proton repulsion; hence 180°, although with polarization it would be 90°. (It actually is 103°.)

For the first excited configuration (still keeping the protons in the xy plane), the upper orbital is doubly filled, $(2s\, 2p_x\, 2p_y)^5\, 2p_z^2$; the situation is now reversed in that the $(2s\, 2p_x\, 2p_y)^5$ part is an open shell. Assuming that the sp energy difference is comparatively high leads to having the vacancy, or hole, almost pure p, say p_x. The configuration $2s^2\, 2p_y^2\, 2p_x^1$ is no longer cylindrically symmetrical around the z axis so it is not necessary to use polarization to find the bond angle. The protons go into the regions of maximum density, which are on opposite sides of the nitrogen ion and on the y axis, so the predicted angle is 180°. The hole thus takes a position of maximum stability! In a sense, $2s^2\, 2p_y^2$ is a closed-shell configuration, hence for the ionic model there is no advantage in using linear combinations. In other words, although digonal hybrid orbitals may be formed

$$d_\pm = 2^{-1/2}\,(2s \pm 2p_y)$$

the Slater determinant based on $d_+^2\, d_-^2$ is the same as the one based on $2s^2\, 2p_y^2$. Somewhat surprisingly, the excited configuration $2s^2\, 2p_y^2\, 2p_x^1\, 2p_z^2$ is degenerate with $2s^2\, 2p_y^2\, 2p_x^2\, 2p_z^1$ for the 180° bond angle so that our viewpoint restricting the protons to the xy plane is an oversimplified one. There is an electronic transition for NH_2 at 5600 Å, and the analysis of the vibronic band structure* shows the molecule to be linear, or nearly so, in the excited state, and confirms that transition is to a degenerate upper orbital.

This description of NH_2 starting from an ionic model is an example of ligand field theory.† The theory has been extensively applied to the 3d open shell of transition metals.

Now we switch away from the ionic point of view. We shall again consider water as an example, but using a new picture; namely, one in which the molecule is thought to consist of the neutral atoms 2H, O modified

* J. A. Pople and H. C. Longuet-Higgins, *Mol. Phys.*, **1** (1958), 372; and K. Dressler and D. A. Ramsay, *Phil. Trans. Roy. Soc.* (London), **251** A (1959), 553.

† J. S. Griffith, *The Theory of Transition-Metal Ions* (New York: Cambridge University Press, 1961); Leslie E. Orgel, *An Introduction to Transition-Metal Chemistry: Ligand-Field Theory* (New York: John Wiley & Sons, Inc., 1960).

by a perturbation. That the ionic viewpoint is probably insufficient may be seen by considering the molecular ingredients, the atoms, widely separated, as a starting point. With the atoms so disposed, the energy required to form the ions from the atoms is negative. That is, the electron affinities

$$O + e^- = O^- \qquad \textit{circa} \quad 3 \text{ e.v.}$$

$$O^- + e^- = O^= \qquad \textit{circa} \ -5 \text{ e.v.}$$

total -2 e.v. Further, the energy of formation of two H ions is an additional 27 e.v. Thus the energy of the separated ionic state $2H^+$, $O^=$ is 29 volts or so above the energy of the separated atoms. When the ions are brought together (H—O distance ≈ 0.96 Å), according to simple electrostatic considerations only 25 e.v. is returned. The apparent ionic binding energy thus may well be negative. Whether the polarization can make up this difference without covalent bond formation being said to have occurred is problematical.*

The way directed valence appears with the atomic model (Pauling) is linked with the idea of electron pair bonds. Just as with the Heitler-London function, the requirement for an electron pair bond between two atoms is two free (half-filled) orbitals, one on each of the centers which are to be bonded. In the case of water, the free orbitals on the hydrogens are the $1s$ orbitals. The makeup of the oxygen atom requires some examination. For in this case, we are not dealing with a closed-shell configuration, and as noted above in our study of the NH_2 radical, the nature of the basis set affects the energy. The rule for forming the basis is to start from a closed-shell configuration and remove electrons in such a way that the holes remaining are as low in energy as possible. Thus the lowest value of the ionization potential for

$$O^= \rightarrow O^- + e^-$$

is obtained when the hole in O^- is a $2p$ orbital. The other extreme is represented by a $2s$ orbital, because of the step-up in energy between s and p for many-electron atoms. Here we are not concerned with the fact that $O^=$ itself may be represented in different ways, but simply with finding the best orbital for the hole in O^-. A second electron would have to be removed from a different $2p$ orbital to guarantee that two free orbitals

* It is sometimes forgotten that agreement with experiment in a narrow sense is no proof of the correctness of a theory. For example, the polarized ionic model leads to a reasonably correct bond angle for water; it must not be inferred, however, that the bond in water is necessarily ionic.

be available for binding with the $1s$ orbitals of the hydrogen atoms. When the directional property of exchange integrals involving p orbitals is considered, this all leads to the prediction of a 90° bond angle in water; moreover, the observed angle, which is similar (actually 15° greater), is believed to be explainable mainly on this basis.

To go into the subject further we need to consider semiquantitatively the $2s$, $2p$ energy differences. For atomic oxygen, the differences are $\sim 17 \pm 8$ e.v. (depending on Hund's rules effects). The first three ionization potentials of water are *circa* 12, 14, and 16 e.v., and the first and third have been interpreted as involving respectively $2p$ and $2s$ electrons. The $2s$ electrons would not be the same in a molecular environment as in an isolated atom and to use the difference $16 - 12 = 4$ e.v. for the step-up or promotion energy may include this effect. Now the energy of formation of holes with various hybridizations may be roughly assessed. For example, to make a hole with tetrahedral hybridization

$$t = \sqrt{\tfrac{1}{4}}\, 2s + \sqrt{\tfrac{3}{4}}\, 2p$$

requires $\frac{1}{4}$ of the promotion energy (one uses the coefficient squared of the $2s$ part) or, by consideration of the various values mentioned above, between 1 and 4 volts. The strength of a Heitler-London bond as calculated depends on the magnitude of the exchange integral, which in turn depends on the orbital shapes. It has long been known that p orbitals are not optimal because they have electron density equally on the side toward the atom being bonded and on the opposite side. Tetrahedral orbitals are much better in that, for them, the electron density is concentrated in a given forward direction, so to speak. Forming a bond between a $1s$ orbital on hydrogen and an oxygen t orbital may liberate an extra volt or so as compared with forming a bond involving a pure $2p$ orbital, which stabilization would tend to compensate the promotion energy. Thus the holes in $O^{=}$ obtained by removing electrons might easily have each an appreciable $2s$ component. As is well known, the maximum density regions with t orbitals are tetrahedrally placed.* Hybridization then may be the main reason why the bond angle in water is greater than 90°, approaching 109°; although the question of the relative contributions of this compared with other effects, like the proton-proton repulsion, must be considered.

In Chapter 3, we shall see that exchange integrals between electrons

* The regions of overlap with outside orbitals are then not spherically symmetrical even with a half-filled shell, Unsold's theorem notwithstanding. See also J. E. Lennard-Jones, *J. Chem. Phys.*, **20** (1952), 1024.

which are paired, but not to each other, are large and come in with a sign opposite to that for the case of bonding—causing repulsion. If we assume tetrahedral hybridization in water, consideration of this effect (as realized by Lennard-Jones and Pople*) leads to the conclusion that the exchange repulsion involving electrons in the two non-bonding orbitals will be considerable; this repulsion, moreover, more than outweighs the similar repulsion between one bond and the other. The reason is that the lone pairs are concentrated more around the oxygen center. Consideration of the lone-pair repulsion thus leads one qualitatively to expect that the bonds will be forced together as the lone-pairs move apart under the influence of the repulsion and rehybridization. This counteracts the proton-proton repulsion.

The foregoing material on directed valence illustrates what is frequently found in the application of quantum mechanics to chemistry. Whereas the broad outlines are clear, the details are confusing; so that, considering the present state of the art, one is well advised to pay close attention to experimental findings. That the bond angle in water is 105° stands out from the web of qualitative explanations. This is an abnormal state of affairs in a physical science because ordinarily the function of theory is to unify and condense, whereas experimental findings are expected to be the proliferation of the theory. We shall see a return to this state of affairs when the time comes that the potential energy surface for H_2O can be calculated with an accuracy commensurate with the employment of the non-relativistic Hamiltonian within the Born-Oppenheimer approximation.

Appendix to Chapter 1

1.6 THE BORN-OPPENHEIMER APPROXIMATION

The Born-Oppenheimer approximation underlies by far the majority of applications of quantum mechanics to molecules.

At the start of the approximation process, nuclear repulsions may be neglected. An energy eigenvalue equation referring to the motion of the electrons is solved for various values of the nuclear coordinates considered as parameters. This gives a set of electronic energy eigenvalues which, for a continuous set of nuclear coordinates as parameters, constitutes a potential energy surface. To finish the approximation process, nuclear repulsions are incorporated in order to get a corrected potential energy surface, and

* J. E. Lennard-Jones and J. A. Pople, *Proc. Roy. Soc.* (London), **205** A (1951), 155.

an energy eigenvalue equation for the nuclei is solved using this surface for the potential. The total wave function is a product

$$|Qq\rangle \mid Q\rangle$$

where the left-hand factor symbolizes the electronic function, with Q referring to the nuclei as a parameter, and the right-hand factor is the nuclear eigenfunction. The use of the Born-Oppenheimer approximation is illustrated in Section 2.14, which shows how to calculate the intensity for the vibronic transitions in the band envelope of an electronic transition.

The systematic investigation of the range of validity of the approximation involves finding a comparison Hamiltonian, H^0, such that the Born-Oppenheimer function, $|Qq\rangle \mid Q\rangle$, is an eigenfunction. The perturbation, $H—H^0$, may then be investigated, for example, by computing the expectation value of $H—H^0$ over $|Qq\rangle \mid Q\rangle$. It is found that the perturbation is indeed small whenever the characteristic frequencies for vibration of the nuclei are much smaller than the characteristic electronic frequencies. For practical purposes, this usually requires that the nuclear masses be much larger, which, of course, they are.

The systematic justification of the Born-Oppenheimer approximation is a difficult job. Yet the underlying physical idea is simple enough—having heavy and light particles so changes the character of the mechanical problem that it may be solved in two steps, during the first of which the inertia of the heavy particles is exploited. We shall try to gain familiarity with the method by working out an elementary example with considerable use of classical mechanics. This has the advantage of our being able to compare the solution obtained using the Born-Oppenheimer approximation with one obtained exactly.

We start with the system of particles and springs in Fig. 1.4, (the motion to be confined to one dimension). As shown in the figure, the force constants are respectively k, $2k$, and k;* and the masses are M, as for a nucleus, and m, as for an electron. The displacements from equilibrium are Q and q, going with M and m. Then

$$T = \frac{M}{2}\dot{Q}^2 + \frac{m}{2}\dot{q}^2 \tag{1.21a}$$

$$\begin{aligned} V &= \frac{k}{2}Q^2 + \frac{k}{2}q^2 + \frac{1}{2}(2k)(q - Q)^2 \\ &= \frac{3k}{2}Q^2 - 2kQq + \frac{3k}{2}q^2 \end{aligned} \tag{1.21b}$$

* Having all the force constants comparable gives a resemblance to the situation found in molecules where, independent of mass, all forces are coulombic.

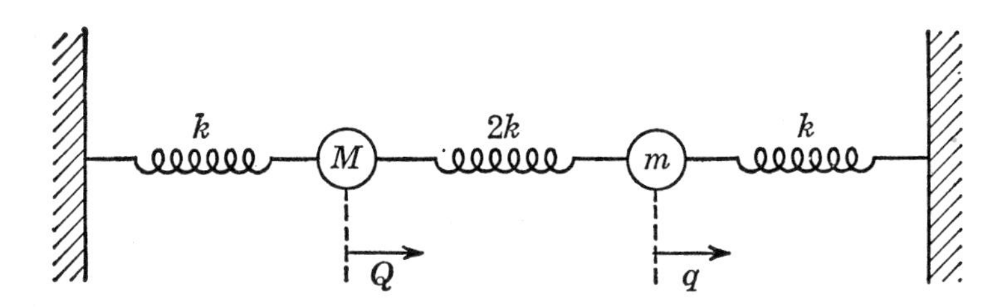

Figure 1.4

We need to get these expressions over into a form such that Lagrange's equations lead to separated equations of motion.* We first switch to mass-weighted coordinates

$$q_1 = \sqrt{m}\, q$$

$$q_2 = \sqrt{M}\, Q$$

whence Eq. (1.21a) and Eq. (1.21b) become

$$2T = \dot{q}_1^2 + \dot{q}_2^2$$

$$2V = \frac{3k}{m} q_1^2 - \frac{4k}{\sqrt{mM}} q_1 q_2 + \frac{3k}{M} q_2^2$$

These may be written in matrix form

$$2T = \tilde{\dot{\mathbf{q}}}\dot{\mathbf{q}}$$

$$2V = \tilde{\mathbf{q}}\mathbf{G}\,\mathbf{q}$$

where, for example,

$$\mathbf{q} = \begin{pmatrix} q_1 \\ q_2 \end{pmatrix}$$

and

$$\mathbf{G} = \begin{pmatrix} \dfrac{3k}{m} & \dfrac{-2k}{\sqrt{mM}} \\ \dfrac{-2k}{\sqrt{mM}} & \dfrac{3k}{M} \end{pmatrix}$$

The normal coordinates are

$$\mathbf{x} = \mathbf{S}\mathbf{q}; \qquad \mathbf{q} = \mathbf{S}^{-1}\mathbf{x}$$

where

$$\tilde{\mathbf{q}}\mathbf{G}\mathbf{q} = \tilde{\mathbf{x}}\tilde{\mathbf{S}}^{-1}\,\mathbf{G}\mathbf{S}^{-1}\,\mathbf{x}$$

* H. Goldstein, *Classical Mechanics* (Reading, Mass: Addison-Wesley Publishing Company, 1950), chap. 10.

and $\mathbf{S}$, the matrix of an orthogonal transformation, is selected so that $\tilde{\mathbf{S}}^{-1}\,\mathbf{G}\mathbf{S}^{-1}$ is diagonal. The potential energy can then be expressed as a quadratic form with no cross terms. It is "diagonal." After the transformation, the kinetic energy is still diagonal

$$2T = \tilde{\dot{\mathbf{x}}}\dot{\mathbf{x}}$$

and Lagrange's equations lead directly to the separated equations of motion

$$\ddot{x}_j = -\lambda_j x_j \qquad j = 1, 2$$

where λ_j is a diagonal matrix element of $\tilde{\mathbf{S}}^{-1}\,\mathbf{G}\mathbf{S}^{-1}$. The solution of the separated equations is

$$x_j = \text{const } e^{i\sqrt{\lambda_j}t}$$

so that the circular frequencies are given by

$$\omega_j^2 = \lambda_j$$

According to an algebraic theorem, moreover, the λ's are the eigenvalues of the original matrix $\mathbf{G}$ (a symmetric matrix). Thus, to find the frequencies, we must solve a secular equation, namely

$$\begin{vmatrix} \dfrac{3k}{m} - \lambda & \dfrac{-2k}{\sqrt{mM}} \\ \dfrac{-2k}{\sqrt{mM}} & \dfrac{3k}{M} - \lambda \end{vmatrix} = 0$$

With the abbreviations $\alpha = k/M$ and $\beta = k/m$, this becomes

$$\begin{vmatrix} 3\beta - \lambda & -2\sqrt{\alpha\beta} \\ -2\sqrt{\alpha\beta} & 3\alpha - \lambda \end{vmatrix} = \lambda^2 - 3(\alpha + \beta)\lambda + 5\alpha\beta = 0$$

The exact solution is

$$\frac{3(\alpha + \beta) \pm \sqrt{9\alpha^2 - 2\alpha\beta + 9\beta^2}}{2}$$

Having $M \gg m$ gives $\beta \gg \alpha$. This last inequality makes it possible to approximate the square root* and leads to

$$\frac{3(\alpha + \beta) \pm (3\beta - \alpha/3)}{2}$$

* If $x \gg y$, $\sqrt{x^2 + y} = x + y/2x$. As briefly noted above, having the masses disparate is not a fundamental requirement. Fundamentally, the inequality involves k/m ratios, or squares of characteristic frequencies. This applies in actual cases. With higher Rydberg orbits, the electronic frequencies are much lower than the molecular vibration frequencies, and the Born-Oppenheimer approximation is inapplicable.

so that the squares of the circular frequencies become

$$\lambda_m = 3\beta + \frac{4}{3}\alpha = 3\frac{k}{m} + \frac{4}{3}\frac{k}{M}$$

$$\cong 3\frac{k}{m} \tag{1.22a}$$

(through the further application of $\beta \gg \alpha$) and

$$\lambda_M = \frac{3}{2}\alpha + \frac{\alpha}{6} = \frac{5}{3}\frac{k}{M} \tag{1.22b}$$

λ_m and λ_M here take the place of λ_1 and λ_2 because the λ's in question refer mainly to light and heavy particle motion respectively.

To solve the problem quantum mechanically, we use the well-known connection between the classical and quantal treatments. Remembering that $\omega_j^2 = \lambda_j$, we have

$$E = \sum_{j=1}^{2} (n_j + \tfrac{1}{2})\hbar\omega_j$$

In the approximation made possible when $\beta \gg \alpha$, this becomes

$$E \cong (n_M + \tfrac{1}{2})\hbar\omega_M + (n_m + \tfrac{1}{2})\hbar\omega_m \tag{1.23}$$

where ω_M goes with λ_M, ω_m with λ_m Eq. (1.22).

Let us now solve the problem by the Born-Oppenheimer approximation. We shall displace the heavy particle (M) a distance Q, in which case the situation for the light particle may be visualized as in Fig. 1.5 (the heavy

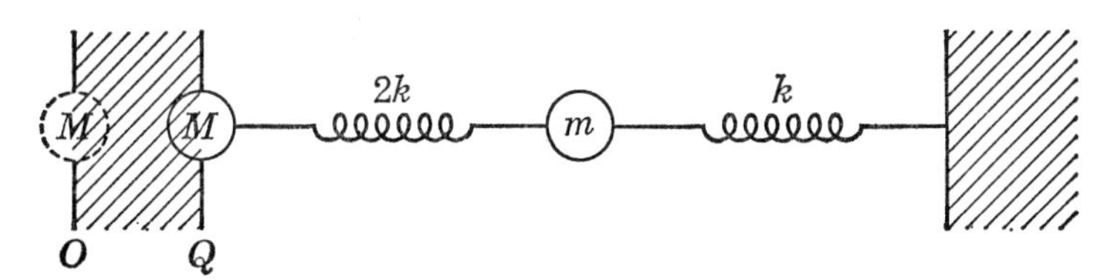

Figure 1.5

particle, here considered as having infinite mass, is like one of the walls). The potential insofar as the light particle is concerned is [see Eq. (1.21b)]

$$V(q) = -2kQq + \tfrac{3}{2}kq^2 \tag{1.24}$$

and $q = 0$ is no longer the equilibrium position. Since the left-hand spring is the stronger, m will move to the right so as to leave the left spring compressed only one-half as much as the right, and the new equilibrium will occur at $q = \frac{2}{3}Q$. Formally we obtain this result by setting the force, $-\partial V/\partial q = 0$. Next we rewrite Eq. (1.24) so as to involve the displacement $\bar{q}$ from equilibrium. That is, $\bar{q} = q - \frac{2}{3}Q$. Substituting into Eq. (1.24), we find

$$V(\bar{q}) = \tfrac{3}{2}k\bar{q}^2 - \tfrac{2}{3}kQ^2$$

The classical frequency is obtained immediately from

$$T = \tfrac{1}{2}m\dot{q}^2 = \tfrac{1}{2}m\dot{\bar{q}}^2$$
$$V = \tfrac{3}{2}k\bar{q}^2$$
$$|\tfrac{3}{2}k - \tfrac{1}{2}m\lambda_m| = 0$$

and is $\omega_m = (3k/m)^{1/2}$. This result is equivalent to the classical approximate result Eq. (1.22a).

The quantal result is readily obtained, once we have the classical frequency. We must be sure to remember that the springs are under tension, however; hence the quantal result referred to the original zero of energy must reflect this state of affairs.

$$E_m = (n_m + \tfrac{1}{2})\hbar\omega_m - \tfrac{2}{3}kQ^2$$

This is the "potential energy surface." To calculate the motion of the heavy particle we must now add the potential energy of the heavy particle, $\frac{3}{2}kQ^2$—the part of Eq. (1.21b) we have been neglecting. The corrected potential energy surface which results is

$$V(Q) = \tfrac{1}{2}(\tfrac{5}{3}k)Q^2 + (n_m + \tfrac{1}{2})\hbar\omega_m$$

where the final term is a constant as far as the motion of the heavy particle is concerned. The classical frequency squared is therefore

$$\lambda_M = \frac{5}{3}\frac{k}{M}$$

again in agreement with the approximate value found from the normal coordinate analysis Eq. (1.22b). The quantal energy is immediately obtained by using

$$(n_M + \tfrac{1}{2})\hbar\omega_M$$

and adding the constant final term in the potential energy of the heavy particle. The energy becomes

$$E \cong (n_M + \tfrac{1}{2})\hbar\omega_M + (n_m + \tfrac{1}{2})\hbar\omega_m$$

which is the same as Eq. (1.23), the approximate expression obtained in the normal coordinate analysis. Using the Born-Oppenheimer approximation, however, it was obtained through the solution of simple single equations, first for the light particle and then for the heavy particle.

The negative potential energy, $-\frac{2}{3}kQ^2$, which is a correction to the heavy particle potential, $\frac{3}{2}kQ^2$, may be understood as follows: If the light particle does not move and the heavy particle moves a distance Q, the potential becomes $\frac{3}{2}kQ^2$ Eq. (1.21b). The light particle, however, will shift so as to minimize the spring tensions in the second and third springs and lower the potential somewhat. Actually, the light particle may vibrate additionally, with a high frequency. But so far as the spring tensions governing the motion of the heavy particle are concerned, it is evidently permissible to consider the average position of the light particle, a position identical to the static equilibrium position for each value of Q.

CHAPTER 2

The Molecular Orbital Method

The modified Hartree-Fock method for atoms (Chapter 1) has the effect of reducing the many-electron problem to a one-electron problem centering around the eigenvalue relation

$$H_\nu^0 \mid i\nu) = \lambda_i \mid i\nu)$$

where

$$H_\nu^0 = T_\nu + U_\nu$$

For a considerable portion of this chapter we shall be dealing with but a single electron. Under this circumstance, it will be convenient frequently to omit the electron label, like ν above, so that for example we write $H^0 \mid i) = \lambda_i \mid i)$. The effective one-electron potential in the modified Hartree-Fock method, U, gives the average repulsion between the other electrons and the one in question and in such a very particular way that the many-electron expectation value $\langle \psi \mid H \mid \psi \rangle$ is simply the sum of the λ's over occupied orbitals. The generalization for molecules is theoretically straightforward, in that the nuclear attraction part of U has merely to be replaced by a sum over all attracting nuclei. The Hartree-Fock method has not received much favor for application to molecules, partly because of the difficulty of solving even the one-electron eigenvalue relations, and partly because the best energy obtained using a single Slater determinant is not accurate enough for chemistry anyway. Under this latter circumstance, it is reasonable to look for simpler orbital approaches.*

The simplification which has dominated the literature (and which originated with Hund, Mulliken, and Hückel) is the use of molecular orbitals which do not have the most general shape possible, but which are linear combinations of atomic orbitals (LCAO's). Thus an extreme variant of the Hartree-Fock method is to approximate a solution of the one-electron eigenvalue relation by means of a linear variation calculation. The elements of the secular equation refer to atomic orbitals and the solution gives approximate λ's and optimal coefficients of atomic orbitals in the molecular orbitals. These LCAO molecular orbitals have to be used in U and an iteration scheme carried out along the same lines as described in Chapter 1. When patterned after the unmodified Hartree-Fock, the method is called the LCAO SCF (self-consistent field) method. It was first worked out by Roothaan.†

2.1 THE HÜCKEL THEORY

A related approach is even more simple, the widely used Hückel theory. In this theory the coefficients of the atomic orbitals are not obtained so as to minimize the variational integral over the complete Hamiltonian but only so as to satisfy some less stringent variational principal.

In this chapter, we shall concentrate on the Hückel theory and a perturbation approach which it engenders. In a not highly developed form,

* If the Hartree-Fock method must be supplemented, as by a second-order perturbation calculation, it is reasonable to attempt to discover an easy first-order theory which, when supplemented, is accurate enough. Thus it might turn out to be extremely impractical to go to all the trouble of finding optimal molecular orbitals when orbitals which are less than optimal can, in effect, have their shape improved at a higher-order stage during which correlation also is being introduced.

† C. C. J. Roothaan, *Rev. Mod. Phys.*, **23** (1951), 69. Among the applications are F. O. Ellison and H. Shull, *J. Chem. Phys.*, **23** (1955), 2348; R. C. Sahni, *J. Chem. Phys.*, **25** (1956), 332; R. A. Ballinger, *Mol. Phys.*, **2** (1959), 139.

the theory consists of determining the nuclear charge (as orbital exponent) in the AO's intuitively, and selecting the coefficients in the linear combinations using an assumed variation method secular equation. The MO's are then used in various ways, such as in predicting gross features of electron distribution; and sometimes even the one-electron eigenvalues are treated as bonafide orbital energies, just as with the Hartree-Fock method. As an example of the Hückel theory, we shall consider the four π electrons in butadiene

```
H         H
 \       /
  C═══C       H
 /       \   /
H         C═══C
         /      \
        H        H
```

The MO's are linear combinations (LC's) of $2p\pi$ AO's usually considered to have $Z \sim 3.2$. A set of effective orbital energies and the coefficients of the AO's are determined by the linear variation method centering around the secular equation

$$\begin{vmatrix} \alpha - \lambda & \beta - s\lambda & 0 & 0 \\ \beta - s\lambda & \alpha - \lambda & \beta - s\lambda & 0 \\ 0 & \beta - s\lambda & \alpha - \lambda & \beta - s\lambda \\ 0 & 0 & \beta - s\lambda & \alpha - \lambda \end{vmatrix} = 0 \tag{2.1}$$

The α's are matrix elements over the AO's, $(i \mid H^0 \mid i)$, and, as in Eq. (2.1), are often taken as independent of which AO is involved (sometimes the independence follows from considerations of symmetry). The β's are $(i \mid H^0 \mid j)$, and it is assumed that such integrals, including also $s = (i \mid j)$, are appreciable only when the orbitals being designated as $(i|$ and $|j)$ are adjacent, owing to the exponential fall-off of the functions. The one-electron effective Hamiltonian is supposed to take into account the other electrons and to lead to the sort of secular equation described above, but is not specified! "Integrals" over such a Hamiltonian have to be determined empirically.* An unspecified unperturbed Hamiltonian is of limited usefulness because it is not possible to define a perturbation. We shall go a step further, considering the Hückel theory as stemming from an explicit effective one-electron Hamiltonian, and shall eventually go on to consider perturbation effects. Our immediate goal is seeing how explicitly

* For a comprehensive treatment of the simple form of Hückel theory, together with an extensive compilation of applications, see A. Streitwieser, Jr., *Molecular Orbital Theory for Organic Chemists*, New York: John Wiley & Sons, Inc., 1961.

to obtain a one-electron effective potential energy operator (like U in the Hartree-Fock method) which acknowledges the presence of the other electrons, though in as simple a way as possible.

We shall restrict our consideration to hydrogen atoms. The potential of a representative electron is very nearly $-1/r_i$ when it is on the ith proton, and when this electron moves to the jth proton, the potential changes to $-1/r_j$. This occurs because the other electrons having the same spin move out of the way of the electron in question, at the same time covering the ith proton. The space around an electron resulting from the repulsion of the other electrons is called the *Fermi hole.* Less stringently, the same sort of effective potential is obtained even with electrons having opposite spins, as is evident from the fact that the Heitler-London function, $|a\nu)\,|\,b\mu) + |a\mu)\,|\,b\nu)$, is so nearly correct. An example of the Fermi hole which is particularly straightforward is afforded by a molecular state of highest multiplicity (for example, all electrons having a spin α) in which case the many-electron function is a Slater determinant with each MO half-filled

$$|\psi\rangle = \sum_P (-1)^P P\,|\,m\alpha 1)\,|\,l\alpha 2)\,|\,k\alpha 3), \ldots$$

($m, l, k, \ldots$ are molecular orbitals). It can be shown by a linear transformation of the MO's that this is equal to the many-electron function

$$\sum_P (-1)^P P\,|\,a\alpha 1)\,|\,b\alpha 2)\,|\,c\alpha 3), \ldots$$

where $a, b, c, \ldots$ are equivalent orbitals, very much like atomic orbitals. The form of $|\psi\rangle$ after transformation is a sum of products, each product having one electron per equivalent orbital, and each equivalent orbital surrounding a given proton. Considering the resulting screening, we find that the expectation value of the potential energy over a product has a contribution for a representative electron which is essentially the attraction exerted by just the proton which the electron surrounds.

We are now ready to see how a one-electron potential operator may be constructed so as to take into account the other electrons. It will consist of two parts: a "diagonal" part for the bare protons

$$-\sum_k \frac{1}{r_k}$$

and a non-diagonal part, that is, a part containing terms having the dyadic form $|i)(i|$. Each term $|i)(i|$ is multiplied by a number, or "coefficient," the purpose of which is to cancel off unwanted proton attractions, as we shall see. The non-diagonal part is

$$\sum_i \left[(i \mid \sum_{k \neq i} \frac{1}{r_k} \mid i) \right] |i)(i|$$

Here the $|i)$'s are essentially atomic orbitals except that, as will be explained in the next section, they are mutually orthogonal. The coefficients are in square brackets.

The matrix element of the diagonal part for a particular atomic orbital, say, $|2)$, has the attraction of an electron at 2 for all the protons

$$-(2 \mid \sum_k \frac{1}{r_k} \mid 2)$$

The matrix element of the non-diagonal part is, apart from the coefficients

$$(2 \mid \sum_i \mid i)(i \mid 2) = \delta_{2i}$$

Going to the full expression for the non-diagonal potential, we see that this brings in the one coefficient

$$(2 \mid \sum_{k \neq 2} \frac{1}{r_k} \mid 2)$$

which cancels all terms in the diagonal part but the appropriate one. Thus the matrix element all together is

$$(2 \mid \left[-\sum_k \frac{1}{r_k} + \sum_{k \neq 2} \frac{1}{r_k} \right] \mid 2) = -(2 \mid \frac{1}{r_2} \mid 2)$$

As a result, wherever the electron "is" (whichever diagonal matrix element is used), the only attraction is for the proton corresponding to the label of the orbital.

Before going on to see how this particular explicit potential energy works out in practice, we need to digress to consider transformation theoretical aspects of the problem, and orthogonal atomic orbitals. This digression is the subject of the following section.

2.2 THE OAO REPRESENTATION

The Hückel theory secular equation (2.1) resembles an expression for the calculation of the eigenvalues of a matrix, except for the non-orthogonality integrals, s. In fact, if we use orthogonal atomic orbitals (OAO's), we can transform the one-electron Hamiltonian into a new representation such that the eigenvalue calculation for a block of the one-electron energy matrix in the new representation is carried out using an equation like (2.1) without s's. The transformation theoretical point of view will be adopted here. In order to use a set of orthogonal atomic orbitals for carrying out a change of basis, we first need to verify the unitarity condition

$$\mathbf{S}\,\mathbf{S}^\dagger = \mathbf{I}$$

which is easily seen to be fulfilled if we write the transformation matrices as involving the OAO's

$$\mathbf{S} = \begin{bmatrix} (1| \\ (2| \\ (3| \\ \cdot \\ \cdot \\ \cdot \end{bmatrix} \quad \mathbf{S}^\dagger = [|1)\,|\,2)\,|\,3)\ldots]$$

It is helpful to regard S as similar to a rectangular matrix, in which case the wave function corresponding to $(1|$ is the first row. The entries (going across the row) are the values of the function for the various values of the argument. A similar interpretation is given $\mathbf{S}^\dagger$ except that rows and columns are interchanged.

If we continue to consider hydrogen atoms, we shall find composing the set of OAO's one for each 1*s* ordinary AO, hence, one for each atomic nucleus.

The one-electron energy matrix involves

$$H^0 = T + U \tag{2.2}$$

where as explained above

$$U = \sum_i -\frac{1}{r_i} + \sum_i \left[(i\,|\sum_{k\neq i} \frac{1}{r_k}\,|\,i) \right] |\,i)(i| \tag{2.2a}$$

After transformation, the energy in the new representation is $\mathbf{S}H^0\mathbf{S}^\dagger$. As we shall see in Section 2.3, the diagonal elements are approximately equal

$$(i\,|\,H^0\,|\,i) \approx \alpha$$

and only the off-diagonal elements between adjacent centers are appreciable

$$(i\,|\,H^0\,|\,i \pm 1) \approx \beta$$

If we consider four H atoms, a system analogous to the π electrons in butadiene, we find after transformation the following block of the one-electron energy matrix

$$H^0 = \begin{pmatrix} \alpha & \beta & 0 & 0 \\ \beta & \alpha & \beta & 0 \\ 0 & \beta & \alpha & \beta \\ 0 & 0 & \beta & \alpha \end{pmatrix}$$

The dimensions of the matrix are the same as the number of atoms, with the result that there will be as many linearly independent MO's based on $1s$ AO's as there are AO's. The eigenvalues of the matrix are found from

$$|H^0 - \lambda I| = 0$$

a secular equation which, as promised above, closely resembles Eq. (2.1), the only difference being that there is no s term off the diagonal.

Having become acquainted with Hückel theory as an end product of the application of a unitary transformation to an effective Hamiltonian, we need to consider the elements of the unitary transformation and its action on the effective Hamiltonian. First we see how to find these elements (orthogonal atomic orbitals) starting from a set of ordinary atomic orbitals. (Construction of OAO's has been systematically studied by Löwdin.*)

The overlap integrals between ordinary AO's may be collected in a matrix, with matrix elements $(i_o \mid j_o)$ (here the subscript o is used to signify ordinary as compared with orthogonal AO's). The entire matrix may be written as a product of a column times a row

$$\mathbf{\Delta} = \begin{bmatrix} (1_o| \\ (2_o| \\ \cdot \\ \cdot \\ \cdot \end{bmatrix} [|1_o) \mid 2_o) \ldots]$$

The transformation which diagonalizes $\mathbf{\Delta}$ is called $\mathbf{T}$. The columns of $\mathbf{T}^\dagger$ are accordingly the (orthonormal) eigenvectors of $\mathbf{\Delta}$, and

$$\mathbf{T\Delta T}^\dagger = \boldsymbol{\lambda}$$

where $\boldsymbol{\lambda}$ is the diagonal matrix of eigenvalues of $\mathbf{\Delta}$. Using the explicit form of $\mathbf{\Delta}$ above, we have

$$\mathbf{T} \begin{bmatrix} (1_o| \\ (2_o| \\ \cdot \\ \cdot \\ \cdot \end{bmatrix} [|1_o) \mid 2_o) \ldots] \mathbf{T}^\dagger = \boldsymbol{\lambda}$$

so that

$$\boldsymbol{\lambda}^{-1/2}\, \mathbf{T} \begin{bmatrix} (1_o| \\ (2_o| \\ \cdot \\ \cdot \\ \cdot \end{bmatrix} [|1_o) \mid 2_o) \ldots] \mathbf{T}^\dagger \boldsymbol{\lambda}^{-1/2} = \mathbf{I}$$

* P. O. Löwdin, *Advances in Physics*, 5 (1956), 1.

This shows that the linear combinations

$$\sum_j (\boldsymbol{\lambda}^{-1/2}\,\mathbf{T})_{ij}\,(j_o| = (i_1|$$

and correspondingly

$$\sum_i (\boldsymbol{\lambda}^{-1/2}\,\mathbf{T}^\dagger)_{ij}\,|i_o) = |j_1)$$

form an orthonormal set

$$\begin{bmatrix} (1_1| \\ (2_1| \\ \cdot \\ \cdot \\ \cdot \end{bmatrix} [|1_1)\mid 2_1)\ldots] = \mathbf{I}$$

The new orbitals with subscripts 1 are not localized like atomic orbitals. In fact, they are more like Hückel theory molecular orbitals. What is needed is to go back in the original direction to get a new set

$$\begin{bmatrix} (1| \\ (2| \\ \cdot \\ \cdot \\ \cdot \end{bmatrix} = \mathbf{T}^\dagger \begin{bmatrix} (1_1| \\ (2_1| \\ \cdot \\ \cdot \\ \cdot \end{bmatrix}$$

and

$$[|1)\mid 2)\ldots] = [|1_1)\mid 2_1)\ldots]\,\mathbf{T}$$

The new orbitals remain orthonormal because the transformation is unitary. They are reasonably well localized, moreover, because essentially what has been done is transform using first $\mathbf{T}$ and then $\mathbf{T}^{-1}$ $(=\mathbf{T}^\dagger)$. This gives the results

$$\begin{bmatrix} (1| \\ (2| \\ \cdot \\ \cdot \\ \cdot \end{bmatrix} = \mathbf{T}^\dagger\,\boldsymbol{\lambda}^{-1/2}\,\mathbf{T} \begin{bmatrix} (1_o| \\ (2_o| \\ \cdot \\ \cdot \\ \cdot \end{bmatrix} \tag{2.3a}$$

$$[|1)\mid 2)\ldots] = [|1_o)\mid 2_o)\ldots]\,\mathbf{T}^\dagger\boldsymbol{\lambda}^{-1/2}\,\mathbf{T} \tag{2.3b}$$

Thus in Eq. (2.3) we have a scheme formally and systematically for going from ordinary AO's $|i_o)$ to orthogonal AO's $|i)$.

For the sake of simplicity, we do not actually use Eq. (2.3) in what follows, but instead shall use the transformation giving the $|i)$'s only to the first order in the overlap between adjacent orbitals. Moreover, we shall be working with the particular example of four hydrogen atoms, all in a line. For this case, the OAO's can be constructed by simply adding adjacent ordinary AO's multiplied by coefficients $-s/2$, for example,

$$|1) = |1_o) - \frac{s}{2}|2_o)$$

where

$$s = (1_o|2_o) = (2_o|3_o) = (3_o|4_o)$$

and it is assumed

$$(1_o|3_o) = (2_o|4_o), \text{ and so on } = 0$$

The orthonormality may be readily verified. For example,

$$(1|2) = \left[(1_o| - \frac{s}{2}(2_o|\right]\left[-\frac{s}{2}|1_o) + |2_o) - \frac{s}{2}|3_o)\right]$$

$$= -\frac{s}{2} + s - \frac{s}{2} + \text{terms in } s^3$$

Before taking up the example of H_4 in earnest, we shall, by way of summary, look at what the Hückel theory is, and just as important, what it is not.

In the version of the Hartree-Fock method given in Chapter 1, a particular one-electron effective Hamiltonian is used such that in addition to $\delta\langle\psi|H|\psi\rangle = 0$ also $\langle\psi|V|\psi\rangle = 0$. In consequence, the variational integral

$$\langle\psi|H|\psi\rangle = \langle\psi|H^0|\psi\rangle$$

Since $H^0 = \Sigma H^0_\nu$ is a sum of one-electron parts, this last is a simple sum of one-electron integrals, or equivalently for closed shell configurations, the sum of the λ's over occupied orbitals.

In the Hückel theory, we have an explicit H^0_ν, Eq. (2.2), so we can define a V

$$H^0 = \sum_\nu H^0_\nu,$$

$$V = H - H^0 \tag{2.4}$$

It is not true, however, that $\langle\psi|V|\psi\rangle = 0$, so we cannot use $\langle\psi|H^0|\psi\rangle$ with any pretense at rigor, but to make a proper use of the variation method should calculate the integral

$$\langle\psi|H|\psi\rangle = \langle\psi|H^0|\psi\rangle + \langle\psi|V|\psi\rangle$$

Of course, a further difference from the Hartree-Fock method is that the full expectation value $\langle\psi|H|\psi\rangle$ is by no means the best one, but is simply a variation integral over what is hoped to be a reasonably accurate many-electron function.

The expectation value of the unperturbed part of the Hamiltonian is an integral part if not the whole part, and by virtue of our result, for the expectation value of one-electron operators in Chapter 1 is the sum of the λ's over occupied orbitals. Here the λ's are eigenvalues of the H_ν^0 matrix or equivalently integrals of H_ν^0 over the Hückel orbitals, the LCAO MO's.

In a very rough way, the expectation value of V Eq. (2.4) is zero because of the effect of the non-diagonal operator in H_ν^0. The one-electron parts each turn out to have one attraction and the sum has n attractions, which last is also what is found on analyzing the true Hamiltonian. This result

$$\langle\psi \mid V \mid \psi\rangle \sim 0$$

establishes a similarity to the version of the Hartree-Fock method given in Chapter 1 and, because the energy should be roughly the sum of the orbital energies, confers additional importance on work with the unperturbed part. In the next few sections we shall use H^0 as an abbreviation for H_ν^0, the one-electron effective Hamiltonian.

2.3 FOUR HYDROGEN ATOMS

Here we shall assume that the nuclei, four protons, are in line and equally spaced

$$\begin{matrix} + & \quad + & \quad + & \quad + \\ 1 & \quad 2 & \quad 3 & \quad 4 \end{matrix}$$

The one-electron effective Hamiltonian, Eq. (2.2), is

$$H^0 = T - \sum_{i=1}^{4} \frac{1}{r_i} + \sum_{i=1}^{4} \left[(i \mid \sum_{k \neq i} \frac{1}{r_k} \mid i) \right] \mid i)\,(i \mid$$

where the $|i)$'s are OAO's based on 1*s* ordinary AO's. The matrix in the OAO representation has a typical diagonal element

$$(2 \mid \left[T - \sum_{i=1}^{4} \frac{1}{r_i} \right] \mid 2) + (2 \mid \left\{ \sum_{i=1}^{4} \left[(i \mid \sum_{k \neq i} \frac{1}{r_k} \mid i) \right] \mid i)\,(i \mid \right\} \mid 2)$$

The second term is zero unless $i = 2$, giving all together

$$(2 \mid H^0 \mid 2) = (2 \mid T - \frac{1}{r_2} \mid 2)$$

Substituting the expression for $|2)$ in terms of ordinary AO's, accurate to the first order in the overlap of adjacent orbitals, we obtain

$$\left[(2_o \mid - \frac{s}{2} (1_o \mid - \frac{s}{2} (3_o \mid \right] \left[T - \frac{1}{r_2} \right] \left[\mid 2_o) - \frac{s}{2} \mid 1_o) - \frac{s}{2} \mid 3_o) \right]$$

$$= (2_o \mid T - \frac{1}{r_2} \mid 2_o) - \frac{s}{2} (1_o \mid T - \frac{1}{r_2} \mid 2_o) + \cdots$$

Employing the fact that $|2_o)$ is a $1s$ wave function for the second atom

$$(T - \frac{1}{r_2})|\,2_o) = E_o\,|\,2_o)$$

we then find

$$= E_o - \frac{s}{2}\,(1_o\,|\,E_o\,|\,2_o) + \ldots$$

or to the first order

$$= E_o$$

Turning to the off-diagonal elements, we find typically

$$(2\,|\,H^0\,|\,3) = (2\,|\left[T - \sum_{i=1}^{4}\frac{1}{r_i}\right]|\,3) + (2\,|\sum_{i=1}^{4}\left[(i\,|\sum_{k\neq i}\frac{1}{r_k}\,|\,i)\right]|\,i)\,(i\,|\,3)$$

$$= (2\,|\left[T - \sum_{i=1}^{4}\frac{1}{r_i}\right]|\,3)$$

The simplification occurs because the matrix element of the operator

$$(2\,|\,i)(i\,|\,3)$$

is zero, for all i. Substituting the ordinary AO's, we find to the first order

$$\left[(2_o\,| - \frac{s}{2}\,(1_o\,| - \frac{s}{2}\,(3_o\,|\right]\left[T - \sum_{i=1}^{4}\frac{1}{r_i}\right]\left[|\,3_o) - \frac{s}{2}\,|\,2_o) - \frac{s}{2}\,|\,4_o)\right]$$

Energy integrals between adjacent $|i_o)$'s are also considered as small quantities of the first order, so we retain only the following

$$-\frac{s}{2}\,(2_o\,|\left[T - \sum_{i=1}^{4}\frac{1}{r_i}\right]|\,2_o) - \frac{s}{2}\,(3_o\,|\left[T - \sum_{i=1}^{4}\frac{1}{r_i}\right]|\,3_o)$$

$$+ (2_o\,|\left[T - \sum_{i=1}^{4}\frac{1}{r_i}\right]\Big|\,3_o\Big)$$

In each expression, we can take out an E_o, and when we combine, this part disappears. What remains is

$$-\frac{s}{2}\,(2_o\,| - \frac{1}{r_1} - \frac{1}{r_3} - \frac{1}{r_4}\,|\,2_o) - \frac{s}{2}\,(3_o\,| - \frac{1}{r_1} - \frac{1}{r_2} - \frac{1}{r_4}\,|\,3_o)$$

$$+ (2_o\,| - \frac{1}{r_1} - \frac{1}{r_2} - \frac{1}{r_4}\,|\,3_o)$$

The site of the overlap is $2 - 3$. The terms involving protons distant from the site essentially cancel. For example, for $-1/r_4$

$$-\frac{s}{2}\,(2_o\,| - \frac{1}{r_4}\,|\,2_o) - \frac{s}{2}\,(3_o\,| - \frac{1}{r_4}\,|\,3_o)$$

almost cancels

$$(2_o| - \frac{1}{r_4} | 3_o)$$

as can be seen if one pictures the shapes of the wave functions occurring in the various integrals. What remains is terms referring to the site of the overlap

$$-(2_o | \frac{1}{r_2} | 3_o) + \frac{s}{2} (2_o | \frac{1}{r_3} | 2_o) + \frac{s}{2} (3_o | \frac{1}{r_2} | 3_o)$$

This residual quantity is by no means inappreciable. Roughly, it represents the attraction of the fraction s of an electron between 2 and 3 for 2, from which is subtracted the attraction of half this charge on 2 for 3 and half this charge on 3 for 2. The net effect is thus attraction, of the order of

$$s\left(-\frac{1}{D/2} + \frac{1}{D}\right) = -\frac{s}{D}$$

where D is the interatomic distance. To a fair degree of approximation, all the off-diagonal elements referring to adjacent centers are the same. The matrix elements connecting non-adjacent OAO's contain terms involving the overlap of non-adjacent ordinary atomic orbitals, which may be set equal to zero, and also higher-order terms in the strict sense. In summary, we have found for the diagonal elements, which we shall call α,

$$\alpha \approx E_o$$

and for the off-diagonal elements, which we shall call β

$$\beta \sim -\frac{s}{D} < 0$$

The secular equation is thus

$$\begin{vmatrix} \alpha - \lambda & \beta & 0 & 0 \\ \beta & \alpha - \lambda & \beta & 0 \\ 0 & \beta & \alpha - \lambda & \beta \\ 0 & 0 & \beta & \alpha - \lambda \end{vmatrix} = 0 \tag{2.5}$$

Dividing by β^4 (one for each row) and putting $(\alpha - \lambda)/\beta = x$ (so that the x-energy is in units of $-\beta$ and measured from α as a zero point) we have

$$\begin{vmatrix} x & 1 & 0 & 0 \\ 1 & x & 1 & 0 \\ 0 & 1 & x & 1 \\ 0 & 0 & 1 & x \end{vmatrix} = x^4 - 3x^2 + 1 = 0 \tag{2.5a}$$

The solutions are obtained from

$$x^2 = \frac{3 \pm \sqrt{5}}{2}$$

or -1.618, -0.618, 0.618, and 1.618. The root -1.618 gives a λ value

$$\alpha - \lambda = -1.618\,\beta$$

$$\lambda = \alpha + 1.618\,\beta$$

which is lowest because of $\beta < 0$. The unperturbed energy of four hydrogen atoms works out to be $4\alpha + 3.236\beta + 1.236\beta$, because we put only two electrons in an orbital. The binding energy is $4E_o$ minus this quantity, or, in the Hückel approximation, $-4.472\,\beta$.

This is greater than twice the binding energy of two atoms (or -4β) by -0.472β. This excess binding energy (resonance energy) is probably in disagreement with the experimental fact that H_4 is unstable

$$H_4 \rightarrow 2H_2$$

(presumably with the evolution of heat), which illustrates a well-known insufficiency of the molecular orbital approach in the simple form where $\langle\psi \mid H^0 \mid \psi\rangle$ is considered but $\langle\psi \mid V \mid \psi\rangle$ is not.

2.4 WAVE FUNCTIONS AND INTERPRETATION*

The functions are combinations of $|i)$'s determined by the linear homogeneous simultaneous equations with coefficients the same as in the secular equation (2.5) or Eq. (2.5a). Calling the coefficients k_i, for $x = -1.618$, we have

$$\begin{aligned} -1.618\,k_1 + k_2 &= 0 \\ k_1 - 1.618\,k_2 + k_3 &= 0 \\ k_2 - 1.618\,k_3 + k_4 &= 0 \\ k_3 - 1.618\,k_4 &= 0 \end{aligned}$$

After normalization, the solution for $x = -1.618$ is†

$$|1_1) = 0.37 \mid 1) + 0.60 \mid 2) + 0.60 \mid 3) + 0.37 \mid 4)$$

The other solutions have sign reversals (nodes), with the energy higher the more nodes there are. These other functions are

$$|2_1) = 0.60 \mid 1) + 0.37 \mid 2) - 0.37 \mid 3) - 0.60 \mid 4)$$

$$|3_1) = 0.60 \mid 1) - 0.37 \mid 2) - 0.37 \mid 3) + 0.60 \mid 4)$$

$$|4_1) = 0.37 \mid 1) - 0.60 \mid 2) + 0.60 \mid 3) - 0.37 \mid 4)$$

* Interpretation of wave functions has recently been considered by R. S. Mulliken, *J. Chem. Phys.*, **23** (1955), 1833.

† The distinguishing subscript, 1, is needed because the notation: $|i)$ is reserved for orthogonal atomic orbitals.

corresponding to $x = -0.618$, $+0.618$ and $+1.618$ respectively. The orbital energy may now be calculated anew as the expectation value of H^0; thus for the first molecular orbital,

$$
\begin{aligned}
(1_1 \mid H^0 \mid 1_1) = {} & 0.37^2\,(1 \mid H^0 \mid 1) \\
& + 0.60^2\,(2 \mid H^0 \mid 2) + 0.60^2\,(3 \mid H^0 \mid 3) + 0.37^2\,(4 \mid H^0 \mid 4) \\
& + 0.37 \times 0.60\,[(1 \mid H^0 \mid 2) + (2 \mid H^0 \mid 1)] \\
& + 0.60 \times 0.60\,[(2 \mid H^0 \mid 3) + (3 \mid H^0 \mid 2)] \\
& + 0.37 \times 0.60\,[(3 \mid H^0 \mid 4) + (4 \mid H^0 \mid 3)] + \text{terms involving non-adjacent } |i)\text{'s}
\end{aligned}
$$

The diagonal elements are $\alpha(= E_o$ to the first order), which may be factored to give the contribution from squared terms

$$\alpha(0.37^2 + 0.60^2 + 0.60^2 + 0.37^2) = \alpha$$

and the terms referring to adjacent orbitals, in the approximation that

$$(1 \mid H^0 \mid 2) = (2 \mid H^0 \mid 3) = \cdots = \beta$$

give

$$2\beta(0.37 \times 0.60 + 0.60 \times 0.60 + 0.37 \times 0.60) = 1.618\,\beta$$

Since $\beta < 0$, the stabilization with respect to α as a zero point evidently depends on having the cross terms enter with positive signs, which in turn depends on the absence of nodes in the lowest energy function, $|1_1)$. Correspondingly, the presence of nodes in the remaining functions raises the energy through the influence on the β or cross terms. (Note that the sum of squared terms always comes out α.) It becomes a matter of interest to be able to focus on a particular overlap site, or bond, looking at the nodes as a measure of the degree to which the site may be considered as stabilized or destabilized, and especially considering the cumulative effect from all occupied orbitals. We shall obtain a formal scheme for assessing the effect quantitatively, although as a preliminary we need to consider in a general way how probability distribution is handled with the bracket notation.

The eigenvector of "position" at the particular point x' will be called $(x'|$ with corresponding wave function $\delta(x - x')$. An orbital, $|k)$, may be considered as expanded in terms of the set of all $|x)$ in which case a particular coefficient in the expansion is $(x' \mid k)$ and the probability that the particle be found at x' is the coefficient times its complex conjugate

$$(x' \mid k)(k \mid x')$$

Any one such term may be regarded as a diagonal matrix element $(x' = x'')$

over $(x'|$ and $|x'')$ of the central operator, $|k)(k|$. Since $(x' \mid \sigma \mid x'')$ is also the Schrödinger representative of any operator σ, one sees that in the Schrödinger representation along the diagonal of the operator $|k)(k|$ is the probability distribution function. The central operator is called ρ_ν, the density matrix for the orbital $|k)$, and the point of view leads automatically to our considering a possible physical significance for off-diagonal matrix elements of the density matrix. As we shall see, appropriate off-diagonal elements over OAO's of the density matrix for an MO give a quantitative measure of the nodal properties of a site.*

The density matrix for the first MO is

$$\begin{aligned} |1_1)(1_1| = 0.14 \mid 1)(1 \mid &+ 0.36 \mid 2)(2 \mid + 0.36 \mid 3)(3 \mid + 0.14 \mid 4)(4| \\ &+ 0.22\,[|1)(2 \mid + \mid 2)(1 \mid + \mid 3)(4 \mid + \mid 4)(3|] \\ &+ 0.36\,[|2)(3 \mid + \mid 3)(2|] + \ldots \end{aligned}$$

The coefficient of the overlap at the 1, 2 site is 0.22, occurring twice, which is the same as governs the contribution to the total stabilization of 1.618 β coming from this site (given above as the factor 0.37×0.60 occurring twice). To generalize, we define the "bond order" between adjacent centers i and j as the average of matrix elements

$$\frac{[(i \mid \rho_\nu \mid j) + (j \mid \rho_\nu \mid i)]}{2}$$

The total bond order is then a sum of contributions like the above. For the lowest configuration of the H_4 molecule, we have two contributions from $|1_1)(1_1|$ and two from $|2_1)(2_1|$.

As an example, we compute the 2, 3 bond order. The part over the first orbital (doubly occupied) is

$$\frac{2[(3 \mid 1_1)(1_1 \mid 2) + (2 \mid 1_1)(1_1 \mid 3)]}{2} = 0.72$$

Similarly, one finds -0.28 from the second orbital, also doubly occupied. For the four electrons, the total bond order is 0.44. The 1, 2 and 3, 4 total bond orders are each computed to be 0.88, giving the following pattern:

$$\underset{1}{+} \quad 0.88 \quad \underset{2}{+} \quad 0.44 \quad \underset{3}{+} \quad 0.88 \quad \underset{4}{+}$$

The total bond order in H_2 is unity and the sum of the bond orders here for H_4 is greater than twice this value, a fact which is consonant with the total energy being greater in absolute value than 4β.

* C. A. Coulson, *Proc. Roy. Soc.*, **A169** (1939), 413. C. A. Coulson and H. C. Longuet-Higgins, *Proc. Roy. Soc.*, **A191** (1947), 39.

These results are sometimes used in connection with the π electrons in butadiene, so that there is implicit in the 0.88 value a prediction that the 1—2 bond will be longer than the corresponding bond in ethylene (1.35 Å) with total bond order one. By contrast, the 0.44 value indicates that the center link will be shorter than the value for a C—C single bond (1.54 Å) which has a total π-electron bond order of zero. Indeed, the bond lengths in butadiene follow this pattern. The 1—2 bond is 1.36 Å and the 2—3 bond is 1.46 Å. This is only one of several possible interpretations of the variation of the bond lengths in butadiene.

The diagonal elements of the density matrix summed over filled orbitals are the atomic charge densities. Referring to the density matrix for the first MO one sees that the density on atom one is 0.14 (occurring twice) and for the second MO it is 0.36 (twice) or, totally, 1.00. The ground state of the system of four atoms turns out to have equal charge densities at each atom; moreover, the values, 1.00 for each atom, add up to 4, the number of electrons.

Such uniformity of charge is consistent* with the form of the effective Hamiltonian, which form causes equal diagonal entries, α, to occur in the secular equation. The same type of consistency is not found for the off-diagonal elements, in that the bond orders resulting from equal β's are not themselves equal.

It has frequently been attempted to assign electronic transitions as arising from transfers of an electron between the Hückel theory energy levels.† Thus a first transition represented by the arrow, and involving orbitals $|2_1) \rightarrow |3_1)$ would be expected in the electronic spectrum of butadiene and with $\Delta E = -1.236\beta$. As the technique of experimental electronic spectroscopy has developed, it has been possible to verify some of these assignments and call into question others. What has to be considered is the comparison between calculated and observed frequencies and intensities and; just as important, between calculated and observed polarization directions. The indicated transition for butadiene has not yet been unequivocally identified in the ultraviolet spectrum, but probably corresponds to an actual absorption band with a peak at 209 mμ. Incidentally, consistency with respect to atomic charge

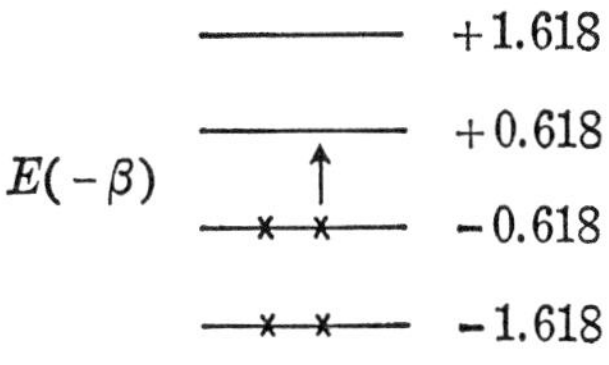

$E(-\beta)$: +1.618, +0.618, −0.618, −1.618

* C. A. Coulson and G. S. Rushbrooke, *Proc. Cambridge Phil. Soc.*, **36** (1940), 193.

† For a comprehensive review of electronic spectra of organic molecules see J. R. Platt, *Ann. Revs. Phys. Chem.*, **10** (Stanford, Calif: Annual Review, Inc., 1960).

densities in the sense described in the preceding paragraph is found also for the configuration formed when the transition $|2_1) \rightarrow |3_1)$ has occurred.

A treatment analogous to the one above for butadiene for the ion

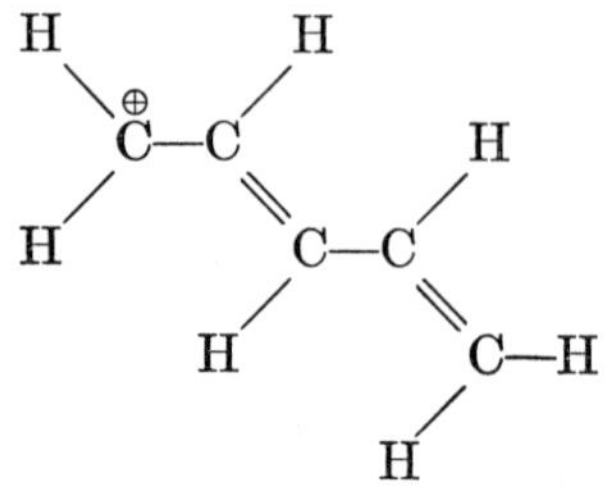

```
H       H
 \⊕    /
  C—C         H
 /    \\     /
H      C—C
      /    \\
     H      C—H
           /
          H
```

(four π electrons in five π orbitals) is the prototype of a simple molecular orbital theory of dyes. (See also Chapter 3.) The elementary Hückel theory as empirically calibrated for one ion leads to predictions about transition energies and intensities for related ions, which predictions are often surprisingly accurate. One reason for the accuracy seems to be that for the dye ions the original assumption of all equal β's leads to theoretical bond orders which are themselves nearly equal.*

In the next section, we shall consider the solution of the unperturbed problem from a more general point of view. This will prove convenient as a starting point for the study of the perturbation part of the Hückel theory.

2.5 GENERAL SOLUTION

The Hückel theory energy matrix has α's on the diagonal and β's at the positions referring to adjacent atoms. If all the atoms are equivalent, as with an infinite chain or a circular arrangement, all α's as well as all β's are strictly equal and may be factored

$$\mathbf{H}^0 = \alpha\mathbf{I} + \beta\mathbf{J}$$

The matrix $\mathbf{J}$ has ones in positions referring to adjacent atoms, and when no atom is adjacent to more than two others this matrix is essentially a finite-difference kinetic energy operator. This implies that the effective mass model discussed in Section 3.13 may be employed, only here at the

* The original assumption of all equal α's does not, however, lead to charge densities uniformly distributed amongst the various centers. It seems to be fairly well established empirically that consistency with respect to bond orders and β's is the overriding consideration, so that assignments of electronic transitions based on Hückel theory are more likely to succeed for the dye ions.

one-electron Hamiltonian level rather than at the many-electron level. Such a use of the effective mass model leads to what is known as the *free-electron method.**

In what follows, we shall work with **J** itself, or rather with the transform of **J** back into the Schrödinger representation, so that we shall be using H^0 without resorting to the free-electron model. Nevertheless, many of the results will bear a strong resemblance to free-particle results, as for example, the appearance of quantum numbers which (for a circular arrangement of atoms) are analogous to angular momentum quantum numbers.†

The **J** matrix in the Schrödinger representation becomes the operator

$$J = \sum_{\substack{i,j \\ \text{adjacent}}} |i)(j|$$

as can be verified by transforming back into the orthogonal atomic orbital representation. We have the result that both the (dimensionless) H^0 and J upon transformation go into **J**, yet $H^0 \neq J$.‡ If we confine ourselves to the $1s$ block or "valence shell," however, we do have the weak equality between one-electron operators

$$H^0 = J$$

a situation which has its analog in the next chapter in connection with the Dirac vector model. The J form of H^0 is particularly convenient because we can use a manifest eigenvalue relation, as we shall see.

If the atoms are in a circle or chain, the J operator becomes§

$$\sum_i [|i-1)(i| + |i+1)(i|]$$

The molecular orbitals are linear combinations of OAO's

$$|k_1) = \sum_j |j)(j \mid k_1)$$

or, with c's for the coefficients,

$$= \sum_j c_j \mid j)$$

The eigenvalue relation is thus

$$\sum_i [|i-1)(i| + |i+1)(i|] \sum_j c_j \mid j) = \lambda \sum_j c_j \mid j)$$

* See, for example, N. S. Bayliss, *Quart. Revs.* (London), **6** (1952), 319.

† J. R. Platt, *J. Chem. Phys.*, **17** (1949), 484.

‡ This occurs because we have not used the full transformation theory but instead have used rectangular matrices appropriate to the $1s$ block.

§ When $|i+1)$ or $|i-1)$ are outside the set of orbitals, they must be specially interpreted. Thus for a circle of n atoms $|n+1)$ must be taken as $|1)$.

Carrying out the operation on the left, we find

$$\sum_i [|i-1) + |i+1)]\, c_i = \lambda \sum_j c_j\, |j)$$

Then, multiplying both sides of the equation by $(s|$,

$$c_{s+1} + c_{s-1} = \lambda c_s$$

Now we assume a trial solution to this system of equations

$$c_s = e^{iks/n}$$

where k/n is a parameter and n is the number of atoms. Then

$$c_{s-1} = e^{ik(s-1)/n}$$

$$c_{s+1} = e^{ik(s+1)/n}$$

and the sum is

$$e^{isk/n}\left(e^{ik/n} + e^{-ik/n}\right) = 2\cos\frac{k}{n}\, c_s$$

This shows that

$$\lambda = 2\cos\frac{k}{n}$$

so that in the case where there are no boundary conditions and all k values are allowed (infinite chain) the energies go from -2 to 2; or, with $H^0 = \beta J$, from 2β to -2β.

We shall specialize to the case of six atoms arranged in a circle, in which case the coefficients are given by

$$c_s = e^{iks/6}$$

The utility of writing k/n as a parameter will become clear as we consider the boundary conditions. If $k = 0$ we have all the coefficients equal, and the lowest energy (β units)

$$\lambda = 2$$

The next value for which the coefficients are single-valued is given by the condition that the coefficients run through a cycle when s runs from 0 to 5 (around once). Thus

$$k = \pm 2\pi$$

which, with $\not{k} = k/2\pi$, may be re-expressed as

$$\not{k} = \pm 1$$

Having the coefficients run through two cycles gives

$$\not{k} = \pm 2$$

and if $k\!\!\!/ = \pm 3$ we have the coefficients for the final high energy state, which is non-degenerate

$$c_s = e^{i(\pm 6\pi)s/6} = e^{\pm i\pi s}$$

For this state, the c's are ± 1, depending on whether s is even or odd. If n is different from 6, we have essentially the same result

$$|k\!\!\!/| = 0, 1, \ldots, \frac{n}{2}$$

$$\lambda = 2 \cos \frac{2\pi k\!\!\!/}{n}$$

The transformation between the MO's and AO's has now been obtained going in one direction. For $n = 6$ and with normalization it is

$$|k\!\!\!/_1) = \frac{1}{\sqrt{6}} \sum_{s=0}^{5} e^{2\pi i k\!\!\!/ s/6} \mid s) \tag{2.6a}$$

Since the $|k\!\!\!/_1)$'s are orthogonal, the rows in the matrix of the coefficients are unitary. Thus the inverse of the transformation is the Hermitian conjugate

$$|s) = \frac{1}{\sqrt{6}} \sum_{|k\!\!\!/|=0}^{3} e^{-2\pi i k\!\!\!/ s/6} \mid k\!\!\!/_1) \tag{2.6b}$$

This transformation will be used in the next section.

2.6 THE PERTURBATION

The first refinement of the Hückel theory consists in making up Slater determinants from the MO's and then using these many-electron functions to calculate expectation values of the perturbation—see Eq. (2.2) and Eq. (2.4):

$$V = H - \sum_{\nu} H_{\nu}^{0}$$

$$= \sum_{i<j} \frac{1}{r_{ij}} + \sum_{\mu<\nu} \frac{1}{r_{\mu\nu}} - \sum_{i\nu} \left[(i\nu \mid \sum_{k\neq i} \frac{1}{r_{k\nu}} \mid i\nu) \right] |i\nu)(i\nu| \tag{2.7a}$$

If the intuitive form of Hückel theory is used (no explicit H^0), much the same result is obtained by calculating the expectation value of the full H, but then the orbital energies as obtained in the one-electron theory must be taken rather lightly. Using the V above, we add the expectation value of the perturbation to the sum of the orbital energies over filled orbitals, so that unperturbed and perturbed energies are delineated. Also the V operator is potentially useful for going to higher orders of perturbation theory, although this possibility will not be explored here.

The nuclear repulsion part of V is, of course, a constant. For a system of atoms of the sort treated in the last section, the operator part is also essentially constant. In order to see this, we note first that by symmetry all the integrals

$$(s\mu \mid \sum_{k \neq s} \frac{1}{r_{k\mu}} \mid s\mu)$$

are the same regardless of where the sth orbital may be located. This makes possible a factoring

$$(s\mu \mid \sum_{k \neq s} \frac{1}{r_{k\mu}} \mid s\mu) \sum_{\nu} \sum_{s} \mid s\nu)(s\nu|$$

Introducing the MO's through the transformation Eq. (2.6b), we obtain

$$|s\nu)(s\nu| = \frac{1}{n} \sum_{\not k} e^{-2\pi i \not k s/n} \mid \not k_1\, \nu) \sum_{\not k'} e^{2\pi i \not k' s/n} (\not k_1'\, \nu|$$

If, however, $\not k \neq \not k'$, the subsequent sum on s gives zero. Carrying out this summation, one obtains for the operator part*

$$(s\mu| \sum_{k \neq s} \frac{1}{r_{k\mu}} \mid s\mu) \sum_{\nu} \sum_{|\not k| = 0}^{n/2} \mid \not k_1\, \nu)(\not k_1\, \nu|$$

Matrix elements over

$$\sum_{\not k} \mid \not k_1\, \nu)(\not k_1\, \nu|$$

are zero unless the νth electron is in the same orbital, on either side of the matrix element. If the orbitals match, a factor of 1 is introduced. Therefore, the matrix element over the full operator

$$\sum_{\nu} \sum_{\not k} \mid \not k_1\, \nu)(_1\not k\, \nu|$$

between simple matching products of filled orbitals introduces a factor n, the number of electrons. It can be shown that this is also true for the diagonal matrix element between Slater determinants (each describing the same configuration) and that non-diagonal matrix elements between Slater determinants vanish. The configurations have to involve only orbitals selected from among the valence shell set, $|\not k| = 0$ to $n/2$, but with this proviso we have

$$\sum_{\nu \not k} \mid \not k_1\, \nu)(\not k_1\, \nu| = n$$

* The sum over $|\not k| = 0$ up to $n/2$ for $n = 6$ is to be understood as over $\not k = 0, \pm 1, \pm 2, 3$. Similar qualification must be understood in subsequent parts of this section.

The perturbation, Eq. (2.7a), becomes

$$V = \sum_{i<j} \frac{1}{r_{ij}} - n\left[(i\nu \mid \sum_{k\neq i} \frac{1}{r_{k\nu}} \mid i\nu) \right] + \sum_{\mu<\nu} \frac{1}{r_{\mu\nu}} \tag{2.7b}$$

The only non-constant part is the interelectronic interaction. We shall now work out a simplification for this part using an approach analogous to the one above (though, understandably, more complicated).

The general electron repulsion integral on the valence shell (between orthogonal atomic orbitals) is

$$(r\mu|\ (s\nu \mid \frac{1}{r_{\mu\nu}} \mid t\mu)\ |u\nu)$$

This may be written in the following (seemingly redundant) fashion

$$(r\mu|\ (s\nu| \left\{ \sum_{ijkl} \left[(i\mu|\ (j\nu \mid \frac{1}{r_{\mu\nu}} \mid k\mu)\ |l\nu) \right] |i\mu)\ |j\nu)\ (k\mu|\ (l\nu| \right\} |t\mu)\ |u\nu)$$

which, however, gives the formal result that on the valence shell

$$\frac{1}{r_{\mu\nu}} = \sum_{rstu} \left[(r\mu|\ (s\nu \mid \frac{1}{r_{\mu\nu}} \mid t\mu)\ |u\nu) \right] |r\mu)\ |s\nu)(t\mu|\ (u\nu|$$

After considerable computational experimentation, it has been discovered (by Pariser and Parr, and by Pople*) that certain electron repulsion matrix elements may for all practical purposes be neglected. These are elements for which one or both electrons are half in one and half in another orthogonal atomic orbital, as for example ($r \neq t$)

$$(r\mu|\ (s\nu \mid \frac{1}{r_{\mu\nu}} \mid t\mu)\ |s\nu)$$

where the μth electron is in such an "overlap distribution." Neglecting these electron repulsion matrix elements greatly simplifies calculation of the effect of the perturbation and is adopted in the following. Thus, we introduce the approximation

$$(r\mu|\ (s\nu \mid \frac{1}{r_{\mu\nu}} \mid t\mu)\ |u\nu) \cong (r\mu|\ (s\nu \mid \frac{1}{r_{\mu\nu}} \mid t\mu)\ |u\nu)\ \delta_{rt}\, \delta_{su}$$

and abbreviation

$$(r\mu|\ (s\nu \mid \frac{1}{r_{\mu\nu}} \mid r\mu)\ |s\nu) \equiv Q_{rs}$$

To this degree of approximation, we therefore have for the interelectronic repulsion

* R. Pariser and R. G. Parr, *J. Chem. Phys.*, **21** (1953), 466, 767. J. A. Pople, *Trans. Far. Soc.*, **49** (1953), 1375. See also *J. Phys. Chem.*, **61** (1957), 6.

$$\frac{1}{r_{\mu\nu}} = \sum_{rs} Q_{rs} \mid r\mu) \mid s\nu) \; (r\mu \mid (s\nu|$$

which, as it occurs in V, Eq. (2.7b), must then be summed over $\mu < \nu$.

The obvious way to proceed is to make up Slater determinants corresponding to configurations of occupied MO's and then to compute matrix elements of the above operator directly. In effect, this is what is usually done. But in the case we have been considering, with all atoms equivalent, another course is open to us.

In fact, the foregoing is unnecessarily formal for calculations using atomic orbitals directly, but it was obtained with the other idea in mind: that of incorporating the transformation between MO's and OAO's, Eq. (2.6b). Making the substitution, we obtain

$$\frac{1}{r_{\mu\nu}} = \sum_{rs} Q_{rs} \frac{1}{n^2} \sum_{|j|=0}^{n/2} e^{-2\pi ijr/n} \mid j\mu) \sum_{|k|=0}^{n/2} e^{-2\pi iks/n} \mid k\nu)$$
$$\times \sum_{|l|=0}^{n/2} e^{2\pi ilr/n} \; (l\mu \mid \sum_{|m|=0}^{n/2} e^{2\pi ims/n} \; (m\nu|$$

Here the $\not{k}$ quantum number for labeling molecular orbitals $|\not{k}_1)$ is represented as j, k, l, and m in turn, and the subscript 1 is omitted (we shall be dealing almost exclusively with molecular orbitals in the next sections).

Focusing on the μth electron and thinking of r as fixed, we may divide the double sum into two parts, one where $j \neq l$ and the other where $j = l$

$$\sum_{|j|=0}^{n/2} e^{-2\pi ijr/n} \, e^{+2\pi ijr/n} \mid j\mu) \; (j\mu \mid + \sum_{j \neq l} e^{-2\pi i(j-l)r/n} \mid j\mu) \; (l\mu|$$

The first expression reduces to the sum

$$\sum_{|j|=0}^{n/2} \mid j\mu) \; (j\mu|$$

which, as we have seen above, is one on the valence shell. The same reasoning applies also for electron ν, leading to

$$\frac{1}{r_{\mu\nu}} = \frac{1}{n^2} \sum_{rs} Q_{rs} \left[1 + \sum_{j \neq l} e^{-2\pi i(j-l)r/n} \mid j\mu) \; (l\mu| \right]$$
$$\times \left[1 + \sum_{k \neq m} e^{-2\pi i(k-m)s/n} \mid k\nu) \; (m\nu| \right]$$

This simplifies to

$$\frac{1}{n^2} \sum_{rs} Q_{rs} \left[1 + \sum_{j \neq l} e^{-2\pi i(j-l)r/n} \mid j\mu) \; (l\mu| \sum_{k \neq m} e^{-2\pi i(k-m)s/n} \mid k\nu) \; (m\nu| \right]$$

only the constant and "quadratic" terms remaining. The reason is that by symmetry

$$\sum_s Q_{rs}$$

is independent of r so that, for example,

$$\sum_r \left\{ \left[\sum_s Q_{rs} \right] e^{-2\pi i(j-l)r/n} \right\} = 0$$

(the coefficients of the OAO's in the j and l MO's are components of orthogonal vectors, $j \neq l$). We shall set aside the constant part

$$\frac{1}{n^2} \sum_{rs} Q_{rs}$$

and go on to consider the quadratic factor which we shall call $Q_{\mu\nu}$. We rewrite this term now with $\alpha = r - s$.

$$Q_{\mu\nu} = \frac{1}{n^2} \sum_{r\alpha} Q_{r,r-\alpha} \sum_{j \neq l} e^{-2\pi i(j-l)r/n} \, |j\mu)\,(l\mu \,| \sum_{k \neq m} e^{-2\pi i(k-m)(r-\alpha)/n} \,|\, k\nu)\,(m\nu|$$

The new index α is employed in order to take advantage of the fact that with a systematic numbering system Q_{rs} depends only on $|\alpha|$ (physically, on the distance between OAO's located at r and s). The sum over r can thus be confined to the operator part, because

$$Q_{r,r-\alpha} = Q_{|\alpha|}$$

is independent of r, and therefore

$$\begin{aligned} Q_{\mu\nu} &= \frac{1}{n^2} \sum_{|\alpha|=0}^{n/2} Q_{|\alpha|} \sum_r \sum_{j \neq l} e^{-2\pi i(j-l)r/n} \, |j\mu)\,(l\mu \,| \\ &\qquad \times \sum_{k \neq m} e^{-2\pi i(k-m)(r-\alpha)/n} \,|\, k\nu)\,(m\nu| \\ &= \sum_{j \neq l} \sum_{k \neq m} \frac{1}{n^2} \sum_{|\alpha|=0}^{n/2} e^{2\pi i(k-m)\alpha/n} \, Q_{|\alpha|} \\ &\qquad \times \sum_r e^{-2\pi i(j-l+k-m)r/n} \,|\, j\mu)\,(l\mu|\,|k\nu)\,(m\nu| \end{aligned}$$

Looking now at the sum over r, we see the result is zero unless

$$j - l + k - m = 0 \quad \text{or} \quad \pm n$$

(the change in "momentum" for μ added to the change for ν must be zero or n), which is a form of selection rule, limiting the operator part and thus allowing only certain configurations to interact. If $j - l + k - m$ is 0 or n, then the sum over r gives n and the interaction becomes

$$K_{k-m} = \frac{1}{n} \sum_{|\alpha|=0}^{n/2} e^{2\pi i(k-m)\alpha/n} Q_{|\alpha|}$$

The formula appears asymmetric between the change for the νth electron $k \rightarrow m$ and the change for the μth, $j \rightarrow l$. These, however, are related by the selection rule in such a way that either could be used. Moreover, the various K's are all real because the sin part has canceling terms by virtue of $Q_\alpha = Q_{-\alpha}$

$$K_{|k-m|} = \frac{1}{n} \sum_{|\alpha|=0}^{n/2} Q_{|\alpha|} \cos \frac{2\pi \mid k - m \mid \alpha}{n} \tag{2.8}$$

Returning to the full interelectronic interaction, we now have

$$\frac{1}{r_{\mu\nu}} = \frac{1}{n^2} \sum_{rs} Q_{rs} + Q_{\mu\nu}$$

where

$$Q_{\mu\nu} = \sum_{\substack{j \neq l \\ j-l+k-m=0 \\ \text{or } n}} \sum_{k \neq m} \mid j\mu) \mid k\nu) (l\mu \mid (m\nu \mid K_{|k-m|} \tag{2.9}$$

We shall principally be applying $Q_{\mu\nu}$ in the following, so that the aim of this section has been accomplished. But before taking up the applications, we might profitably organize the constant parts a little better. The sum over s only,

$$\sum_s Q_{rs}$$

is independent of r. The double sum is thus $n \sum_s Q_{rs}$ and we have

$$\frac{1}{r_{\mu\nu}} = \frac{1}{n} \sum_s Q_{rs} + Q_{\mu\nu}$$

or, summing over all pairs of electrons,

$$\sum_{\mu<\nu} \frac{1}{r_{\mu\nu}} = \frac{n^2 - n}{2n} \sum_s Q_{rs} + \sum_{\mu<\nu} Q_{\mu\nu}$$

We now go back a step, to V, the perturbation itself, Eq. (2.7b). Using our result for the interelectronic interaction, this becomes

$$V = \sum_{i<j} \frac{1}{r_{ij}} - n\,(i\nu \mid \sum_{k \neq i} \frac{1}{r_{k\nu}} \mid i\nu) + \frac{n-1}{2} \sum_s Q_{rs} + \sum_{\mu<\nu} Q_{\mu\nu} \tag{2.7c}$$

The part that is non-constant and therefore non-trivial, Eq. (2.8) and Eq. (2.9)

$$\sum_{\mu<\nu} Q_{\mu\nu}$$

we shall call the *interaction operator*.

The geometrical structure of the nuclear repulsion part is explicit enough. The electronic repulsions brought in by the Q_{rs} term are $(n^2 - n)/2$ in number, as for the nuclear repulsions, and have a similar (though not identical) structure. The attractions are $n^2 - n$ in number and have a geometrical structure which is obviously a fair match for the structure of the repulsions. We see that, at least with respect to number, the attractions and repulsions are already balanced in the constant parts of V; so with our earlier result (Section 2.2) that V is, in a sense, zero we expect the interaction operator itself to be, in a sense, zero. This is corroborated by the fact that the interaction operator introduces only exchange integrals, never coulomb integrals.

2.7 BENZENE MANY-ELECTRON FUNCTIONS

We now shall study the first few energy levels in the valence shell for half-filled orbitals arranged around in a circle, as in the hypothetical molecule H_6. To the extent that the π electrons in benzene may be considered as independent of the rest of the molecule, the results apply to benzene. After the details of the calculations are presented, we shall make a comparison with the benzene spectrum. (The benzene calculation was first done by Goeppert-Mayer and Sklar.*)

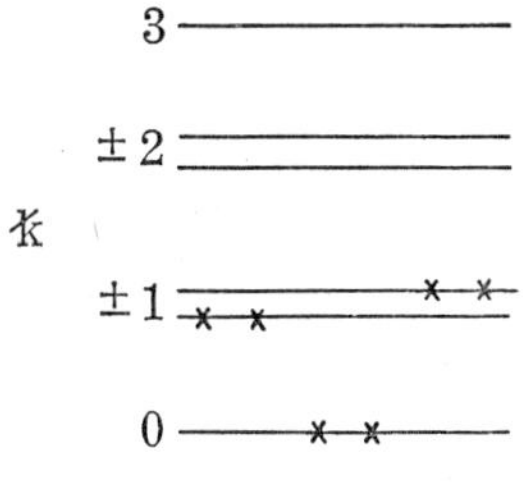

The molecular orbitals have already been found, Eq. (2.6a). They are labeled according to the $\not{k}$ value

$$|0), \; |+1), \; |-1), \; |+2), \; |-2), \; |3)$$

The corresponding energies are $2\beta \cos 2\pi\not{k}/6$.

Figure 2.1

The pattern of filled and empty orbitals in the configuration of lowest energy is shown in Fig. 2.1. The wave function for this configuration is

$$|0\rangle = (6!)^{-1/2} A \mid 0\alpha 1) \mid 0\beta 2) \mid +1\alpha 3) \mid +1\beta 4) \mid -1\alpha 5) \mid -1\beta 6)$$

where the antisymmetrizing operator is abbreviated

$$A \equiv \sum_P (-1)^P P$$

and, for example, $|\not{k}\alpha\nu)$ means electron ν is in the $\not{k}\alpha$ spin orbital.

The first excited configuration is fourfold degenerate because an electron

* M. Goeppert-Mayer and A. L. Sklar, *J. Chem. Phys.*, 6 (1938), 645.

can be shifted from either $|+1\rangle$ or $|-1\rangle$ into either $|+2\rangle$ or $|-2\rangle$. The wave functions for the excited configurations are more complicated, since, with only one electron in an orbital, the spins need not be paired. We shall use linear combinations of Slater determinants, which combinations are antisymmetric when the spins going along with the half-filled orbitals are exchanged. This automatically gives singlet functions, as will be shown in the next chapter. The singlet wave functions for the first excited configuration are labeled according to Δk

$$-1 \rightarrow +2$$

$$|+3\rangle = (2 \cdot 6!)^{-1/2} A\,|0\alpha 1\rangle\,|0\beta 2\rangle \times [|+1\alpha 3\rangle\,|+1\beta 4\rangle\,|-1\alpha 5\rangle\,|+2\beta 6\rangle - |+1\alpha 3\rangle\,|+1\beta 4\rangle\,|-1\beta 5\rangle\,|+2\alpha 6\rangle] \tag{2.10a}$$

$$-1 \rightarrow -2$$

$$|-1\rangle = (2 \cdot 6!)^{-1/2} A\,|0\alpha 1\rangle\,|0\beta 2\rangle \times [|+1\alpha 3\rangle\,|+1\beta 4\rangle\,|-1\alpha 5\rangle\,|-2\beta 6\rangle - |+1\alpha 3\rangle\,|+1\beta 4\rangle\,|-1\beta 5\rangle\,|-2\alpha 6\rangle] \tag{2.10b}$$

$$+1 \rightarrow +2$$

$$|+1\rangle = (2 \cdot 6!)^{-1/2} A\,|0\alpha 1\rangle\,|0\beta 2\rangle \times [|-1\alpha 3\rangle\,|-1\beta 4\rangle\,|+1\alpha 5\rangle\,|+2\beta 6\rangle - |-1\alpha 3\rangle\,|-1\beta 4\rangle\,|+1\beta 5\rangle\,|+2\alpha 6\rangle] \tag{2.10c}$$

$$+1 \rightarrow -2$$

$$|-3\rangle = (2 \cdot 6!)^{-1/2} A\,|0\alpha 1\rangle\,|0\beta 2\rangle \times [|-1\alpha 3\rangle\,|-1\beta 4\rangle\,|+1\alpha 5\rangle\,|-2\beta 6\rangle - |-1\alpha 3\rangle\,|-1\beta 4\rangle\,|+1\beta 5\rangle\,|-2\alpha 6\rangle] \tag{2.10d}$$

We shall be particularly interested in how this first excited configuration splits under the influence of the interelectronic repulsion: the non-constant part of which is the interaction operator, $\sum Q_{\mu\nu}$. There are two ways of approaching the problem. One is to calculate the matrix elements for a 4×4 secular equation, making only the most obvious use of symmetry. The other way, which will be used here, is to work with linear combinations of the $|\Delta k\rangle$ belonging to different species of the space group of the Hamiltonian, so as to give a factoring of the secular equation right at the start. The group for benzene is D_{6h}. If the AO's are π orbitals, the application of standard group theoretical methods (Sections 2.11 and 2.12) shows that $|-1\rangle$ and $|+1\rangle$ are components of a twofold degenerate species E_{1u}, whereas $|+3\rangle$ and $|-3\rangle$ must be taken in linear combinations:

$$|+\rangle = 2^{-1/2}\,(|+3\rangle + |-3\rangle)$$

belongs to B_{1u}, whereas

$$|-\rangle = 2^{-1/2}\,(|+3\rangle - |-3\rangle)$$

belongs to B_{2u}. Since functions belonging to different species do not interact, the perturbation energies may be calculated without solving a secular equation. The energy of the degenerate level may be obtained from either $|+1\rangle$ or $|-1\rangle$, whereas the energies of $|+\rangle$ and $|-\rangle$ require evaluation of a diagonal matrix element (by symmetry the one over $|+3\rangle$ would equal the one over $|-3\rangle$) and the interaction element connecting $|+3\rangle$ with $|-3\rangle$.

The electron-repulsion parameters, Eq. (2.8), are three in number, labeled K_1, K_2, and K_3. Using the values of the Q's in e.v. given by Pariser,*

$$\begin{aligned} Q_0 &= 10.96 \\ Q_1 &= 6.90 \\ Q_2 &= 5.68 \\ Q_3 &= 4.98 \end{aligned}$$

one computes the K's for the π electrons in benzene as (e.v.)

$$K_1 = 1.20 \qquad K_2 = 0.56 \qquad K_3 = 0.59 \tag{2.11}$$

At this point, we are ready to consider in detail the calculation of the various matrix elements.

2.8 MATRIX ELEMENTS OF THE INTERACTION OPERATOR

We first compute the interaction of $|0\rangle$ with itself. Since this function describes a closed-shell configuration, we can use the formula for the expectation value of two-electron operators already considered in Chapter 1, Eq. (1.4). The procedure is to add up all the ordinary pair interactions and then go on to subtract exchange integrals between electrons having the same spin.

The employment of $Q_{\mu\nu}$, Eq. (2.9), allows us to neglect the ordinary integrals. That is, the operator part of $Q_{\mu\nu}$ consists of the sum

$$\sum_{j \neq l} \sum_{k \neq m} |j\mu)\,|k\nu)\,(l\mu|\,(m\nu|$$

so that the μth electron and also the νth must be changing orbitals going from one side of the matrix element to the other. The exchange integrals between electrons having the same spin in $|0\rangle$ contribute

$$-2(0\mu\,|\,(+1\nu\,|\,Q_{\mu\nu}\,|+1\mu)\,|\,0\nu) - 2(0\mu\,|\,(-1\nu\,|\,Q_{\mu\nu}\,|-1\mu)\,|\,0\nu)$$
$$-2(+1\mu\,|\,(-1\nu\,|\,Q_{\mu\nu}\,|-1\mu)\,|+1\nu)$$

By symmetry, this reduces to the two contributions,

* R. Pariser, *J. Chem. Phys.*, **24** (1956), 250.

$$-4(0\mu \mid (+1\nu \mid Q_{\mu\nu} \mid +1\mu) \mid 0\nu) - 2(+1\mu \mid (-1\nu \mid Q_{\mu\nu} \mid -1\mu) \mid +1\nu)$$

Looking at the first, we see that the orbitals are capable of picking out the one term of the interaction operator

$$\mid j\mu) \mid k\nu) \; (l\mu \mid (m\nu \mid K_{|k-m|} = \mid 0\mu) \mid +1\nu) \; (+1\mu \mid (0\nu \mid K_1$$

Moreover, this term actually occurs in $Q_{\mu\nu}$ because it satisfies the selection rule

$$j - l + k - m = 0 \quad \text{or} \quad n$$

In fact,

$$j - l + k - m = 0 - (+1) + (+1) - 0 = 0$$

We therefore have the contribution $-4K_1$. Similarly, from the second we get $-2K_2$ so that

$$\langle 0 \mid \sum Q_{\mu\nu} \mid 0 \rangle = -4K_1 - 2K_2$$

We turn next to the excited state manifold Eq. (2.10) and begin by considering the energy of the E_{1u} state. By reason of the degeneracy, we may focus on the energy of either configurational function; let us pick $|-1\rangle$ Eq. (2.10b). By symmetry, we need not consider the two parts of $|-1\rangle$ on both sides of the matrix element, hence

$$\langle -1 \mid \sum Q_{\mu\nu} \mid -1 \rangle = 2(2 \cdot 6!)^{-1/2} A$$
$$\times (0\alpha 1 \mid (0\beta 2 \mid (+1\alpha 3 \mid (+1\beta 4 \mid (-1\alpha 5 \mid (-2\beta 6 \mid \sum Q_{\mu\nu} \mid -1 \rangle$$

Also, only the leading term of the single determinant needs to be used; all other terms will give the same value, and there are 6! such terms. This gives

$$(0\alpha 1 \mid (0\beta 2 \mid (+1\alpha 3 \mid (+1\beta 4 \mid (-1\alpha 5 \mid (-2\beta 6 \mid \sum Q_{\mu\nu} A$$
$$\times [\mid 0\alpha 1) \mid 0\beta 2) \mid +1\alpha 3) \mid +1\beta 4) \mid -1\alpha 5) \mid -2\beta 6) \tag{2.12}$$
$$- \mid 0\alpha 1) \mid 0\beta 2) \mid +1\alpha 3) \mid +1\beta 4) \mid -1\beta 5) \mid -2\alpha 6)]$$

We look first at the second term on the right interacting with the term on the left. Since electron five has spin α on the left and β on the right, we must find a permutation which gives five the opposite spin: that is, with one, three, or six. Of these, only the permutation with six is usable because the spins of one and three are α on the left and have to stay that way. Counting the factor of -1 for the permutation we therefore have the single term

$$(0\alpha 1 \mid (0\beta 2 \mid (+1\alpha 3 \mid (+1\beta 4 \mid (-1\alpha 5 \mid (-2\beta 6 \mid \sum Q_{\mu\nu}$$
$$\times \mid 0\alpha 1) \mid 0\beta 2) \mid +1\alpha 3) \mid +1\beta 4) \mid -1\beta 6) \mid -2\alpha 5)$$

We are now ready to use the selection rule: For Q_{56} we have $j \neq l\ k \neq m$ and

$$j - l + k - m = -1 - (-2) - 2 - (-1) = 0$$

so we find a contrubution $+K_1$.

Multiple permutations including P_{56} as a factor always lead nowhere because orbitals containing the electrons other than five and six become unmatched. If $\Sigma\, Q_{\mu\nu}$ is to introduce mixing through the orbitals occupied by five and six, then the terms go out upon integration over the other electrons by orbital orthogonality. If $\Sigma\, Q_{\mu\nu}$ is to mix through the other orbitals then the terms each go out upon integration over electrons five and six.

We next consider the part of the matrix element, Eq. (2.12), which involves the first term on the right

$$(0\alpha 1 \mid (0\beta 2 \mid (+1\alpha 3 \mid (+1\beta 4 \mid (-1\alpha 5 \mid (-2\beta 6 \mid \sum Q_{\mu\nu}\, A$$
$$\times \mid 0\alpha 1) \mid 0\beta 2) \mid +1\alpha 3) \mid +1\beta 4) \mid -1\alpha 5) \mid -2\beta 6)$$

We first look at all β permutations. For P_{24} and Q_{24}, we find

$$- \mid 0\alpha 1) \mid 0\beta 4) \mid +1\alpha 3) \mid +1\beta 2) \mid -1\alpha 5) \mid -2\beta 6)$$

with $j - l + k - m = 0 - 1 + 1 - 0 = 0$ which brings in $-K_1$. Similarly we find P_{26} gives

$$- \mid 0\alpha 1) \mid 0\beta 6) \mid +1\alpha 3) \mid +1\beta 4) \mid -1\alpha 5) \mid -2\beta 6)$$

which brings in $-K_2$. Going on in this way we find

Electrons permuted	24	26	46	13	15	35
$-K$ value	1	2	3	1	1	2

The multiple permutations give nothing because of orbital orthogonality. All together, we therefore have

$$\langle -1 \mid \sum Q_{\mu\nu} \mid -1 \rangle = -2K_1 - 2K_2 - K_3$$

and this same result would be found for $\langle +1 \mid \Sigma\, Q_{\mu\nu} \mid +1 \rangle$ by symmetry. Proceeding in the same way, we find

$$\langle +3 \mid \sum Q_{\mu\nu} \mid +3 \rangle = \langle -3 \mid \sum Q_{\mu\nu} \mid -3 \rangle = -4K_1 - 2K_2 + K_3$$

The degenerate state lies above the center of $|+\rangle$ and $|-\rangle$ by

$$\langle -1 \mid \sum Q_{\mu\nu} \mid -1 \rangle - \langle +3 \mid \sum Q_{\mu\nu} \mid +3 \rangle = 2(K_1 - K_3)$$

which is found (using actual K values) to be positive.

We now look at the interaction between $| +3\rangle$ and $|-3\rangle$ which gives the splitting between $|+\rangle$ and $|-\rangle$. Making the preliminary simplifications as in the preceding work, we obtain

$$(0\alpha 1 \mid (0\beta 2 \mid (+1\alpha 3 \mid (+1\beta 4 \mid (-1\alpha 5 \mid (+2\beta 6 \mid \sum Q_{\mu\nu} A$$
$$\times [|0\alpha 1) \mid 0\beta 2) \mid -1\alpha 3) \mid -1\beta 4) \mid +1\alpha 5) \mid -2\beta 6)$$
$$+ |0\alpha 1) \mid 0\beta 2) \mid -1\alpha 3) \mid -1\beta 4) \mid +1\beta 6) \mid -2\alpha 5)]$$

Note that we have already interchanged electrons five and six, which accounts for the plus sign connecting the two terms on the right. Let us look first at the second term on the right. The spins are consonant, but there is a mismatching of orbitals so that we have a contribution only after the permutation $P_{35}\, P_{46}$ is brought in. Then Q_{36} gives us $+K_3$ (the selection rule in this case is satisfied because the net $\not{k}$ change is 6 instead of zero). The contribution from the first term works out to be $-K_2$ from P_{35} and $+K_3$ from $P_{35}\, P_{46}$. Thus

$$\langle +3 \mid \sum Q_{\mu\nu} \mid -3 \rangle = 2K_3 - K_2$$

which, considering actual K values, is positive and shows that the minus state lies below the plus state.

2.9 COMPARISON WITH EXPERIMENT

The ground and first excited singlets may be pictured as differing in energy by the contribution from the effective Hamiltonian, H^0, augmented by the perturbation. The former contribution is $[2 \cos 2\pi(2)/6 - 2 \cos 2\pi(1)/6]\, \beta = -2\beta$. The parts of V in addition to the interaction operator are constant (and of order zero).

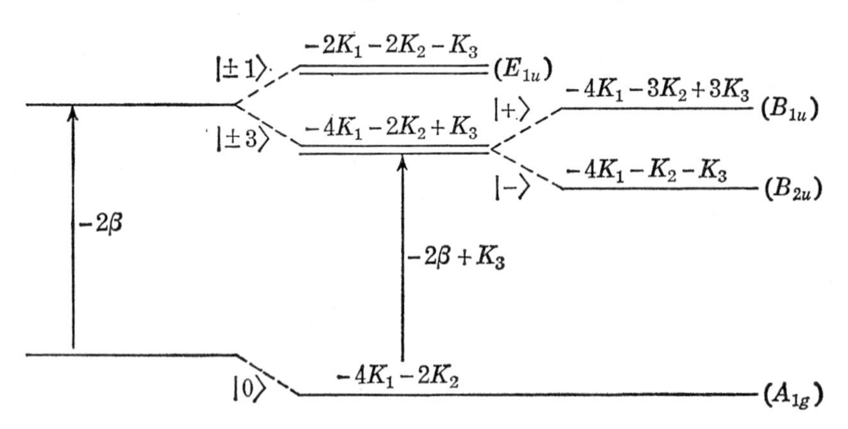

Figure 2.2

In consequence they do not have to be brought in: the exchange integrals represent the perturbation. The energies are summarized diagrammatically (Fig. 2.2). The symmetry species are shown enclosed in parentheses.

The average of the $|0\rangle \rightarrow |\pm\rangle$ transition energy, or the $|0\rangle \rightarrow |\pm 3\rangle$ energy (before the $\langle +3| \Sigma Q_{\mu\nu} | -3\rangle$ matrix element is brought in) is $-2\beta + K_3$. If we estimate β as $-s/D$, as suggested in the section "Four Hydrogen Atoms," we obtain $\beta = -2.7$ e.v. (for $D = 1.39$ Å and $s = 0.25$, as calculated for benzene and adjacent π orbitals). Using the K_3 value listed in Eq. (2.11), we thus predict a $|0\rangle \rightarrow | \pm 3\rangle$ energy of 4.8 e.v. The observed value is dependent on having the correct experimental assignments. It is considered likely, however, that the first two observed transitions in benzene at 2600 Å and 2000 Å are, respectively, $A_{1g} \rightarrow B_{2u}$ and $A_{1g} \rightarrow B_{1u}$. The observed average energy then works out to be 5.6 e.v. In order to circumvent having to make a crude estimate of β, we can use the observed energy to give an empirical β, which then becomes -3.5 e.v. This value might be used for calculations on molecules which are similar to benzene.

The B_{2u} state is calculated to lie below the B_{1u} state, which matches the experimental assignment.* Moreover, the split observed, $\sim$1.3 e.v., agrees well with the split calculated, $2(2K_3 - K_2) = 1.24$ e.v. This is not as satisfactory as it might appear because the Q's and hence the K's have been modified to a certain extent in a way so as to give, among other things, this agreement. The assignment of the strong absorption at 1800 Å as $A_{1g} \rightarrow E_{1u}$ is unquestioned, and this fits the calculation, which puts $|0\rangle \rightarrow |\pm 1\rangle$, also $A_{1g} \rightarrow E_{1u}$, at the highest energy. The $|\pm 1\rangle \rightarrow |\pm 3\rangle$ split, $2(K_1 - K_3)$ is calculated to be 1.22 e.v. and is observed to be $\sim$1.7 e.v.

The ordering of the levels corresponds to the experimental assignments, and even the calculated transition energies agree fairly well; all of which is astonishing, considering the approximations, and that we are dealing with π electrons as if they could be isolated from the rest of the electrons.† Before we are in a position to draw reasonably firm conclusions about the success or failure of the theoretical approach, we need to consider the intensities. The intensities for the $A_{1g} \rightarrow B_{2u}$ and the $A_{1g} \rightarrow B_{1u}$ transitions are zero in the lowest approximation (Section 2.13) and this agrees tolerably

* A. C. Albrecht and W. T. Simpson, *J. Chem. Phys.*, **23** (1955), 1480; *J. Am. Chem. Soc.*, **77** (1955), 4454.

† When higher approximations are brought in, it is found that an $A_{1g} \rightarrow E_{2g}$ transition should have a similar energy to the transition energies computed here—see R. G. Parr, D. P. Craig, and I. G. Ross, *J. Chem. Phys.*, **18** (1950), 1561. Since this transition is highly forbidden, its presence or absence has not yet been unequivocally established.

well with experiment. The intensity for the $A_{1g} \rightarrow E_{1u}$ transition will be our next consideration.

2.10 TRANSITION PROBABILITY

Let us begin by assuming that the electronic charge is unity, and also that no transition moment is generated out-of-plane or z. The transition moment matrix element between $|0\rangle$ and $|-1\rangle$ Eq. (2.10b) will be the same in absolute value as between $|0\rangle$ and $|+1\rangle$, provided that we treat the electric moment operator properly as a vector. We therefore confine the treatment to the calculation of

$$\langle 0 \mid \mathbf{i} \sum_{\nu} x_{\nu} + \mathbf{j} \sum_{\nu} y_{\nu} \mid -1 \rangle$$

$$= 2^{-1/2} (0\alpha 1 \mid (0\beta 2 \mid (+1\alpha 3 \mid (+1\beta 4 \mid (-1\alpha 5 \mid (-1\beta 6 \mid \left[\mathbf{i} \sum_{\nu} x_{\nu} + \mathbf{j} \sum_{\nu} y_{\nu}\right] A\, [\mid 0\alpha 1) \mid 0\beta 2) \mid +1\alpha 3) \mid +1\beta 4) \mid -1\alpha 5) \mid -2\beta 6) + \mid 0\alpha 1) \mid 0\beta 2) \mid +1\alpha 3) \mid +1\beta 4) \mid -1\beta 6) \mid -2\alpha 5)]$$

Here we have simplified in the usual way, and have also written the second term on the right the way it appears after the $5 - 6$ permutation. Consideration of spin orthogonality and orbital orthogonality, coupled with the fact that the operator acts on only one numbered electron at a time, shows that the only terms not vanishing are the ones based on the identity permutation in A. The first of these is

$$2^{-1/2} (0\alpha 1 \mid (0\beta 2 \mid (+1\alpha 3 \mid (+1\beta 4 \mid (-1\alpha 5 \mid (-1\beta 6 \mid \times \left[\mathbf{i} \sum_{\nu} x_{\nu} + \mathbf{j} \sum_{\nu} y_{\nu}\right] \mid 0\alpha 1) \mid 0\beta 2) \mid +1\alpha 3) \mid +1\beta 4) \mid -1\alpha 5) \mid -2\beta 6)$$
$$= 2^{-1/2} [\mathbf{i}(-1\beta 6 \mid x_6 \mid -2\beta 6) + \mathbf{j}(-1\beta 6 \mid y_6 \mid -2\beta 6)]$$

The second is the same except that electron five is brought in instead of six. The transition moment is thus

$$2 \cdot 2^{-1/2} [\mathbf{i}(-1 \mid x \mid -2) + \mathbf{j}(-1 \mid y \mid -2)]$$

Since the transition probability is proportional to the square of this vector, it is

$$2\{\mid (-1 \mid x \mid -2) \mid^2 + \mid (-1 \mid y \mid -2) \mid^2\}$$

The physical interpretation of the factor of 2 is that there are two electrons in the originating orbital and each acts independently as an absorber.

It remains now to calculate the one-electron matrix elements. For the x moment, using Eq. (2.6a), we have the result in terms of integrals over orthogonal atomic orbitals

$$\tfrac{1}{6}\sum_s e^{2\pi is/6}\,(s \mid x \sum_t e^{-2\pi it/3} \mid t)$$

$$= \tfrac{1}{6}\Big[\sum_s e^{-2\pi is/6}\,(s \mid x \mid s) + \sum_{s\neq t} e^{2\pi i(s-2t)/6}\,(s \mid x \mid t)\Big]$$

The terms where $s \neq t$ are zero, as will now be shown. Write in place of x

$$a\bar{x} + b\bar{y} + c$$

where $\bar{x}$ and $\bar{y}$ are new variables with origin at the midpoint between atoms s and t, and where $\bar{x}$ joins the centers. We then have to evaluate terms like

$$a(s \mid \bar{x} \mid t)$$

This particular term is zero because what is involved is an integration over a symmetric function (product of equivalent orthogonal atomic orbitals) and an antisymmetric function ($\bar{x}$). The same holds for the $\bar{y}$ term. The term $c\,(s \mid t)$ is zero because $|s)$ and $|t)$ are orthogonal. We can evaluate a typical term for which $s = t$ similarly. The origin of the coordinate system is fixed at the center of the atom and only the constant term remains after integration, which constant is the coordinate of the center of the atom referred to a previously chosen coordinate system for the entire molecule.

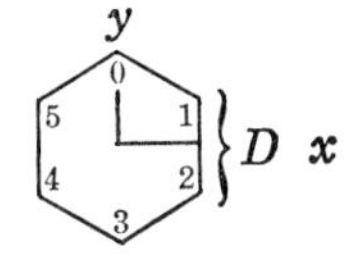

Figure 2.3

We now choose a particular coordinate system (Fig. 2.3) where the interatomic distance is D. The x moment is

$$(-1 \mid x \mid -2) = \tfrac{1}{6}\sum_{s=0}^{5} e^{-2\pi is/6}\,(s \mid x \mid s)$$

$$= \left[1, \frac{1}{2} - \frac{\sqrt{3}}{2}i, -\frac{1}{2} - \frac{\sqrt{3}}{2}i, -1, -\frac{1}{2} + \frac{\sqrt{3}}{2}i, \frac{1}{2} + \frac{\sqrt{3}}{2}i\right]\begin{bmatrix} 0 \\ \frac{\sqrt{3}}{2}D \\ \frac{\sqrt{3}}{2}D \\ 0 \\ -\frac{\sqrt{3}}{2}D \\ -\frac{\sqrt{3}}{2}D \end{bmatrix}$$

$$= -\frac{iD}{2}$$

Similarly, the y moment between MO's is

$$(-1 \mid y \mid -2) = \frac{D}{2}$$

so that the transition moment squared for $|0\rangle \rightarrow |-1\rangle$ becomes

$$2\left[\frac{D^2}{4} + \frac{D^2}{4}\right] = D^2$$

The same applies for the transition $|0\rangle \rightarrow |+1\rangle$, so the total intensity (expressed as the square of a moment) for the $A_{1g} \rightarrow E_{1u}$ transition is calculated to be $2D^2$. The relation between the intensity of a band of vibronic transitions and the electronic transition moment is derived in the Appendix (Section 2.14). The integrated intensity (Section 4.8) for hexamethylbenzene has been found to correspond to a transition moment in the plane of the molecule of ~1.3 Å for each half of the degenerate transition, a value which compares favorably with the calculated one (D = 1.39 Å).* The value for benzene itself is, however, probably only 0.6 of the theoretical one and the discrepancy has been attributed to the effect of higher-order perturbations.† The agreement with experiment is quite good, all things considered, so that it may be concluded that the theory of the degenerate manifold for benzene presented in this chapter is a realistic one.

Appendix to Chapter 2

2.11 GROUP THEORETICAL CONSIDERATIONS

We shall start with an outline of the application of group representation theory to quantum mechanics. The symmetry operations are easiest to work with in the Schrödinger representation (and we shall use ψ functions instead of brackets to begin with). Curiously, one almost never uses an explicit representation of an operator, but deals with it in terms of its effect, instead. For example, the operation G of replacing x by $-x$ for functions of a single variable has the explicit form

$$G(x', x) = \delta(x - (-x')) = \delta(x + x')$$

whence the transform of ψ

$$\psi'(x') = \int_{dx} G(x', x)\, \psi(x) = \int_{dx} \delta(x + x')\, \psi(x) = \psi(-x')$$

a result which one usually writes down immediately without attempting to use G mechanically.

* R. C. Nelson and W. T. Simpson, *J. Chem. Phys.*, **23** (1955), 1146.
† C. L. Bevan and D. P. Craig, *Trans. Faraday Soc.*, **47** (1951), 564.

In the Heisenberg representation, the symmetry operations have the form of infinite strings of irreducible representation matrices. The matrix for G has elements

$$G_{ij} = \int_{dx'} \psi_i(x') \int_{dx} G(x'x)\, \psi_j(x)$$

For harmonic oscillator wave functions as basis functions, this becomes the matrix

$$\begin{pmatrix} 1 & 0 & 0 & 0 & \\ 0 & -1 & 0 & 0 & \\ 0 & 0 & 1 & 0 & \\ 0 & 0 & 0 & -1 & \\ & & & & \ddots \end{pmatrix}$$

signifying that the functions are alternately even and odd. Usually one deals with finite parts of these matrices, the sets of irreducible representation matrices. Our first main result will be the theorem just illustrated, that the energy eigenfunctions constitute a basis for irreducible representations of the group of symmetry operations.

We start by adopting the point of view that an operation (like reflection or inversion) in the Schrödinger representation gives a simple, almost trivial change of basis—into a "double-primed representation"

$$\psi'' = R\psi$$

According to transformation theory, dynamical variables transform in tensor fashion

$$H'' = RHR^{-1}$$

If the new H'' is the same as H, R is defined as a symmetry operation.

We next suppose that R and also S are symmetry operations

$$RHR^{-1} = SHS^{-1} = H$$

and in addition define the product

$$T = SR$$

whence

$$T^{-1} = R^{-1}S^{-1}$$

and

$$THT^{-1} = SRHR^{-1}S^{-1} = H$$

showing that the product is also a symmetry operation. This gives the closure property, the main reason why the symmetry operations form a group. The Schrödinger operators (the explicit form of which has not been specified in the preceding material) strictly speaking constitute a reducible representation of the group.

Suppose now that

$$H\psi = W\psi$$

This must also hold in the double-primed representation

$$H''\psi'' = W\psi''$$

so that

$$(RHR^{-1})\,(R\psi) = W(R\psi)$$

Then because of $RHR^{-1} = H$, this becomes

$$H(R\psi) = W(R\psi)$$

showing that if ψ_i is an eigenfunction belonging to W_i, $(R\psi_i)$ must also be an eigenfunction belonging to the same eigenvalue. Most generally there is degeneracy, in which case one is led to conclude

$$R\psi_i = \sum_j R'_{ji}\,\psi_j \tag{2.13}$$

where the ψ_j fall in the degenerate manifold. The coefficients (with labels chosen for later convenience) constitute a matrix, and this matrix may be considered as a generalized eigenvalue. Thus we can switch our viewpoint, so that R is regarded not as a change of basis operator, but as a kind of dynamical variable. Since R'_{ij} also turns out to be the matrix of some particular irreducible representation, we can think of ψ_i as belonging to that same representation. This is an elementary way of thinking about the meaning of the symmetry of a function. A function having symmetry may be thought of as a generalized eigenfunction corresponding to a particular irreducible representation matrix as generalized eigenvalue.

We shall now treat the symmetry operations formally as dynamical variables. Then we may compute the matrix of, for example, R in the Heisenberg representation using transformation theory, which we proceed to do as follows:

$$R' = \begin{bmatrix} \langle\psi_1| \\ \langle\psi_2| \\ \langle\psi_3| \\ \cdot \\ \cdot \\ \cdot \end{bmatrix} R\,[|\psi_1\rangle\,|\psi_2\rangle\,|\psi_3\rangle\,.\,.\,.] \equiv UR\overline{U}$$

where the ψ_1, ψ_2, and so on, are energy eigenfunctions. The new dynamical variables multiply together the same as the old. That is, if

$$SR = T$$

then

$$S'R' = US\bar{U}\, UR\bar{U} = USR\bar{U} = T'$$

so the matrices, with elements

$$R'_{ij} = \langle \psi_i \mid R \mid \psi_j \rangle$$

form a representation of the group.

We shall see that this representation is in a sense irreducible. The plan is to rederive our generalized eigenvalue equation (2.13). Starting from

$$UR\bar{U} = R'$$

and multiplying by $\bar{U} = U^{-1}$,* one obtains

$$R\bar{U} = \bar{U}R'$$

or

$$R\begin{bmatrix} |\psi_1\rangle \; |\psi_2\rangle \; |\psi_3\rangle \cdots \\ \\ \\ \\ \end{bmatrix} = \begin{bmatrix} |\psi_1\rangle \; |\psi_2\rangle \; |\psi_3\rangle \cdots \\ \\ \\ \\ \end{bmatrix}\begin{bmatrix} R'_{11} & R'_{12} & R'_{13} & \dots \\ R'_{21} & R'_{22} & R'_{23} & \dots \\ R'_{31} & R'_{32} & R'_{33} & \dots \\ \cdot & & & \\ \cdot & & & \\ \cdot & & & \end{bmatrix}$$

Equating corresponding columns on the left and right gives

$$\begin{aligned} R \mid \psi_1\rangle &= |\psi_1\rangle R'_{11} + |\psi_2\rangle R'_{21} + |\psi_3\rangle R'_{31} + \dots \\ R \mid \psi_2\rangle &= |\psi_1\rangle R'_{12} + |\psi_2\rangle R'_{22} + |\psi_3\rangle R'_{32} + \dots \\ &\cdot \\ &\cdot \\ &\cdot \end{aligned} \tag{2.14}$$

The generalized eigenvalue equation (2.13) is much the same. We used more stringent conditions in deriving it, however, and indeed found that it limits the linear combinations to members of a degenerate manifold. This shows that most of the R'_{ij} in Eq. (2.14) are zero. For example, if the first two functions spanned a twofold manifold, we should have

$$\begin{aligned} R \mid \psi_1\rangle &= |\psi_1\rangle R'_{11} + |\psi_2\rangle R'_{21} \\ R \mid \psi_2\rangle &= |\psi_1\rangle R'_{12} + |\psi_2\rangle R'_{22} \\ R \mid \psi_3\rangle &= \qquad\qquad\qquad\qquad\quad |\psi_3\rangle R'_{33} + \dots \end{aligned}$$

* That $U\bar{U} = 1$ is easier to verify than the transpose, $\bar{U}U = 1$; this latter is $\sum_i |\psi_i\rangle\langle\psi_i|$, an operator which is unity in a representation in which the $|\psi_i\rangle$'s are basis vectors, hence in all representations.

and so on. This shows that the full R' has a block pattern. The same pattern is obtained for the other transformed symmetry operators (like S') because it depends solely on the groupings of the $|\psi_i\rangle$'s into the various degenerate manifolds. Furthermore, by the rule for matrix multiplication, the individual blocks multiply the same way as the full matrices. The matrices of the symmetry operations in the Heisenberg representation are much reduced. That these matrices are fully reduced (irreducible) cannot strictly be proved. But, if the blocks of R', S', and so on, singled out by a particular set of degenerate functions could be further reduced, this would imply the divisibility of the manifold into two (or more) submanifolds. The transformation which effected the reduction could be used on the set of degenerate eigenfunctions instead, generating a new set in terms of which the blocks of R', S', and so on, would be simultaneously in factored form. This situation, although theoretically possible, almost never occurs in practice, so that when it does occur the fact that the functions in each submanifold belong to the same energy eigenvalue is described as accidental degeneracy. We can therefore say that energy eigenfunctions constitute bases for irreducible representations of the group.

At this point, we have the main theorem, but it is not in the form we need. In the work on benzene (Chapter 3), we have used the idea that functions belonging to different irreducible representations do not interact through the Hamiltonian. This is part of a related theorem which appears thus, in wave mechanical form:

*matrix elements $\int \psi^i (\alpha\varphi)^j \, d\tau$ are zero if ψ^i and $(\alpha\varphi)^j$ belong respectively to different species, Γ_i and Γ_j.**

To understand this theorem, we have to see first that, when a well-behaved function belonging to a particular species is expanded using energy eigenfunctions, these energy eigenfunctions must belong exclusively to that same species. We now obtain this result under the simplifying assumption of no degeneracy.

Suppose that ψ^i belongs to Γ_i and is expanded in terms of energy eigenfunctions ψ_s^i, each belonging to Γ_i, and one ψ_t^j, which belongs to Γ_j.

$$\psi^i = \sum_s c_s \psi_s^i + c_t \psi_t^j \tag{2.15}$$

Since we are assuming no degeneracy, the irreducible representation matrices are 1×1 and are equal to the characters. Also, since $\Gamma^i \neq \Gamma^j$, for at least one operation, R, the characters must be different

$$\chi^i (R) \neq \chi^j (R)$$

* We avoid talking about the species of the operator α.

The fact that ψ^i belongs to Γ_i implies

$$R\psi^i = \chi^i(R)\,\psi^i$$

and similar relations hold for the ψ_s^i and ψ^j. Equation (2.15) is

$$\psi^i - \sum_s c_s\,\psi_s^i = c_t\,\psi_t^j$$

Operating on each side with R gives

$$\chi^i(R)\left(\psi^i - \sum_s c_s\,\psi_s^i\right) = \chi^j(R)c_t\,\psi_t^j$$

Because the characters are different, the factors multiplying them would have to vanish

$$\psi^i - \sum_s c_s\,\psi_s^i = c_t\,\psi_t^j = 0$$

so that $c_t = 0$.

Returning to the question of the matrix element $\int \psi^i\,(\alpha\varphi)^j\,d\tau$, we now expand ψ^i in terms of energy eigenfunctions belonging to Γ_i and $(\alpha\varphi)^j$ in terms of energy eigenfunctions belonging to Γ_j. These sets of eigenfunctions are disjoint, so the integral is zero by the orthogonality of eigenfunctions of H. In case α is just H, our result becomes simpler; namely $\int \psi^i\,H\,\psi^j\,d\tau$ is zero whenever $\Gamma_i \neq \Gamma_j$ (because if ψ^j belongs to the species Γ_j, then $H\psi^j = H\sum c_s\,\psi_s^j = \sum W_s\,c_s\,\psi_s^j$ also belongs to Γ_j).

We now can see how in the benzene calculation we avoided having to set up the full 4×4 secular equation connecting $|+1\rangle$, $|-1\rangle$, $|+3\rangle$, and $|-3\rangle$ Eq. (2.10). The linear combinations $|3\rangle + |-3\rangle$ and $|3\rangle - |-3\rangle$ fail to interact because each belongs to a different irreducible representation. Moreover, these irreducible representations are distinct from the one for $|+1\rangle$ and $|-1\rangle$ (which is degenerate). This does not tell us how we managed to select the proper linear combinations, or how we know what species each belongs to.

In order to understand these points, we need to study the action of the so-called *character operator*. This operator is

$$\sum_R \chi^i(R)\,R \tag{2.16}$$

where R is an operation of the group, $\chi^i(R)$ is the corresponding character for Γ_i, and the sum is over all operations. When this operator is applied to a wave function which does not belong to any particular species, it generates a new function which belongs to Γ_i, or if this is impossible, it generates zero. To see this in a simple case imagine that the function ψ is composed of two parts which belong to different species, Γ_i and Γ_j

$$\psi = \psi^i + \psi^j$$

Then

$$\sum_R \chi^i (R) R\psi = \sum_R \chi^i (R) R\psi^i + \sum_R \chi^i (R) R\psi^j$$

We avoid complication as in the case of the last theorem by postulating no degeneracy. This allows us to use

$$R\psi^j = \chi^j (R)\psi^j$$

in the third sum above. The sum vanishes

$$\sum_R \chi^i (R) R\psi^j = \psi^j \sum_R \chi^i (R) \chi^j (R) = 0$$

because of the well-known orthogonality relation for the characters of the irreducible representations. Thus the character operator for Γ_i working on the function ψ above "washes out" the part of ψ that does not belong to Γ_i. For the benzene problem, the character operator for B_{1u} working on, for example, (see Eq. (2.10a))

$$|+3\rangle = \tfrac{1}{2} [|+3\rangle + |-3\rangle] + \tfrac{1}{2} [|+3\rangle - |-3\rangle]$$

washes out the part which does not belong to B_{1u}, namely,

$$|-\rangle = |+3\rangle - |-3\rangle \; (B_{2u})$$

leaving the part which does belong

$$|+\rangle = |+3\rangle + |-3\rangle \; (B_{1u})$$

The character operator for B_{2u} working on $|+3\rangle$ generates $|-\rangle$ (B_{2u}). Character operators for all other irreducible representations generate zero. In the next section, we shall work out some of the details.

2.12 SYMMETRY OF BENZENE FUNCTIONS

Benzene belongs to D_{6h}, which has the character table given in Table 2.1.

The selection of symmetry-adapted functions through the character operator Eq. (2.16) requires that we know the action of this operator on more or less arbitrarily selected functions which may not themselves be symmetry adapted. We shall be particularly concerned with $|+3\rangle$ Eq. (2.10a) as an example. At the outset, we define the action of R on a many-electron function and consider the effect of using Slater determinants. The operation R which leaves the many-electron Hamiltonian unchanged must be taken as giving a displacement of each one-electron part in a product of one-electron parts, for example,*

* Formally, $R = \prod_\nu R_\nu$.

Table 2.1

D_{6h}	E	$2C_6$	$2C_3$	C_2	$3C_2'$	$3C_2''$	i	$2S_3$	$2S_6$	σ_h	$3\sigma_d$	$3\sigma_v$
A_{1g}	1	1	1	1	1	1	1	1	1	1	1	1
A_{2g}	1	1	1	1	−1	−1	1	1	1	1	−1	−1
B_{1g}	1	−1	1	−1	1	−1	1	−1	1	−1	1	−1
B_{2g}	1	−1	1	−1	−1	1	1	−1	1	−1	−1	1
E_{1g}	2	1	−1	−2	0	0	2	1	−1	−2	0	0
E_{2g}	2	−1	−1	2	0	0	2	−1	−1	2	0	0
A_{1u}	1	1	1	1	1	1	−1	−1	−1	−1	−1	−1
$A_{2u}(z)$	1	1	1	1	−1	−1	−1	−1	−1	−1	1	1
B_{1u}	1	−1	1	−1	1	−1	−1	1	−1	1	−1	1
B_{2u}	1	−1	1	−1	−1	1	−1	1	−1	1	1	−1
$E_{1u}(xy)$	2	1	−1	−2	0	0	−2	−1	1	2	0	0
E_{2u}	2	−1	−1	2	0	0	−2	1	1	−2	0	0

$$
\begin{array}{lllll}
R\,|+3\rangle|+3\rangle & -\,|+3\rangle|+3\rangle & -\,|+3\rangle|-3\rangle - |-3\rangle & -\,|+3\rangle|+3\rangle - |+3\rangle|+3\rangle & -\,|-3\rangle|-3\rangle \\
 & -\,|+3\rangle|+3\rangle & |-3\rangle - |-3\rangle & |+3\rangle - |+3\rangle & -\,|-3\rangle|-3\rangle \\
 & & |-3\rangle - |-3\rangle & & -\,|-3\rangle|-3\rangle
\end{array}
$$

$$
\begin{aligned}
R\mid 0\alpha 1)\,&|0\beta 2)\,|+1\alpha 3)\,|+1\beta 4)\,|-1\alpha 5)\,|-1\beta 6) \\
&= R_1\mid 0\alpha 1)\,R_2\mid 0\beta 2)\,R_3\,|+1\alpha 3)\,R_4\,|+1\beta 4)\,R_5\,|-1\alpha 5)\,R_6\,|-1\beta 6)
\end{aligned}
$$

Since R commutes with the operation A of forming a determinant, we can work with just the leading term. The leading term of $|+3\rangle$, with electron numbers suppressed, is characterized with the letter l

$$
l\mid +3\rangle = \quad |0)\,|0)\,|+1)\,|+1)\,|-1)\,|+2)
$$

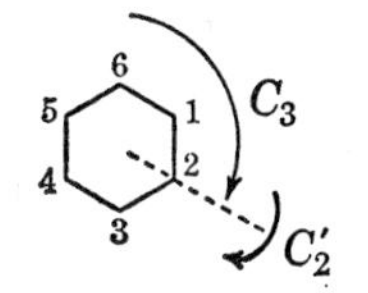

Figure 2.4

We now need to have the result of the various operations of the group, D_{6h}, on this product of functions. We shall consider in detail three typical operations, C_3 (clockwise rotation by 120°); C_2' (rotation about the points of the hexagon at 2 and 5); and i (inversion). Although most of the material in the foregoing applies equally to H_6 or benzene we shall regard the AO's as π orbitals so the discussion here applies directly to benzene.

The action of one of two operations C_3 is to advance an orbital function by $2\pi/3$ in the clockwise direction (Fig. 2.4). Apart from normalization

$$
C_3\mid \not{k}) = C_3 \sum_s e^{2\pi i \not{k} s/6}\,|s) = \sum_s e^{2\pi i \not{k}(s-2)/6}\,|s) = e^{-4\pi i \not{k}/6}\,|\not{k})
$$

Thus

$$
C_3\, l\mid +3\rangle = e^{-4\pi i(0+0+1+1-1+2)/6}\, l\mid +3\rangle = e^{-2\pi i}\, l\mid +3\rangle = l\mid +3\rangle
$$

For the actual function, we have

$$C_3 A\, l\,|+3\rangle = A\, C_3 l\,|+3\rangle = A\, l\,|+3\rangle$$

so

$$C_3\,|+3\rangle = |+3\rangle$$

We next look at a particular one of the operations C_2' (Fig. 2.4) and begin by turning a function around until the real coefficient is unity not at atom six but at atom two as apex, obtaining

$$C_3\,|\,\not{k})$$

If we operate on this rotated function with C_2' (remembering that the AO's have a nodal plane), we find for the AO's $|2) \to -\,|\,2)$, $|3) \to -\,|\,1)$, and so on (here the numbers are the atoms, not the $\not{k}$ values). This makes the real and imaginary parts transform differently (cos and sin are symmetrical and antisymmetrical on either side of the apex)

$$C_2'\,[C_3\,|\,\not{k})] = -\,[C_3\,|\,\not{k})]^* = -e^{4\pi i \not{k}/6}\,|-\not{k})$$

(Here we use $|\not{k})^* = |-\not{k})$.) Thus,

$$C_2' e^{-4\pi i\not{k}/6}\,|\,\not{k}) = -e^{4\pi i \not{k}/6}\,|-\not{k})$$

$$C_2'\,|\,\not{k}) = -e^{4\pi i \not{k}/3}\,|-\not{k})$$

Working on the many-electron function an even number of times gives, Eq. (2.10)

$$C_2' l\,|+3\rangle = +e^{4\pi i(0+0+1+1-1+2)/3}\, l\,|-3\rangle = l\,|-3\rangle$$

or

$$C_2'\,|+3\rangle = |-3\rangle$$

Now considering the operation of inversion, i, we have the AO's $|1) \to -\,|\,4)$, $|2) \to -\,|\,5)$, and so on, which is equivalent to rotating by π and multiplying by -1

$$i\,|\,\not{k}) = -e^{-\pi i \not{k}}\,|\,\not{k})$$

Working on $l\,|\,+3\rangle$ we find

$$il\,|+3\rangle = e^{-\pi i(0+0+1+1-1+2)}\, l\,|+3\rangle = -l\,|+3\rangle$$

or

$$i\,|+3\rangle = -\,|+3\rangle$$

Continuing in this fashion, we find the $R\,|+3\rangle$'s as shown on the last line of the D_{6h} character table (Table 2.1).*

We are now ready to apply the character operator to $|+3\rangle$. If we use the characters for B_{1u} we obtain immediately

$$E\,|+3\rangle - C_6\,|+3\rangle - C_6\,|+3\rangle + C_3\,|+3\rangle + C_3\,|+3\rangle - C_2\,|+3\rangle + \ldots$$

* In the present case, but not in general, the several $R_i\,|\,+3\rangle$'s are the same when the R_i are equivalent.

which, after incorporation of our results for the $R\mid +3\rangle$'s, becomes

$$12\,|+3\rangle + 12\,|-3\rangle$$

Similarly, putting in the characters for B_{2u}, we find that the difference function is generated

$$12\,|+3\rangle - 12\,|-3\rangle$$

The result is the same except for phase if we start with $|-3\rangle$. Using the characters for any other species results in the generation of no function. Analogously, $|0\rangle$ is found to belong to A_{1g}, and the only non-vanishing symmetry adapted function which can be generated from $|+1\rangle$ is one belonging to E_{1u}.

2.13 SELECTION RULES

The intensity of a transition is proportional to the transition moment matrix element squared; accordingly, when this matrix element vanishes by symmetry, we have a symmetry-forbidden transition. The electric moment operator has components

$$e\sum x_\nu,\ e\sum y_\nu,\ e\sum z_\nu$$

(where the sum is over all electrons) so that we have to consider integrals of the form $\langle i \mid \Sigma\, x_\nu \mid j\rangle$, and so on, or using one of the examples encountered with benzene,

$$\langle + \mid \sum x_\nu \mid 0\rangle = \langle + \mid \sum x_\nu\, 0\rangle$$

If the species of the part $\mid \Sigma\, x_\nu\, 0\rangle$ is not the same as the species of $\langle +|$ (in this case B_{1u}), and the same thing is found for the y and z components, the transition $|0\rangle \rightarrow |+\rangle$ ($A_{1g} \rightarrow B_{1u}$) will be symmetry forbidden.

To compute the species of $\mid \Sigma\, x_\nu\, 0\rangle$ we consider a one-electron part x_μ operating on $|0\rangle$ to give $|x_\mu\, 0\rangle$ and calculate the effect of the operation R, namely, $R \mid x_\mu\, 0\rangle$. The computation can be most easily carried out in the Schrödinger representation—for then $x_\mu\, \psi(q)$ is a new wave function, a product of two functions, x and ψ. R working on this product results in $Rx_\mu\, R\psi(q)$. We already know $R\psi(q)$, in fact for the case we are considering, $R\psi(q)$ is $\psi(q)$ because $\psi(q)$ represents the totally symmetric $|0\rangle$. The transformation properties of $|x_\mu\, 0\rangle$ depend on how x_μ itself transforms

$$R \mid x_\mu\, 0\rangle = (Rx_\mu) \mid 0\rangle$$

also

$$R \mid \sum x_\nu\, 0\rangle = R \sum_\nu \mid x_\nu\, 0\rangle = \sum_\nu (Rx_\nu) \mid 0\rangle$$

We must remember that $R = R_1 R_2 \ldots R_\mu \ldots$. This string of R's working on the function x_μ, however, is $R_\mu x_\mu$. Moreover, these same considerations apply for any μ, each term in the sum, whence also for the sum. The final result is that $| \Sigma x_\nu 0\rangle$ transforms the same as the coordinate of a single electron considered as a function in the Schrödinger representation. For example, if

$$R_\mu x_\mu = - x_\mu$$

then

$$R \mid \sum x_\mu 0\rangle = - \mid \sum x_\mu 0\rangle$$

(as pointed out above $R \mid 0\rangle$ comes in, but $R \mid 0\rangle = |0\rangle$). The species of the character system showing how this or that coordinate transforms is usually listed in the group table, just as in Table 2.1. If there is degeneracy, the situation is not altered beyond expectation.

For D_{6h}, the group of benzene, z* belongs to A_{2u} and x and y together belong to E_{1u}. Thus Σz_ν operating on $|0\rangle$, a totally symmetric function, gives a function which belongs to A_{2u}. Similarly, Σx_ν and Σy_ν throw $|0\rangle$ over into functions which belong to E_{1u}.

Now we look at the transition moment matrix elements to see whether any can be shown to vanish on the grounds of symmetry. For the $|0\rangle \rightarrow |+\rangle$ transition ($A_{1g} \rightarrow B_{1u}$), we are led to examine $\langle +|$, which is B_{1u}, going with $| \Sigma z_\nu 0\rangle$, which is A_{2u}; and the x, y ones, which are E_{1u}. Since A_{2u} and E_{1u} are not B_{1u}, the matrix elements are all zero and the transition is symmetry forbidden. The same holds for $\langle -|$, (B_{2u}); whereas the pair, $\langle +1| \langle -1|$, belongs to E_{1u}, so that the transition from $|0\rangle$ is allowed, in-plane. At the end of Chapter 2, we saw how the intensity of this transition is computed, and in the next section, we go into the question of intensities considered as involving vibrations as well as electronic motion, and there see how certain vibrations make, for example, the symmetry-forbidden B_{1u} and B_{2u} transitions allowed.

2.14 VIBRONIC BAND THEORY

Assuming the applicability of the Born-Oppenheimer approximation (see Section 1.6), we represent vibrational states within an electronic state, vibronic states, as

$$|rQq\rangle \, |mrQ\rangle$$

where the ket, or loosely, the wave function, is a product of two factors. The left-hand factor is a function of the electronic variables, symbolized

* The relations in Table 2.1 are based on, among other things, the convention that the sixfold axis be called z.

by the lower-case coordinate, q; whereas the right-hand factor is a function of the nuclear variables, symbolized by Q. A complete electronic wave function is fixed by specifying r, the electronic quantum number, and Q, the parameter locating a point on the potential energy surface. A complete vibrational function has m, symbolizing the complex of vibrational quantum numbers, and r, naming the potential energy surface.

The electric moment involves all charged particles in a system. Therefore the vector transition moment matrix element for a vibronic transition must include the electric moment operator for the nuclei $\boldsymbol{\mu}(Q)$ as well as Eq. (2.17), the operator for the electrons

$$\boldsymbol{\mu}(q) = e \sum (\mathbf{i}x_\nu + \mathbf{j}y_\nu + \mathbf{k}z_\nu) \tag{2.17}$$

(where $\mathbf{i}$, $\mathbf{j}$, $\mathbf{k}$ are unit vectors along the coordinate axes). The transition moment is therefore

$$\langle nsQ| \langle sQq| [\boldsymbol{\mu}(Q) + \boldsymbol{\mu}(q)] |rQq\rangle |mrQ\rangle$$

However,

$$\langle nsQ| \langle sQq \mid \boldsymbol{\mu}(Q) \mid rQq\rangle |mrQ\rangle = \langle nsQ \mid \boldsymbol{\mu}(Q) \langle sQq \mid rQq\rangle |mrQ\rangle$$

and for any value of Q as a parameter

$$\langle sQq \mid rQq\rangle = \delta_{rs}$$

Since $r \neq s$ for an electronic transition, this leaves the part over $\boldsymbol{\mu}(q)$ only Eq. (2.17)

$$\langle \boldsymbol{\mu} \rangle = \langle nsQ| \langle sQq \mid \boldsymbol{\mu}(q) \mid rQq\rangle |mrQ\rangle \tag{2.18}$$

To proceed (following Herzberg and Teller), we write an expression, correct to the first order, for the family of electronic wave functions in the neighborhood of some fixed configuration, Q_0.

$$\langle sQq| = \langle sQ_0\, q| - \sum_t{}' \frac{\langle sQ_0\, q \mid V(qQ) \mid tQ_0\, q\rangle}{E_t^0 - E_s^0} \langle tQ_0\, q|$$

Here

$$V(qQ) = -e^2 \sum_{i\nu} Z_i \frac{\delta \mathbf{Q}_i \cdot \mathbf{q}_{\nu i}}{|q_{\nu i}|^3}$$

where Z_i is the charge of the ith nucleus, $\mathbf{q}_{\nu i}$ is the radius vector to the νth electron, and $\delta\mathbf{Q}_i$ is the displacement from the fixed configuration. The electronic function can be written more simply as

$$\langle sQy| = \langle sQ_0\, q| - \sum_t{}' \sum_i w_{sti}\, \delta\mathbf{Q}_i \langle tQ_0\, q|$$

or grouping the $\delta \mathbf{Q}_i$ into normal modes $\delta Q_m = \sum_i k_{mi}\, \delta \mathbf{Q}_i$, and so on,

$$= \langle sQ_0\, q| - {\sum_t}' \sum_m v_{stm}\, \delta Q_m \langle tQ_0\, q| \tag{2.19}$$

The same can be done for $|rQq\rangle$. Using Eq. (2.19) in the electronic part of Eq. (2.18), we have

$$\begin{aligned}\langle sQq \mid \boldsymbol{\mu}(q)\, |rQq\rangle \\ &= \langle sQ_0\, q \mid \boldsymbol{\mu}(q)\, |rQ_0\, q\rangle - {\sum_t}' {\sum_m}' v_{stm}\, \delta Q_m \langle tQ_0\, q \mid \boldsymbol{\mu}(q)\, |rQ_0\, q\rangle \\ &\quad - {\sum_t}' \sum_m v_{rtm}\, \delta Q_m \langle tQ_0\, q \mid \boldsymbol{\mu}(q)\, |sQ_0\, q\rangle\end{aligned} \tag{2.20}$$

If $r = 1$ (ground state) and Q_0 is an average Q which appropriately for r and s minimizes the effect of $V(qQ)$, and if the ground state is unexcited vibrationally, we compute a zero-order $\langle \boldsymbol{\mu} \rangle$ Eq. (2.18) from the leading term of Eq. (2.20)

$$\langle sQ_0\, q \mid \boldsymbol{\mu}(q)\, |1Q_0\, q\rangle \langle nsQ \mid 01Q\rangle$$

If the left-hand factor, the electronic moment, is nonvanishing, the transition is allowed. The sum of transition moments squared is

$$\langle sQ_0\, q \mid \boldsymbol{\mu}(q)\, |1Q_0\, q\rangle^2 \sum_n \langle nsQ \mid 01Q\rangle^2 = \langle sQ_0\, q \mid \boldsymbol{\mu}(q)\, |1Q_0\, q\rangle^2$$

The summation is unity, as it is simply the normalization condition for coefficients in the expansion

$$|01Q\rangle = \sum_n k_{sn} \mid nsQ\rangle$$

Thus to the first approximation, the sum of all the vibronic transition probabilities within an allowed electronic band is given by the square of the electronic transition moment evaluated at some representative point Q_0 on the potential energy surfaces.

If the transition moment is zero,

$$\langle sQ_0\, q \mid \boldsymbol{\mu}(q)\, |1Q_0\, q\rangle = 0$$

we now say that the transition is Frank-Condon forbidden. We must then bring in the full Eq. (2.20), which has a part representing mixing with the state r and a part representing mixing with the state s. Considering mixing with the upper state $\langle s|$, we must look at the various t terms, for example,

$$\langle nsQ \mid {\sum_m}' v_{stm}\, \delta Q_m \langle tQ_0\, q \mid \boldsymbol{\mu}(q)\, |1Q_0\, q\rangle\, |01Q\rangle$$

until we find one for which

$$\langle tQ_0\, q \mid \boldsymbol{\mu}(q) \mid 1Q_0\, q\rangle \neq 0$$

The question arises whether there exists a normal mode δQ_m such that also

$$v_{stm} \neq 0$$

If one can be found, then in $\langle\boldsymbol{\mu}\rangle$ Eq. (2.18) the transition moment $\langle tQ_0\, q \mid \boldsymbol{\mu}(q) \mid 1Q_0\, q\rangle$ is to be multiplied by

$$v_{stm}\, \langle nsQ \mid \delta Q_m \mid 01Q\rangle$$

There are restrictions on n. We may classify the vibrational wave functions by species of the group having the least symmetry common to the potential energy surfaces involved. Then $|01Q\rangle$ is totally symmetric, and δQ_m transforms like a diagram for the particular normal vibration m that brings in the t electronic state through v_{stm} Eq. (2.19). This shows that the wave function for the $\langle nsQ|$ vibrational state has to transform like the mth normal mode in order that the integral used to evaluate $\langle nsQ \mid \delta Q_m \mid 01Q\rangle$ be nonvanishing. This implies an odd number of units of excitation in m, any number in the totally symmetric modes, and an even number in all vibrations that are not totally symmetric. Thus using ψ_k for the vibrational wave function for the kth mode we should have $|nsQ\rangle$ represented by such examples as

$$\psi_0^0\, \psi_1^0\, \psi_2^0 \ldots \psi_m^1 \ldots \psi_n^0 \quad \text{or}$$

$$\psi_0^1\, \psi_1^0\, \psi_2^2 \ldots \psi_m^3 \ldots \psi_n^0$$

(where ψ_0 is a function for a totally symmetric mode).

Now we investigate how the symmetry of m is determined. Since $V(qQ)$ must be totally symmetric (it is a part of the Hamiltonian), the electronic part of V transforms like δQ_m. The electronic part must mix $\langle sQ_0\, q|$ with $\langle tQ_0\, q|$ where $\langle tQ_0\, q|$ is connected with the original state $|rQ_0\, q\rangle$ so as to give a nonvanishing moment. If r is totally symmetric, t then has the species of a translation. Knowing the species of s, one can then list the possible species of the electronic part of $V(qQ)$ and equivalently of δQ_m. That is, δQ_m must be able to connect s with t.

Using benzene as an example, we have for the A_{1g}, B_{2u} transition the result that $\langle sQ_0\, q \mid \boldsymbol{\mu}(q) \mid 1Q_0\, q\rangle = 0$ (the transition is Frank-Condon forbidden). In-plane intensity requires that the "t state" E_{1u} be brought in, this because the transition A_{1g}, E_{1u} is allowed according to the transformation properties of x,y as listed in Table 2.1. Thus, E_{1u} must be mixed with B_{2u}. The electronic part of $V(qQ)$ must work on a B_{2u} function to give a new function with symmetry E_{1u}. By an argument resembling the one in

Section 2.12, it is found that the electronic part, therefore, must transform like E_{2g} (the "direct product" $E_{1u} \times B_{2u} = E_{2g}$). Concomitantly, the species of the vibrational part of $V(qQ)$ will be the same, e_{2g}. It turns out that there *is* an e_{2g} vibration for benzene. In fact, the structure of the A_{1g}, B_{2u} transition has been analyzed as showing symmetrical progressions with one unit of excitation in the e_{2g} mode for the upper potential energy surface (Sponer, Nordheim, Sklar, and Teller).*

If we carry out this analysis for the B_{1u} band, we again find that the e_{2g} vibration should appear in connection with mixing-in of the E_{1u} state, the strong in-plane transition. For the out-of-plane, A_{2u}, transition, the effective vibration would be b_{2g} (b_{1g} for the first considered case, $A_{1g} \rightarrow B_{2u}$). There is a b_{2g} (out-of-plane) vibration in benzene, though its assignment is uncertain and it will appear only weakly in the B_{1u} vibronic band. There is no b_{1g} vibration. In consequence there is a possibility for distinguishing between B_{1u} and B_{2u} by considering the vibrational perturbation, although the possibility is a bare one.

* H. Sponer, G. Nordheim, A. L. Sklar, and E. Teller, *J. Chem. Phys.*, 7 (1939), 207. See also A. D. Liehr, *Revs. Mod. Phys.*, **32** (1960), 436, and references therein.

CHAPTER 3

The Valence Bond Method

In our work with the molecular orbital method, we have frequently claimed to be treating nothing more elaborate than hydrogen atoms. In this way we have avoided considering such complications as inner shells, and so on.* Actually, we have tried to apply our results to more complicated situations, notably to π electrons considered apart from the other electrons, but without justification.

In the next few sections, we shall see the development of methods which will allow us in principle to treat the interaction of many-electron atoms. We shall then return to the model of a collection of hydrogen atoms with some better appreciation of its wider applica-

* For a treatment of inner shells see O. Sinanoğlu, *J. Chem. Phys.*, **33** (1960), 1212.

bility and treat such a collection by the valence bond method, which sometimes works better than the molecular orbital method.

The energy required to separate a hydrogen molecule into infinitely separated protons and electrons is 32 e.v., whereas the energy needed to separate the molecule into atoms is 4.7 e.v., or about 15 per cent of the total. For more complicated molecules, the total energy goes up rapidly, becoming of the order of thousands of electron volts even for molecules containing just first-row atoms. The binding energies and first transition energies remain of the order of tens of electron volts. Thus if we wish to calculate from first principles binding energies and transition energies to within 10 per cent, we are required to calculate total energies to within 0.1 per cent. This accuracy has not yet been achieved, although through use of the large electronic computers it will probably be realized within the next several decades.

The small magnitudes of binding energies make one think that it would be possible to calculate these energies as perturbations using atomic wave functions. Even this is not a straightforward matter, for several reasons: first, because, practically speaking, good atomic wave functions are not available any more than good molecular wave functions are; second, because the atomic excited states are low-lying (virtually degenerate) so that simple perturbation theory including only the exchange degeneracy is ruled out, and a fairly large secular equation would actually have to be used. The difficulty about the lack of good atomic wave functions typically introduces extremely large errors in the total energy, which then show up as correspondingly large errors in the binding energy. This difficulty can be partially circumvented by using experimental atomic term values for certain required matrix elements. The approximate wave functions are then being used in such a way that their inadequacy is less seriously reflected in the calculated total energy, and hence the binding energy. (This was first systematically outlined by Moffitt,* who named his method appropriately "Atoms in Molecules.") Thus, by foregoing total calculation and using empirical quantities for the atomic parts, we might be able to achieve a satisfactory degree of accuracy for chemical calculations—binding energies, even activation and transition energies.

Although a start has been made, such a program has not to date been successfully carried out, partly because of the second difficulty: the need for bringing in a comparatively large number of low-lying excited atomic states. Nevertheless, it is believed that the idea of treating chemical cal-

* W. Moffitt, *Proc. Roy. Soc. (London)*, **A 210** (1951), 224, 245. See also A. C. Hurley, *Proc. Phys. Soc. (London)*, **69A** (1956), 49 and *J. Chem. Phys.*, **28** (1958), 532.

culations by perturbation theory is important, and the rudiments of such a theory are described in the next sections, illustrated by the interaction of two lithium atoms.

3.1 TWO LITHIUM ATOMS*

There are six electrons in the two atoms and thus already a considerable complication from the permutation degeneracy. This will be dealt with by using antisymmetrizing operators

$$A \equiv \sum_P (-1)^P P$$

for the atoms separately, together with a "residual" antisymmetrizer, A', which brings in the exchanges from one atom to the other. If we confine our work to the states with $\Sigma\, m_z = 0$ we have the spins of the electrons in the outer orbits on the separate atoms having to be opposite, and we may use these spins to specify the wave functions. Thus the simple single-configuration wave function for a lithium atom (where the first number labels the orbital and the last the electron)

$$6^{-1/2} A \mid 1\alpha 1) \mid 1\beta 2) \mid 2\alpha 3)$$

which has α in the outer orbital, may be written as

$$6^{-1/2} A_a \mid a\alpha\rangle$$

where a means the ath lithium atom. (Note the new Dirac bracket signifying a many-electron function.) Also, a more general function in which the inner-shell electrons are treated (in principle) quite accurately can be formally represented in the same way

$$6^{-1/2} A_a \mid \alpha\beta\rangle \mid 2\alpha 3) = 6^{-1/2} A_a \mid a\alpha\rangle$$

(Here $|\alpha\beta\rangle$ stands for the inner-shell wave function.) If we could neglect the extra terms brought in by A' there would be the following two product functions for the system of two atoms (labeled a and b)

$$6^{-1} A_a \mid a\alpha\rangle A_b \mid b\beta\rangle \quad \text{and} \quad 6^{-1} A_a \mid a\beta\rangle A_b \mid b\alpha\rangle$$

where the electrons on atom a might, for example, be the ones numbered 1–3, and on atom b, 4–6. Each product function contains $36 = 3! \times 3!$ terms of the total of $6!$ required, so that the residual antisymmetrizer, A', must bring in an extra 20 terms. The approximate functions satisfying the Pauli principle may therefore be written, for example,

* Treated in detail by T. Arai, *J. Chem. Phys.*, **26** (1957), 435, 451.

$$|a\alpha b\beta\rangle = 20^{-1/2}\, A'\, 6^{-1}\, A_a \mid a\alpha\rangle\, A_b \mid b\beta\rangle$$
$$|a\beta b\alpha\rangle = 20^{-1/2}\, A'\, 6^{-1}\, A_a \mid a\beta\rangle\, A_b \mid b\alpha\rangle$$

The fact that there are two equivalent functions is an example of what is called *exchange degeneracy.*

We would like to use these functions in a perturbation calculation. To apply perturbation theory in the strictest sense for the situation in which the atoms are brought together, we should need exact functions for the case of no perturbation—separated atoms—and should need to consider other functions corresponding to states which lie close to the ground unperturbed state (approximately within the degenerate manifold); but as briefly mentioned above, we shall work with approximate functions, and for the time being, consider just the two.

The scheme for separating out the perturbation will now be described. The Hamiltonian may be taken as

$$H_a + H_b + V$$

where

$$H_a = T_1 + T_2 + T_3 + V_{a1} + V_{a2} + V_{a3} + V_{12} + V_{13} + V_{23}$$

with a similar expression for H_b. Each of H_a and H_b corresponds to the numbering system employed before the residual antisymmetrizer mixes up the electrons. The perturbation is what remains

$$V = V_{a4} + V_{a5} + V_{a6} + V_{b1} + V_{b2} + V_{b3} + V_{14} + V_{15} + V_{16} + V_{24} + V_{25} + V_{26} + V_{34} + V_{35} + V_{36} + V_{ab}$$

A given matrix element, say, the off-diagonal one

$$720^{-1}\,\langle a\alpha \mid A_a\, \langle b\beta \mid A_b\, A'\, HA'\, A_a \mid a\beta\rangle\, A_b \mid b\alpha\rangle$$

is equal to

$$\langle a\alpha \mid \langle b\beta \mid HA'\, A_a \mid a\beta\rangle\, A_b \mid b\alpha\rangle$$

(the standard argument involving the fact that a renumbering of electrons does not change the Hamiltonian). The matrix element is next split into unperturbed and perturbed parts, for example,

$$\langle a\alpha \mid \langle b\beta \mid (H_a + H_b)\, A'\, A_a \mid a\beta\rangle\, A_b \mid b\alpha\rangle$$

and an integral over V. The former is now changed by a reintroduction of the local antisymmetrizers on the left, which gives thirty-six terms in place of the one. Dividing by 6^{-2}, we then have

$$6^{-1}\cdot 6^{-1/2}\,\langle a\alpha \mid A_a\, 6^{-1/2}\,\langle b\beta \mid A_b\, (H_a + H_b)\, A'\, A_a \mid a\beta\rangle\, A_b \mid b\alpha\rangle$$

But if, for example, $6^{-1/2}\langle a\alpha \mid A_a$ were exact, it would be an eigenfunction of H_a (considered as operating to the left) corresponding to an eigenvalue E_0, which is the observed ground state energy of a lithium atom. This is a purely mathematical fact, true no matter where the nucleus and the numbered electrons of the other atom are located.

3.2 INTRODUCTION OF THE OBSERVED ENERGY

In the calculation of the matrix elements, it will now be assumed that the true atomic functions are momentarily introduced on the left for

$$6^{-1/2}\langle a\alpha \mid A_a\, 6^{-1/2}\langle b\beta \mid A_b$$

Thus operating to the left with $(H_a + H_b)$ yields $2E_0$. The unperturbed off-diagonal matrix element is therefore

$$6^{-1}\cdot 6^{-1/2}\langle a\alpha \mid A_a\, 6^{-1/2}\langle b\beta \mid A_b\,(2E_0)\,A'\,A_a \mid a\beta\rangle\, A_b \mid b\alpha\rangle$$
$$= 2E_0\,\langle a\alpha \mid \langle b\beta \mid A \mid a\beta\rangle \mid b\alpha\rangle$$

where the separate antisymmetrizers have once more been removed from the left, and the various antisymmetrizers on the right have been lumped together

$$A = A'\,A_a\,A_b$$

The perturbed part is

$$\langle a\alpha \mid \langle b\beta \mid VA \mid a\beta\rangle \mid b\alpha\rangle$$

The full secular equation is analogous to the one found in the Heitler-London treatment of H_2, as we shall see by introducing some further abbreviations. We regard the perturbed part as analogous to a molecular exchange integral

$$\langle a\alpha \mid \langle b\beta \mid VA \mid a\beta\rangle \mid b\alpha\rangle = K$$

and similarly we obtain a coulomb integral

$$\langle a\alpha \mid \langle b\beta \mid VA \mid a\alpha\rangle \mid b\beta\rangle = J$$

The true atomic functions and also their approximate counterparts are not orthogonal, leading to the necessity of defining*

$$\langle a\alpha \mid \langle b\beta \mid A \mid a\alpha\rangle \mid b\beta\rangle = \Delta_0$$

as well as the more familiar

$$\langle a\alpha \mid \langle b\beta \mid A \mid a\beta\rangle \mid b\alpha\rangle = \Delta$$

* Observe that without A', $6^{-2}\langle a\alpha \mid A_a \langle b\beta \mid A_b\, A_a \mid a\alpha\rangle\, A_b \mid b\beta\rangle = 1$

Using these abbreviations (and taking out atomic eigenvalues wherever possible), we find the following secular equation

$$\begin{vmatrix} 2E_0\,\Delta_0 + J - \lambda & 2E_0\,\Delta + K - \Delta\lambda \\ 2E_0\,\Delta + K - \Delta\lambda & 2E_0\,\Delta_0 + J - \lambda \end{vmatrix} = 0$$

Since the limit of Δ_0 as the atoms are separated is unity, to a fair approximation we should find

$$\begin{vmatrix} J - \lambda' & K - \Delta\lambda' \\ K - \Delta\lambda' & J - \lambda' \end{vmatrix} = 0$$

where $\lambda' = \lambda - 2E_0$, the binding energy; and therefore

$$\lambda' \approx \frac{J \pm K}{1 \pm \Delta}$$

This expression is directly comparable to the one for the hydrogen molecule. It could have been obtained in a more intuitive fashion than was used. The systematic approach, however, is needed as more states are brought in.

3.3 IONIC CONTRIBUTIONS

The contributions of various functions in a perturbation (or variation) calculation are given approximately by the interaction matrix elements divided by the diagonal energy differences. Thus the contribution of a wave function corresponding to an ionic structure for Li_2 depends heavily on the energy above $2E_0$ of the (unperturbed) ionic state, leading to the conclusion that this difference as employed should be accurate. This quantity is related to the difference between the ionization potential and electron affinity, a fact which affords a check on any approximate computation of the quantity. Several such approximate computations have been made for this or that molecular system with quite erroneous results. This is the main reason for our interest in being able to introduce the empirical quantities. We shall now see how energies of ionic states may be introduced in the case of Li_2.

The wave functions of the ionic states will be written

$$48^{-1/2} A_a \mid a^+\rangle A_b \mid b^-\rangle$$

$$48^{-1/2} A_a \mid a^-\rangle A_b \mid b^+\rangle$$

where the local antisymmetrizers are variable depending on whether they work on a positive or a negative ion, being thus two- and four-electron antisymmetrizers respectively.

To evaluate a typical matrix element, we interact the ionic states. It will be convenient to use a division of the Hamiltonian

$$H = H_a\,(12) + H_b\,(3456) + V$$

where electrons one and two are considered as being on atom a and the remaining electrons on b. The interaction matrix element is thus

$$\begin{aligned} &15^{-1}\,48^{-1}\,\langle a^+ \mid A_a \langle b^- \mid A_b\,A'\,(H_a + H_b + V)\,A'\,A_a \mid a^-\rangle\,A_b \mid b^+\rangle \\ &\quad = \langle a^+ \mid \langle b^- \mid (H_a + H_b + V)\,A \mid a^-\rangle \mid b^+\rangle \\ &\quad = 48^{-1}\,\langle a^+ \mid A_a \langle b^- \mid A_b\,(H_a + H_b + V)\,A \mid a^-\rangle \mid b^+\rangle \end{aligned}$$

where finally the local antisymmetrizers have been reintroduced on the left so that the true wave functions for the ionic states of the separated atoms may be introduced. If we let E_+ and E_- stand for the atomic (ionic) eigenvalues we have

$$\begin{aligned} &= 48^{-1}\,\langle a^+ \mid A_a \langle b^- \mid A_b\,(E_+ + E_- + V)\,A \mid a^-\rangle \mid b^+\rangle \\ &= \langle a^+ \mid \langle b^- \mid (E_+ + E_- + V)\,A \mid a^-\rangle \mid b^+\rangle \end{aligned}$$

Apparently having different numbers of electrons assigned to an atom on two sides of a matrix element poses no problem. The atomic term values taken out may depend on whether the unperturbed Hamiltonian is defined so as to be able to operate, and operates, to the left or to the right. This is easy to see when one considers the interaction between an ionic state and a covalent state. In any event, it is probably best to adopt a particular convention (for example, the Hamiltonian always operates to the left) and stick with it, a practice which will lead to unsymmetrical secular equations.

The introduction of the observed energy, as described generally above, will not simplify actual computations to any remarkable degree. But it offers considerable promise as a way of systematizing molecular calculations involving different kinds of atoms. Whether the method can be elaborated to bring in enough excited states so as to give really satisfactory accuracy, economically with respect to computing effort, is a moot point.

We next go back to the comparatively simple problem of making a perturbation calculation omitting all but the separated atom ground states, so that all that remains is the exchange degeneracy.

3.4 EXCHANGE DEGENERACY

The feature common to the calculation for Li_2 using just the 2×2 secular equation, and the Heitler-

London calculation for H_2, is the singly-occupied (free) orbitals leading to the exchange or permutation degeneracy. When there are more than just two singly-occupied orbitals, naturally the degeneracy is greater, and the problem of which functions satisfy the exclusion principle and of how the secular equation may be simplified can become quite formidable.

To be able to understand the general case is extremely important because of the phenomenon of covalent bond formation in chemistry. That there must ultimately be some simple way of dealing with collections of singly-occupied orbitals is suggested by the straightforwardness and success of the structural theory of organic chemistry. The exchange degeneracy problem may then be considered as directed toward deriving this structural theory from quantum mechanics.

Here we shall consider the orbitals as initially separated and then brought together until there is a first-order interaction, but not so close as to introduce higher-order terms. If the atoms are brought together in such a way that the ratios among the interatomic distances are the same as in actual molecules, the calculations may in favorable cases actually be relevant in the description of the true ground states. Enlarging on this idea, let us refer to the level scheme in Fig. 3.1. The shaded region schematically depicts the results of a first-order treatment of the exchange degeneracy. The levels at the true interatomic distance would be as on the right in the figure. In many cases, however, the pattern in the shaded region might be expected to be maintained on the right, only with magnification. Levels classified as coming from atomic excited states would also be interspersed, but these would not reach down to the ground level and might not interact heavily with the lowest states of the exchange degeneracy problem. Thus the first-order calculation could predict relative binding energies and even low-lying transition energies for molecules similar in nature.

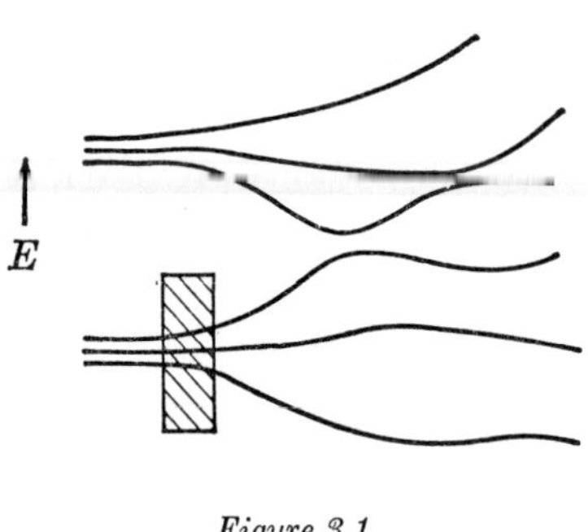

Figure 3.1

Strictly speaking, of course, such a calculation ought to be considered as producing the first derivative of the energy with respect to a parameter expressing the approach of the atoms—the meshing of the outer orbitals. Thus stringently considered, the calculation would in principle be quite accurate, provided that the free orbitals are optimal and that experimental atomic term values are introduced to overcome deficiencies in the inner shell parts of the functions. Using hydrogen atoms in place of heavier atoms each with a free orbital may be considered as representing most simply the satisfaction of these conditions. We shall therefore use hydrogen atoms in the following, a plan which will make it possible to concentrate on the characteristic features of the exchange degeneracy.

The next problem considered is a system of n fixed protons and n electrons to go with them, all atoms being widely, but not infinitely, separated. The procedure will be to use the formalism of transformation theory, as as was done in Chapter 2, only here the basis functions must be many-electron functions.

3.5 PERMUTATION HAMILTONIAN*

We wish to transform the Hamiltonian in the Schrödinger representation into a representation such that the unit vectors are spinless eigenfunctions of the system: atoms removed to infinity. We restrict our consideration to the degenerate 1s block and begin with a digression in which a system is built up for describing all the various functions which are related through the permutation degeneracy.

A many-electron ket is depicted as a product

$$| a\mu) \, | b\nu) \ldots$$

or simply

$$a_\mu \, b_\nu \ldots$$

where $a, b, \ldots$ are 1s orbitals on different protons $a, b, \ldots$ at positions or "centers" $a, b, \ldots$ and where $\mu, \nu, \ldots$ are coordinate labels referring to different numbered electrons.

There are $n!$ equivalent many-electron kets, and these may be generated by coordinate permutations, P, or orbital permutations, R. We shall consider orbital permutations first, and work with the example $n = 3$. For a standard, we take

$$| 0\rangle = a_1 \, b_2 \, c_3$$

and from this generate the following six degenerate kets, arranged according to the group classes of the R's

* P. A. M. Dirac, *Quantum Mechanics* (Oxford: Oxford University Press, 1958), chap. 9.

$$R_0 \mid 0\rangle = \mid 0\rangle = a_1\, b_2\, c_3 \quad R_1 \mid 0\rangle = \mid 1\rangle = b_1\, a_2\, c_3 \quad R_4 \mid 0\rangle = \mid 4\rangle = c_1\, a_2\, b_3$$
$$R_2 \mid 0\rangle = \mid 2\rangle = a_1\, c_2\, b_3 \quad R_5 \mid 0\rangle = \mid 5\rangle = b_1\, c_2\, a_3$$
$$R_3 \mid 0\rangle = \mid 3\rangle = c_1\, b_2\, a_3 \tag{3.1}$$

The action of an R on a ket which is not the standard is found by rearranging the factors until the orbital labels are arranged serially—in the standard order—and then operating on the orbital labels in a way analogous to what was done in Eq. (3.1). For example, for

$$R_2 \mid 3\rangle = R_2\, R_3 \mid 0\rangle$$

we have

$$\begin{aligned} R_2\, c_1\, b_2\, a_3 &= R_2\, a_3\, b_2\, c_1 \\ &= a_3\, c_2\, b_1 = \mid 5\rangle = R_5 \mid 0\rangle \end{aligned}$$

We see, in addition, that if the operand is $\mid 0\rangle$

$$R_2\, R_3 = R_5$$

The action of the P's is taken from the definition Eq. (3.1) in the sense that whatever R_i does to the letters $a, b, c, \ldots$ P_i does to the numbers $1, 2, 3, \ldots$ starting from the same standard order. For example,

$$P_3 \mid 0\rangle = P_3\, a_1\, b_2\, c_3 = a_3\, b_2\, c_1$$

because R_3 is an $a \leftrightarrow c$ interchange so P_3 is a $1 \leftrightarrow 3$ interchange. Using Eq. (3.1), one can convince himself that a P and an R commute when they act on the standard

$$RP \mid 0\rangle = PR \mid 0\rangle$$

We now show that P and R commute generally:

$$RP_i \mid j\rangle = RP_i\, P_k \mid 0\rangle = RP \mid 0\rangle$$

where here $P_k \mid 0\rangle = \mid j\rangle$* and $P_i\, P_k = P$ and continuing

$$\begin{aligned} RP \mid 0\rangle &= PR \mid 0\rangle = P_i\, P_k\, R \mid 0\rangle \\ &= P_i\, RP_k \mid 0\rangle = P_i\, R \mid j\rangle \end{aligned}$$

Since $|j\rangle$ is any ket,

$$RP_i = P_i\, R$$

We now go back to the example we were considering involving the R's

$$R_2\, R_3 \mid 0\rangle = R_5 \mid 0\rangle$$

* The definition of P_k—as doing the same thing to the numbers as R_k does to the letters—does not imply $P_k \mid 0\rangle = \mid k\rangle$ for all k. Thus $P_4 \mid 0\rangle = \mid 5\rangle$.

and operate with some P_k such that

$$P_k \mid 0\rangle = \mid j\rangle$$

obtaining

$$P_k R_2 R_3 \mid 0\rangle = P_k R_5 \mid 0\rangle$$

which, by virtue of the commutability of R's and P's,

$$= R_2 R_3 P_k \mid 0\rangle = R_5 P_k \mid 0\rangle$$

therefore, for any j,

$$R_2 R_3 \mid j\rangle = R_5 \mid j\rangle$$

This demonstrates the essential group property for the R's, the closure property (the same is true for the P's). We shall subsequently need to refer to the group multiplication table.

Before terminating this discussion of the P's and R's, we note an additional property of the two working together, provided that the operand is the standard and the same index is used for both R and P

$$P_i R_i \mid 0\rangle = R_i P_i \mid 0\rangle = \mid 0\rangle$$

whence also

$$P_i \mid 0\rangle = R_i^{-1} \mid 0\rangle \tag{3.2}$$

We are now ready to carry out the actual computation of the Hamiltonian matrix for the 1s block. As discovered by Dirac, this matrix has many repeating elements, the locations of which may be described in a manner which is startling in its simplicity. We shall use the R's to generate the basis functions. The element in the rth row and s^{th} column is

$$\langle r \mid H \mid s\rangle = \langle 0 \mid \overline{R}_r H R_s \mid 0\rangle \tag{3.3}$$

Here the conjugate notation means

$$\overline{R_r \, 1 0\rangle} = \langle 0 \mid \overline{R}_r$$

and it may be shown that

$$R^{-1} = \overline{R}$$

$$P^{-1} = \overline{P}$$

We next, in effect, renumber the coordinates in Eq. (3.3) to bring $R_s \mid 0\rangle$ back to the standard. Formally, and with $\overline{P}_s P_s = 1$,

$$\langle 0 \mid \overline{R}_r H R_s \mid 0\rangle = \langle 0 \mid \overline{R}_r \overline{P}_s P_s H \overline{P}_s P_s R_s \mid 0\rangle$$

$$= \langle 0 \mid \overline{R}_r \overline{P}_s P_s H \overline{P}_s \mid 0\rangle$$

where we have used the previous result

$$P_s R_s \mid 0\rangle = \mid 0\rangle$$

The transform of H may be computed by renumbering all the electrons in H, which leaves H unchanged

$$P_s H \overline{P}_s = H$$

so that

$$\langle r \mid H \mid s \rangle = \langle 0 \mid \overline{R}_r \overline{P}_s H \mid 0 \rangle$$

Next, we use the commutability of P's and R's, giving

$$= \langle 0 \mid \overline{P}_s \overline{R}_r H \mid 0 \rangle$$

and the relation Eq. (3.2), giving finally

$$= \langle 0 \mid \overline{R}_s^{-1} \overline{R}_r H \mid 0 \rangle$$

Now if we define

$$R_t = R_r R_s^{-1} \tag{3.4}$$

this becomes

$$\langle r \mid H \mid s \rangle = \langle 0 \mid \overline{R}_t H \mid 0 \rangle = \langle t \mid H \mid 0 \rangle \tag{3.5}$$

so that all r, s matrix elements Eq. (3.3) are $\langle t \mid H \mid 0 \rangle$, where r and s are linked together through Eq. (3.4), as recorded in the group multiplication table.

We see that many elements of the Hamiltonian matrix are the same and now shall obtain a simple description of how these elements are positioned. To this end, we compute the elements of the matrix representing a particular R, R_t

$$\langle r \mid R_t \mid s \rangle = \langle 0 \mid \overline{R}_r R_t R_s \mid 0 \rangle$$

Because of the (assumed) orthogonality

$$\langle i \mid j \rangle = \delta_{ij}$$

this matrix has non-zero elements, equal to unity, provided that

$$R_r = R_t R_s$$

or equivalently, Eq. (3.4) again,

$$R_t = R_r R_s^{-1}$$

Bringing the findings for the matrix of H and the matrix of R_t together, we have the result that the numbers $\langle t \mid H \mid 0 \rangle$ occur at exactly the same places in $\mathbf{H}$ as the numbers *one* occur in $\mathbf{R}_t$; so that we may take as a partial $\mathbf{H}$ the matrix $\langle t \mid H \mid 0 \rangle \, \mathbf{R}_t$, and for the entire $1s$ block,

$$\mathbf{H} = \sum_t \langle t \mid H \mid 0 \rangle \, \mathbf{R}_t$$

This is true in a representation for which the many-electron kets $|i\rangle$ are unit vectors and also in any other representation, a fact which gives the fundamental equation for the permutation Hamiltonian

$$H = \sum_t \langle t \mid H \mid 0 \rangle R_t \tag{3.6}$$

3.6 THE INTERACTION OPERATOR

For the model of hydrogen atoms well separated, many of the matrix elements, $\langle t \mid H \mid 0 \rangle$, are zero, a fact which makes it profitable to simplify the permutation Hamiltonian further. To begin, we divide the energy into perturbed and unperturbed parts

$$H = \sum_{\nu,i} [T_\nu + V_{i\nu}] + \sum_{\mu<\nu} V_{\mu\nu} + \sum_{i<j} V_{ij}$$

$$H^0 = \sum_{\nu,i} [T_\nu + V_{i\nu}\, \delta_{i\nu}]$$

whence, by difference, $V = H - H^0$ is

$$V = \sum_{\nu,i} [V_{i\nu} - V_{i\nu}\, \delta_{i\nu}] + \sum_{\mu<\nu} V_{\mu\nu} + \sum_{i<j} V_{ij}$$

The Kronecker delta in H^0 results in the retention of attraction terms such that each numbered electron in the standard $|0\rangle$ is attracted specifically to the proton with the same number—therefore

$$H^0 \mid 0 \rangle = nE_o \mid 0 \rangle$$

where n is the number of atoms and E_o is the $1s$ energy eigenvalue. The general matrix element thus becomes

$$\langle t \mid H \mid 0 \rangle = nE_o \langle t \mid 0 \rangle + \langle t \mid V \mid 0 \rangle$$

and the Hamiltonian, Eq. (3.6) becomes

$$H = nE_o + \langle 0 \mid V \mid 0 \rangle + \sum_t{}' \langle t \mid V \mid 0 \rangle R_t \tag{3.6a}$$

where the prime indicates that the $t = 0$ term is to be omitted. Inspection of the "coulomb term" $\langle 0 \mid V \mid 0 \rangle$ shows that it contains a balance of electron-electron and proton-proton repulsions against the distant electron-proton attractions and thus approaches zero when the atoms are removed from one another. The "exchange terms" involve integrals $\langle t \mid V \mid 0 \rangle$ in which a given electron is in an overlap distribution on different centers, so this term also goes to zero when the atoms are removed from one another. This proves our premise that the basis functions which have been used in the transformation of H are eigenfunctions when all interatomic separations are infinite.

When the separations are not quite infinite it is no longer true that the basis functions are orthogonal, that is, $\langle r \mid s \rangle \neq \delta_{rs}$, a fact which calls into question the entire derivation of the permutation Hamiltonian. It turns out that it is possible to rework the derivation with a result which essentially validates Eq. (3.6a). (See Section 3.14 in the Appendix.)

Returning to the Hamiltonian, Eq. (3.6a), we now regard the part involving the R_t's as the significant part. It equals

$$H - nE_o - \langle 0 \mid V \mid 0 \rangle$$

which in turn approximately equals the energy beyond nE_o (the energy of n isolated atoms). This last justifies the name *interaction operator*. As abbreviated, this is

$$H_{\text{int}} = \sum_t{}' \langle t \mid V \mid 0 \rangle R_t \tag{3.7a}$$

The coefficients multiplying the various R_t's are capable of being divided into different categories depending on how the atoms are brought together. Let us suppose the atoms are brought together so that certain pairs are adjacent, with all adjacent distances equal, and so that all non-adjacent interactions are very much smaller. This is possible owing to the exponential fall-off of the wave functions, and the nature of $\langle t \mid V \mid 0 \rangle$. To see this, we look at the integral for the hydrogen molecule. With electron one on proton a and electron two on proton b (and disregarding V_{ab}) the integral is

$$\langle 1 \mid V \mid 0 \rangle = \int a_2\, b_1\, (V_{a2} + V_{b1} + V_{12})\, a_1\, b_2\, d\tau_1\, d\tau_2$$

If a and b are considered as representing adjacent centers, this integral is, say, a first-order infinitesimal, but if they are considered as representing non-adjacent centers the integral is, in effect, zero. To see this integrate over, for example, $d\tau_1$, which gives zero because the integrand is essentially $a_1\, b_1$ (the operator part does not change the function significantly). The function $a_1\, b_1$ is a product of parts which are non-zero in mutually exclusive regions of space; hence the product is everywhere zero. For a spatial distribution of atoms in which the adjacent pairs are equivalent, we can factor the non-vanishing exchange integrals. We thus find for the interaction operator

$$H_{\text{int}} = K \sum_j{}'' R_j \tag{3.7b}$$

where multiple (as opposed to pairwise) exchanges and pairwise exchanges of non-adjacent atoms have disappeared, for reasons similar to what was explained above. The double prime means pairwise exchanges of equivalent adjacent atoms and harmonizes with K, which stands for the non-vanishing exchange integrals.

When account of the non-orthogonality is taken, exchange integrals must be replaced by (see Appendix)

$$B_t = \langle t \mid V \mid 0 \rangle - \langle 0 \mid V \mid 0 \rangle \langle t \mid 0 \rangle$$

This expression has the same sensitivity as K to the overlap of the orbitals involved, and leads to a formula for the interaction like Eq. (3.7b) which is essentially exact to the first order in the overlap.

$$H_{\text{int}} = B \sum_j R_j \tag{3.7c}$$

(For convenience the double prime has been omitted.)

Now, and in the following section as well, we shall consider the various modifications which must be introduced when we drop the restriction to the artificial case of spinless functions. The most fundamental consideration is that the Pauli exclusion principle must be satisfied; this condition is fulfilled by the employment of certain restricted linear combinations of the $R \mid 0\rangle$'s together with spin, namely, Slater determinants. If we begin with the assumption that the states with no total spin angular momentum are of primary interest (n would have to be taken as even), then we further assume that the z component of the total spin is zero, which is guaranteed by using equal numbers of α's and β's in each Slater determinant. An example of such a Slater determinant is the following,

$$A a\alpha_1 \, b\beta_2 \, c\alpha_3 \, d\beta_4$$

where, for example, $a\alpha_1$ means electron one is in orbital a with spin α. In another notation, this example becomes

$$\begin{vmatrix} a\alpha_1 & b\beta_1 & c\alpha_1 & d\beta_1 \\ a\alpha_2 & b\beta_2 & c\alpha_2 & d\beta_2 \\ a\alpha_3 & b\beta_3 & c\alpha_3 & d\beta_3 \\ a\alpha_4 & b\beta_4 & c\alpha_4 & d\beta_4 \end{vmatrix}$$

The Pauli principle is guaranteed by the row antisymmetry. There is also column antisymmetry, and it is this property of the determinants we wish to use. We have been employing operators, R, which permute the orbitals amongst themselves. We now consider the operators, $\mathcal{R}$, which interchange spins going along with orbitals but not the orbitals. In order to interchange a column of a Slater determinant, one must interchange both spins and orbitals, and then the determinant changes sign

$$R\mathcal{R} = -1$$

Since the R's in Eq. (3.7c) are single interchanges we may use for the corresponding $\mathcal{R}$'s

$$\mathcal{R}^{-1} = \mathcal{R},$$

in which case we have $R = -\mathcal{R}$. Employing the interchangeability of R and $-\mathcal{R}$, we come to the final form of the interaction operator (a form which will be very useful after we see how to write the wave functions as crucially involving the $\mathcal{R}$'s).

$$H_{\text{int}} = -B \sum_j \mathcal{R}_j \tag{3.8}$$

This operator is entirely equivalent to Eq. (3.7c), provided that we allow it to operate on Slater determinants.

3.7 FACTORING THE SECULAR EQUATION

In this section and the next, we shall see how to set up the eigenvalue calculation for H_{int} for that part of the $1s$ block corresponding to the z component of the total spin equal to zero and the total spin squared having one of its eigenvalues. In particular, we shall be interested in the block of total spin zero, the singlet block. The procedure for factoring the secular equation in this case is well known; namely, that one can construct functions in which the electrons are "paired" and these functions, being singlets, will fail to interact with the higher multiplet functions. Just what *paired* means is a little subtle, because in a given bond between two distinguishable centers the electrons are numbered every which way. It is really the spins on the centers which are to be paired, and we shall proceed so as to accent the distinction between paired spins on centers and paired numbered electrons.

With this in mind we change the notation for a spinorbital so that instead of, for example,

$$a_\nu \, \alpha_\nu \quad \text{or} \quad a\alpha_\nu$$

(electron ν is in the $a\alpha$ spinorbital), we write

$$\alpha_\nu^a$$

A Slater determinant is generated, as before, by action of the antisymmetrizer on the leading term, for example,

$$A\,\alpha_1^a\,\beta_2^b\,\alpha_3^c \ldots$$

We can further simplify the notation by recognizing that here one Slater determinant differs from another only through the assignment of spins to orbitals. Thus the determinant above may just as well be written as some operator working on a product of spinorbital symbols

$$A\,\alpha_1^a\,\beta_2^b\,\alpha_3^c \ldots = \hat{A}\alpha^a\,\beta^b\,\alpha^c \ldots$$

The new operator $\hat{A}$ may be defined as one which puts in electron numbers as subscripts, 1 corresponding to a, 2 to b, 3 to c, and so on, after which the ordinary antisymmetrization process is carried out. If the spinorbital symbols are arranged serially, then the electron numbers will be entered serially.

For example,

$$\hat{A}\alpha^b\,\beta^a = A\alpha_2^b\,\beta_1^a = A\beta_1^a\,\alpha_2^b$$

The general linear combination of Slater determinants

$$\sum_{\mathcal{R}} k\hat{\mathcal{R}}\mathcal{R}A\,a\alpha_1\,b\beta_2\,c\alpha_3\ldots$$

(where all α, β interchanges $\mathcal{R}$ are represented) becomes in the new notation

$$\hat{A}(k_1\,\alpha^a\,\beta^b\,\alpha^c\ldots + k_2\,\beta^a\,\alpha^b\,\alpha\beta^c\ldots + \ldots)$$

The first term, which has α's and β's alternating, starting with α when the orbital superscripts are arranged serially, will be taken as standard

$$\hat{A}\alpha^a\,\beta^b\,\alpha^c\ldots = |s\rangle$$

At this point, we are ready for the theorem to be used in selecting the proper linear combination of Slater determinants for any possible spin multiplet.

THEOREM 3.1. *The coefficients*, k, *in*

$$\hat{A}(k_1\,\alpha^a\,\beta^b\,\alpha^c\ldots + k_2\,\beta^a\,\alpha^b\,\alpha^c\ldots + \ldots)$$

are to be taken as equal to the corresponding coefficients which show how to combine spin-only functions to give a desired spin multiplet

$$(k_1\,\alpha_1\,\beta_2\,\alpha_3\ldots + k_2\,\beta_1\,\alpha_2\,\alpha_3\ldots + \ldots)$$

The theorem may be proved by studying the action of $\hat{A}$. When the leading term of each Slater determinant in the linear combination is generated inside the parenthesis

$$\hat{A}(k_1\,\alpha^a\,\beta^b\,\alpha^c\ldots + k_2\,\beta^a\,\alpha^b\,\alpha^c\ldots + \ldots)$$
$$= A(k_1\,\alpha_1^a\,\beta_2^b\,\alpha_3^c\ldots + k_2\,\beta_1^a\,\alpha_2^b\,\alpha_3^c\ldots + \ldots)$$

one obtains a result which, in one of the less compact notations, is seen to contain a spin multiplet function as a factor

$$= A\,a_1\,b_2\,c_3\ldots(k_1\,\alpha_1\,\beta_2\,\alpha_3\ldots + k_2\,\beta_1\,\alpha_2\,\alpha_3\ldots + \ldots)$$

Subsequent action of the P's in the conventional antisymmetrizer, A, is merely to produce a renumbering. In consequence, each new spinless part is multiplied by a spin-only factor having the structure of the spin-only factor in the leading term, and thus belonging to the same eigenvalue of the total spin angular momentum.

Granting that we may make use of Theorem 3.1, this still leaves the question of how to select the k's in the spin-only case. This implies that we must study spin angular momentum, (or just "spin" if the factor $\hbar$ is omitted).

The operator for the total spin-squared, S^2_{op}, may be written as involving Pauli matrices*

$$4S^2_{\text{op}} = \boldsymbol{\sigma}^2 = \sum_{\mu=1}^{n} \boldsymbol{\sigma}_\mu \cdot \sum_{\nu=1}^{n} \boldsymbol{\sigma}_\nu \tag{3.9}$$

where for each particle

$$\boldsymbol{\sigma} = \mathbf{i}\sigma_x + \mathbf{j}\sigma_y + \mathbf{k}\sigma_z$$

This gives

$$\boldsymbol{\sigma}^2 = \sum_{\mu=1}^{n} \boldsymbol{\sigma}_\mu^2 + 2 \sum_{\mu<\nu} \boldsymbol{\sigma}_\mu \cdot \boldsymbol{\sigma}_\nu$$

or with

$$\boldsymbol{\sigma}_\mu \cdot \boldsymbol{\sigma}_\mu = 3$$

$$\boldsymbol{\sigma}^2 = 3n + 2 \sum_{\mu<\nu} \boldsymbol{\sigma}_\mu \cdot \boldsymbol{\sigma}_\nu$$

If we now incorporate the Dirac spin-exchange identity (Section 3.16 in the Appendix)

$$P_{\mu\nu} = \tfrac{1}{2}(1 + \boldsymbol{\sigma}_\mu \cdot \boldsymbol{\sigma}_\nu)$$

we obtain

$$\boldsymbol{\sigma}^2 = 3n - 2\left(\frac{n^2 - n}{2}\right) + 4 \sum_{\mu<\nu} P_{\mu\nu}$$

or going back to Eq. (3.9),

$$S^2_{\text{op}} = \sum_{\mu<\nu} P_{\mu\nu} - \frac{n^2 - 4n}{4} \tag{3.10}$$

Thus we may regard the sum of pairwise interchanges as essentially equivalent to S^2_{op}. This sum is a class sum of the permutation group, a dynamical variable in its own right. (For pairwise interchanges $P^{-1} = P$; thus the rule for permutations $\overline{P} = P^{-1}$ implies Hermiticity.)

Briefly now, we shall go on systematically to investigate the selection of linear combinations of spin-only functions as eigenfunctions of $\sum_{\mu<\nu} P_{\mu\nu}$ belonging to this or that eigenvalue. We abbreviate

$$\sum_{\mu<\nu} P_{\mu\nu} \equiv P_{\text{op}}$$

and label the various spin functions, for example,

* Recall that Pauli matrices have eigenvalues ± 1, whereas spin has eigenvalues $\pm \frac{1}{2}$.

$$|1\rangle = \alpha_1\,\beta_2\,\alpha_3\ldots$$
$$|2\rangle = \beta_2\,\alpha_1\,\alpha_3\ldots$$
$$\vdots$$

The action of P_{op} is to throw one function into a linear combination

$$P_{\text{op}}\,|\,i\rangle = \sum_m p_{im}\,|\,m\rangle$$

where the p_{im} have to be worked out by inspection. Thus a linear combination becomes

$$P_{\text{op}} \sum_i k_i\,|\,i\rangle = \sum_{im} k_i\,p_{im}\,|\,m\rangle$$

Now suppose the linear combination is an eigenfunction corresponding to the eigenvalue π

$$P_{\text{op}} \sum_i k_i\,|\,i\rangle = \pi \sum_i k_i\,|\,i\rangle$$

This gives

$$\sum_{im} k_i\,p_{im}\,|\,m\rangle = \pi \sum_i k_i\,|\,i\rangle$$

which on multiplication by $\langle j|$ becomes

$$\sum_i k_i\,p_{ij} = \pi k_j$$

leading to the secular equation

$$|\,p_{ij} - \pi\delta_{ij}\,| = 0$$

The eigenvalues may be obtained in advance by combining the known eigenvalues

$$S^2_{\text{op}} \doteq S(S+1)$$

with Eq. (3.10), with the result

$$P_{\text{op}} \doteq \pi_{n,s} = S(S+1) + \frac{n^2 - 4n}{4} \tag{3.11}$$

but since we mainly need the eigenvectors, this still requires the evaluation first of the p's and then of the k's. It turns out that there is a way to select the k's to give correct linear combinations especially for the singlet block without going through the procedure just cited.

3.8 BOND EIGENFUNCTIONS

For the present, we shall continue to deal with the spin-only case. The singlets are obtained by the Rümer procedure, which is begun by arranging all the spins and electron numbers in a circle in the standard fashion (alternating α's and β's starting with α). For example, if $n = 6$ we have

$$\begin{array}{ccc} & \alpha_1 & \\ \beta_6 & & \beta_2 \\ & & \\ \alpha_5 & & \alpha_3 \\ & \beta_4 & \end{array}$$

Now every $\alpha\beta$ pair is joined by a line and in such a manner that no lines cross. In this manner, the numbered electrons are paired. For $n = 6$, this gives five diagrams:

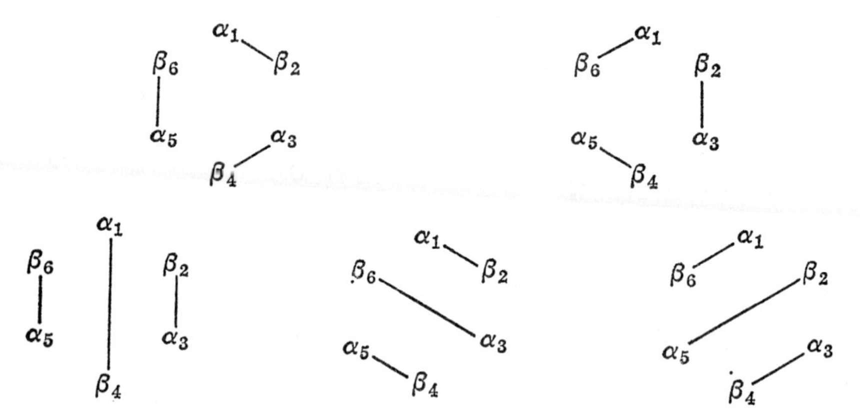

Each diagram may then be made the basis of a singlet by using every operator $(1 - P_{ij})$, referring to the paired electrons ij joined by a line, operating on the standard. For example, for the third diagram we would have

$$(1 - P_{14})(1 - P_{23})(1 - P_{56})\ \alpha_1\,\beta_2\,\alpha_3\,\beta_4\,\alpha_5\,\beta_6$$

Not only will a wave function so constructed be a singlet, but also the number of such diagrams is equal to the number of linearly independent functions for a given n, and the functions are independent.

We now investigate the action of P_{op} on such a function. The essential features are illustrated with the example $n = 4$, and one way of pairing the electrons gives the same result as another. Consider, for example,

$$(P_{12} + P_{13} + P_{14} + P_{23} + P_{24} + P_{34})(1 - P_{12})(1 - P_{34})\ \alpha_1\,\beta_2\,\alpha_3\,\beta_4$$

The P_{12} and P_{34} collapse into the operator, giving -1 apiece, and therefore,

$$(-1 + P_{13} + P_{14} + P_{23} + P_{24} - 1)(1 - P_{12})(1 - P_{34})\ \alpha_1\,\beta_2\,\alpha_3\,\beta_4$$

In order to obtain the -1 eigenvalues, we use operator algebra, for example,

$$P_{12}(1 - P_{12}) = P_{12} - P_{12}^2 = P_{12} - 1 = -(1 - P_{12})$$

In the general case there results $-n/2$, which is the negative of the number of connecting lines. There are four terms remaining and the sum of these four terms commutes* with the operator $(1 - P_{12})(1 - P_{34})$, giving

$$(1 - P_{12})(1 - P_{34})(P_{13} + P_{14} + P_{23} + P_{24})\,\alpha_1\,\beta_2\,\alpha_3\,\beta_4$$

In general, the terms remaining are $(n^2 - n)/2 - n/2$ in number. The P's remaining are divisible into two halves. One half permutes electrons having the same spin, which introduces a $+2$ here or $[(n^2 - n)/2 - n/2]/2$ generally, and the other half permutes electrons having opposite spins but which are not "bonded," for example,

$$P_{14}\,\alpha_1\,\beta_2\,\alpha_3\,\beta_4 = \alpha_4\,\beta_2\,\alpha_3\,\beta_1$$

This always results in a function which is annihilated by the operator for the bonds because in some bond two spins are alike

$$(1 - P_{12})\,\alpha_4\,\beta_2\,\alpha_3\,\beta_1 = 0$$

Therefore a function with all electrons paired is an eigenfunction of the class sum with the eigenvalue

$$\pi_n = -\frac{n}{2} + \frac{[(n^2 - n)/2 - n/2]}{2} = \frac{n^2 - 4n}{4}$$

(In the present case with $n = 4$, we have $\pi_4 = 0$.) Comparing with Eq. (3.11), we now recognize that the functions constructed according to the Rümer procedure must also be eigenfunctions of S_{op}^2 Eq. (3.10) corresponding to $S(S + 1) = 0$. Thus $S = 0$, and the multiplicity, $2S + 1$, is one.

To round out the picture, we should need to prove the completeness and independence of the functions constructed according to the Rümer procedure. We shall not investigate the latter property, but with respect to the completeness, we may bring in the branching diagram. It will be observed that the number of functions obtained using the Rümer method is equal to the appropriate entry in the branching diagram. This entry gives the total number of independent spin states—though by an apparently quite different procedure. Figure 3.2 shows a portion of the branching diagram. The number five at $n = 6$ and $S = 0$ harmonizes with the fact that there are five Rümer diagrams, any one of which corresponds to an

* The entire P_{op} commutes with the projection operator. The terms P_{12} and P_{34} then may be collapsed into the projection operator from the right.

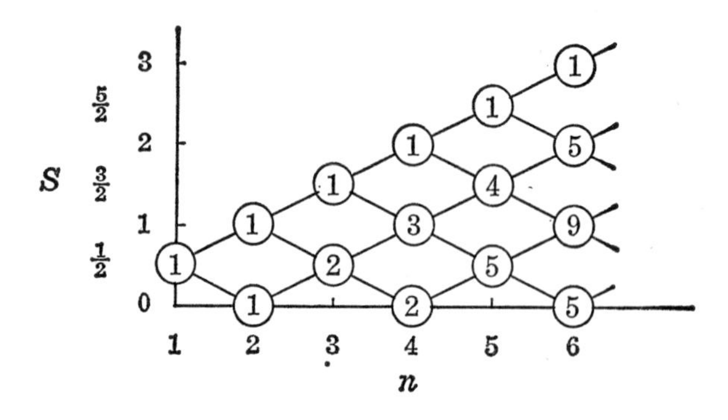

Figure 3.2

independent function for the pairing of six electrons. The branching diagram is constructed by observing that, for example, a spin of one can be obtained in three ways for $n = 4$: by compounding an $S = \frac{1}{2}$ state for a single electron with either of the two spins for $n = 3$, $S = \frac{3}{2}$ (one state already) or $S = \frac{1}{2}$ (two states already). The compounding is done using $S = -\frac{1}{2}$ in the former case and $S = +\frac{1}{2}$ in the latter.

Going back to Theorem 3.1, we can now translate the results obtained through the study of the spin-only case. We recall that the Slater determinants are to be combined using the same k's as used with the spin-only basis functions. With the Rümer procedure, this is automatically accomplished by starting with a spin arrangement labeled using the orbital designations

$$\begin{array}{ccc} & \alpha^a & \\ \beta^f & & \beta^b \\ \alpha^e & & \alpha^c \\ & \beta^d & \end{array}$$

Thus for the diagram analogous to the third, preceding, we have

$$\begin{array}{ccc} & \alpha^a & \\ \beta^f & | & \beta^b \\ | & | & | \\ \alpha^e & | & \alpha^c \\ & \beta^d & \end{array}$$

and for the function

$$\hat{A}(1 - \mathcal{R}_{ad})(1 - \mathcal{R}_{bc})(1 - \mathcal{R}_{ef})\ \alpha^a\ \beta^b\ \alpha^c\ \beta^d\ \alpha^e\ \beta^f$$

It is readily shown that the $\mathcal{R}$'s commute with $\hat{A}$, giving

$$(1 - \mathcal{R}_{ad})(1 - \mathcal{R}_{bc})(1 - \mathcal{R}_{ef})\ \hat{A}\alpha^a\ \beta^b\ \alpha^c\ \beta^d\ \alpha^e\ \beta^f = (1 - \mathcal{R}_{ad})(1 - \mathcal{R}_{bc})(1 - \mathcal{R}_{ef})\ |s\rangle$$

Thus we see how to write a singlet wave function (not normalized) as an operator which is a function of the $\mathcal{R}$'s working on $|s\rangle$, the standard Slater determinant. In the example, the spins on a and d, b and c, and e and f are paired. In general, the pairing is among spins on centers.

Just as certain linear combinations of Slater determinants are singlets, triplets, and so on, depending upon the k's, so also a given Slater determinant is (or may be considered to be) a linear combination of singlets, triplets, and so on, taken as components. The product of factors operating on the standard determinant

$$\ldots (1 - \mathcal{R}_{ij})(1 - \mathcal{R}_{kl})\ \ldots\ |s\rangle$$

may then be considered as an operator which projects $|s\rangle$ (a linear combination of singlets, triplets, and so on) on the "singlet axis." A projection operator working on a once projected function creates nothing new, a property which is expressed in operator form

$$O^2 = O$$

Each factor $(1 - \mathcal{R}_{ij})$ has this property if multiplied by $\frac{1}{2}$

$$[\tfrac{1}{2}(1 - \mathcal{R}_{ij})]^2 = \tfrac{1}{4}(1 - 2\mathcal{R}_{ij} + \mathcal{R}_{ij}^2) = \tfrac{1}{4}(2 - 2\mathcal{R}_{ij}) = \tfrac{1}{2}(1 - \mathcal{R}_{ij})$$

(here we have used $\mathcal{R}_{ij}^2 = 1$). Since the factors $(1 - \mathcal{R}_{ij})$ commute, all together the product of factors $(1 - \mathcal{R}_{ij})$ may be considered as a projection operator.

The $\mathcal{R}$'s used in the foregoing are the same permutations we previously used in setting up the final form of the interaction operator Eq. (3.8). A function generated from the standard which contains the factor (pairing centers i and j)

$$\ldots (1 - \mathcal{R}_{ij}) \ldots$$

in the projection operator will bring in a stabilization represented by $+B$ (and $B < 0$) if there is a corresponding term in the interaction operator*

$$-B\mathcal{R}_{ij}$$

* In Eq. (3.8), we have used single subscripts to label the single interchanges serially. Here, we use double subscripts to indicate the centers among which the α,β interchanges occur.

because $+B$ is an eigenvalue

$$-B\mathcal{R}_{ij}(1 - \mathcal{R}_{ij}) = -B(\mathcal{R}_{ij} - \mathcal{R}_{ij}^2)$$
$$= B(1 - \mathcal{R}_{ij})$$

Following Slater, Penney, Van Vleck, Pauling, and others, we then say that there is an electron pair bond between i and j. Because of this possibility, moreover, we call the singlets constructed according to the plan outlined in the foregoing *bond eigenfunctions*. This demonstration foreshadows the subject of the next section which is the calculation of matrix elements working mainly with the projection operators.

3.9 INTERACTION MATRIX ELEMENTS

As a first illustration, we shall set up the $S = 0$ secular equation for a system of four atoms in a line, with equal nearest neighbor distances. Calling the atoms a, b, c, and d, in order, we then have, Eq. (3.8)

$$H_{\text{int}} = -B(\mathcal{R}_{ab} + \mathcal{R}_{bc} + \mathcal{R}_{cd}) \tag{3.12}$$

signifying a is adjacent to b, etc. The Rümer diagrams* are

$$\begin{matrix} \alpha^a \text{---} \beta^b \\ \beta^d \text{---} \alpha^c \end{matrix} \qquad \begin{matrix} \alpha^a \\ | \\ \beta^d \end{matrix} \qquad \begin{matrix} \beta^b \\ | \\ \alpha^c \end{matrix}$$

leading to bond eigenfunctions

$$|1\rangle = N_1(1 - \mathcal{R}_{ab})(1 - \mathcal{R}_{cd})\,|s\rangle$$
$$|2\rangle = N_2(1 - \mathcal{R}_{ad})(1 - \mathcal{R}_{bc})\,|s\rangle$$

The N's are normalizing factors. In $|1\rangle$ there are bonds between a and b and between c and d. In $|2\rangle$ there is no bond between a and d even though the spins on a and d are paired, because $\mathcal{R}_{ad}$ does not appear in H_{int}. The diagonal matrix element for the function with two bonds is

$$\langle 1 \mid H_{\text{int}} \mid 1\rangle =$$
$$-BN_1^2\,\langle s|\,(1 - \mathcal{R}_{ab})(1 - \mathcal{R}_{cd})(\mathcal{R}_{ab} + \mathcal{R}_{bc} + \mathcal{R}_{cd})(1 - \mathcal{R}_{ab})(1 - \mathcal{R}_{cd})\,|s\rangle \tag{3.13}$$

* The fact that the Rümer diagrams form a square should not imply that atoms a and d are adjacent, which they are not. What is important is the absence of $\mathcal{R}_{ad}$ from H_{int}.

Here we have been able to use $\overline{\mathcal{R}} = \mathcal{R}$ because $\overline{\mathcal{R}} = \mathcal{R}^{-1}$, and $\mathcal{R}^{-1} = \mathcal{R}$ for single interchanges. Using $\mathcal{R}_{ab}(1 - \mathcal{R}_{ab}) = -(1 - \mathcal{R}_{ab})$ and the same for $\mathcal{R}_{cd}$ and remembering that the bond eigenfunctions are normalized, we have

$$\langle 1 \mid H_{\text{int}} \mid 1\rangle - 2B =$$

$$-BN_1^2 \langle s|\,(1 - \mathcal{R}_{ab})(1 - \mathcal{R}_{cd})\,\mathcal{R}_{bc}\,(1 - \mathcal{R}_{ab})(1 - \mathcal{R}_{cd})\,|s\rangle \quad (3.13\text{a})$$

The matrix element of $\mathcal{R}_{bc}$ requires some study. First we observe that it is the same as for all the transforms*

$$\begin{aligned}
\mathcal{R}_{bc} &= \mathcal{R}_{bc} \\
\mathcal{R}_{ab}\,\mathcal{R}_{bc}\,\mathcal{R}_{ab} &= \mathcal{R}_{ac} \\
\mathcal{R}_{cd}\,\mathcal{R}_{bc}\,\mathcal{R}_{cd} &= \mathcal{R}_{bd} \\
\mathcal{R}_{ab}\,\mathcal{R}_{cd}\,\mathcal{R}_{bc}\,\mathcal{R}_{cd}\,\mathcal{R}_{ab} &= \mathcal{R}_{ad}
\end{aligned}$$

where every $\mathcal{R}$ in the projection operator which would fail to commute with $\mathcal{R}_{bc}$ is brought in. To see why, for example, the matrix element over $\mathcal{R}_{ac}$ is the same as the one over $\mathcal{R}_{bc}$ we note that the property $\mathcal{R}_{ab}(1 - \mathcal{R}_{ab}) = -1(1 - \mathcal{R}_{ab})$ and $(1 - \mathcal{R}_{ab})\,\mathcal{R}_{ab} = -1\,(1 - \mathcal{R}_{ab})$ may be used

$$\begin{aligned}
&\langle s|\,(1 - \mathcal{R}_{ab})(1 - \mathcal{R}_{cd})\mathcal{R}_{ab}\,\mathcal{R}_{bc}\,\mathcal{R}_{ab}\,(1 - \mathcal{R}_{ab})(1 - \mathcal{R}_{cd})\,|s\rangle \\
&\qquad = \langle s|\,(1 - \mathcal{R}_{ab})(1 - \mathcal{R}_{cd})\,\mathcal{R}_{bc}\,(1 - \mathcal{R}_{ab})(1 - \mathcal{R}_{cd})\,|s\rangle
\end{aligned}$$

We may now use the sum

$$\mathcal{R}_{\text{sum}} \equiv \tfrac{1}{4}(\mathcal{R}_{bc} + \mathcal{R}_{ac} + \mathcal{R}_{bd} + \mathcal{R}_{ad})$$

in place of $\mathcal{R}_{bc}$ and be assured that the matrix element will be the same as the one over $\mathcal{R}_{bc}$. Unlike the single $\mathcal{R}_{bc}$, the sum commutes with the projection operator

$$\mathcal{R}_{\text{sum}}\,(1 - \mathcal{R}_{ab})(1 - \mathcal{R}_{cd}) = (1 - \mathcal{R}_{ab})(1 - \mathcal{R}_{cd})\,\mathcal{R}_{\text{sum}}$$

To see this, we would need to show that, for example,

$$\mathcal{R}_{\text{sum}}\,\mathcal{R}_{ab} = \mathcal{R}_{ab}\,\mathcal{R}_{\text{sum}}$$

or, since $\mathcal{R}_{ab} = \mathcal{R}_{ab}^{-1}$,

$$\mathcal{R}_{ab}\,\mathcal{R}_{\text{sum}}\,\mathcal{R}_{ab} = \mathcal{R}_{\text{sum}}$$

which the reader can verify by using the original form for $\mathcal{R}_{\text{sum}}$

$$\tfrac{1}{4}(\mathcal{R}_{bc} + \mathcal{R}_{ab}\,\mathcal{R}_{bc}\,\mathcal{R}_{ab} + \mathcal{R}_{cd}\,\mathcal{R}_{bc}\,\mathcal{R}_{cd} + \mathcal{R}_{ab}\,\mathcal{R}_{cd}\,\mathcal{R}_{bc}\,\mathcal{R}_{cd}\,\mathcal{R}_{ab})$$

We may now write the sum immediately to the left of the standard, so that the right-hand side of Eq. (3.13a) becomes

* In simplifying, for example, $\mathcal{R}_{ab}\,\mathcal{R}_{bc}\,\mathcal{R}_{ab} = \mathcal{R}_{ac}$, we are using a theorem which holds quite generally.

$$-BN_1^2 \langle s|\, (1 - \mathcal{P}_{ab})(1 - \mathcal{P}_{cd})(1 - \mathcal{P}_{ab})(1 - \mathcal{P}_{cd}) \\ \tfrac{1}{4}(\mathcal{P}_{bc} + \mathcal{P}_{ac} + \mathcal{P}_{bd} + \mathcal{P}_{ad})\, \hat{A}\alpha^a \beta^b \alpha^c \beta^d$$

Of the four terms in the sum, two ($\mathcal{P}_{ac}$ and $\mathcal{P}_{bd}$) convert the standard Slater determinant into itself, for example,

$$\mathcal{P}_{ac}\, \hat{A}\alpha^a \beta^b \alpha^c \beta^d = \hat{A}\, \mathcal{P}_{ac}\, \alpha^a \beta^b \alpha^c \beta^d = \hat{A}\alpha^a \beta^b \alpha^c \beta^d$$

The other two convert the standard into new determinants, for example,

$$\mathcal{P}_{bc}\, \hat{A}\alpha^a \beta^b \alpha^c \beta^d = \hat{A}\, \alpha^a \alpha^b \beta^c \beta^d$$

Subsequent action of the projection operator on these new determinants gives zero, for example,

$$(1 - \mathcal{P}_{ab})\, \hat{A}\alpha^a \alpha^b \beta^c \beta^d \\ = \hat{A}\, (1 - \mathcal{P}_{ab})\, \alpha^a \alpha^b \beta^c \beta^d = \hat{A}(\alpha^a \alpha^b \beta^c \beta^d - \alpha^a \alpha^b \beta^c \beta^d) = 0$$

Thus we have remaining only two of the original four terms

$$-BN_1^2 \langle s|\, (1 - \mathcal{P}_{ab})(1 - \mathcal{P}_{cd})\, \mathcal{P}_{bc}\, (1 - \mathcal{P}_{ab})(1 - \mathcal{P}_{cd})\, |s\rangle \\ = -BN_1^2 \langle s|\, (1 - \mathcal{P}_{ab})(1 - \mathcal{P}_{cd})\, \tfrac{2}{4}\, (1 - \mathcal{P}_{ab})(1 - \mathcal{P}_{cd})\, |s\rangle \\ = -B/2$$

In consequence, Eq. (3.13) becomes

$$\langle 1 \mid H_{\text{int}} \mid 1\rangle = 2B - \frac{B}{2} = \frac{3B}{2}$$

Similarly,

$$\langle 2 \mid H_{\text{int}} \mid 2\rangle = B - \frac{B}{2} - \frac{B}{2} = 0$$

The off-diagonal matrix element of H_{int} is

$$-BN_1 N_2 \langle s|\, (1 - \mathcal{P}_{ab})(1 - \mathcal{P}_{cd}) \\ (\mathcal{P}_{ab} + \mathcal{P}_{bc} + \mathcal{P}_{cd})(1 - \mathcal{P}_{ad})(1 - \mathcal{P}_{bc})\, |s\rangle$$

The terms in the interaction operator are allowed to operate either to the left, as for $\mathcal{P}_{bc}$, or to the right, as for $\mathcal{P}_{ab}$ and $\mathcal{P}_{cd}$. For each one an eigen-relation holds: $\mathcal{P}(1 - \mathcal{P}) = -\,(1 - \mathcal{P})$, so we have

$$\langle 1 \mid H_{\text{int}} \mid 2\rangle = 3B\, \langle 1 \mid 2\rangle$$

The non-orthogonality integral is computed by noting that the bonding scheme in $|1\rangle$ may in effect be transferred onto different atoms to give $|2\rangle$ by an *orbital* permutation

$$R_{bd}\, N_1\, (1 - \mathcal{P}_{ab})(1 - \mathcal{P}_{cd})\, |s\rangle \\ = N_1\, (1 - \mathcal{P}_{ad})(1 - \mathcal{P}_{bc})\, R_{bd}\, |s\rangle$$

$$= N_1 (1 - \mathcal{R}_{ad})(1 - \mathcal{R}_{bc})(-\mathcal{R}_{bd}) \hat{A}\alpha^a \beta^b \alpha^c \beta^d$$

$$= -N_1 (1 - \mathcal{R}_{ad})(1 - \mathcal{R}_{bc}) |s\rangle = -\frac{N_1}{N_2} |2\rangle$$

Thus

$$R_{bd} |1\rangle = -\frac{N_1}{N_2} |2\rangle$$

or

$$\mathcal{R}_{bd} |1\rangle = \frac{N_1}{N_2} |2\rangle$$

As it turns out, N_1/N_2 is not strictly unity unless $|1\rangle$ and $|2\rangle$ are related by symmetry; nevertheless, the factor B in the matrix element

$$3B \langle 1 \mid 2 \rangle$$

is already a small quantity of the first order so we may approximate N_1/N_2 by unity, finding

$$\langle 1 \mid H_{\text{int}} \mid 2 \rangle = 3B \langle 1 \mid \mathcal{R}_{bd} \mid 1 \rangle$$

This last quantity is one we have in effect just finished studying (it is like $\langle 1 \mid \mathcal{R}_{bc} \mid 1 \rangle$) so that we find

$$\langle 1 \mid 2 \rangle = \frac{1}{2} \quad \text{and} \quad \langle 1 \mid H_{\text{int}} \mid 2 \rangle = \frac{3B}{2}$$

The secular equation for the singlet block of H_4 is

$$\begin{vmatrix} \frac{3B}{2} - \lambda & \frac{3B}{2} - \frac{\lambda}{2} \\ \frac{3B}{2} - \frac{\lambda}{2} & -\lambda \end{vmatrix} = 0 \tag{3.14}$$

An approximation to the lowest root is obtained by ignoring the interaction, in which case, $\lambda = 3B/2$. To ignore the contribution of all but a single bond eigenfunction is called the *approximation of perfect pairing.* In this approximation, the energy is always a sum of B's for the bonds and $-B/2$'s for the uncoupled spins on adjacent centers (this last is easy to prove as an extension of our result for $\langle 1 \mid \mathcal{R}_{bc} \mid 1 \rangle$ for H_4).

The actual lowest root of Eq. (3.14) is

$$\lambda = \sqrt{3}\, B$$

and for the corresponding function

$$c_1 \mid 1\rangle + c_2 \mid 2\rangle$$

the contributions are

$$\left(\frac{c_1}{c_2}\right)^2 = 7.45$$

The meaning of this ratio is not transparent because $|2\rangle$ has some $|1\rangle$ already in it ($\langle 1 \mid 2 \rangle \neq 0$). The actual ground state function, however, is certainly predominantly $|1\rangle$ indicating an approach to perfect pairing.

As realized by Pauling, a study of the implications of our treatment of H_4 very likely shows why the valence bond structures of organic chemistry are so successful. This does not mean that a valence bond structure as used by an organic chemist is literally equivalent to a pure bond eigenfunction. It could well be that a structure appropriately stands for not just $|1\rangle$ but the entire function

$$c_1 \mid 1\rangle + c_2 \mid 2\rangle$$

One can go even further by assuming that the structural formula should be considered as applying at the true internuclear separations, and thus includes just the right contribution from atomic excited states (for example, so-called ionic terms), as depicted schematically on the right of Fig. 3.1. In any event, the structural formulas of organic chemistry have no property of being positive or negative and thus should be considered as representing the square of a wave function, with concomitant implications about probability distribution.

There are some cases for which the perfect pairing approximation obviously could not hold. For four atoms at the corners of a square, the two functions $|1\rangle$ and $|2\rangle$ become equivalent because of the extra term—compare Eq. (3.12)—in the interaction operator

$$-B(\mathcal{R}_{ab} + \mathcal{R}_{bc} + \mathcal{R}_{cd} + \mathcal{R}_{ad})$$

(this gives $\langle 1 \mid H_{\text{int}} \mid 1\rangle = \langle 2 \mid H_{\text{int}} \mid 2\rangle$). The Kekulé resonance in benzene is almost surely an example of this effect, there being no single most stable pairing scheme for the π electrons because of the cyclic nature of the π orbital arrangement. The Kekulé structures which an organic chemist draws need not be taken as referring literally to the bond eigenfunctions, or their squares. Still, the connection between what is inferred intuitively using the structures, and what may be found from the bond eigenfunctions, is most suggestive.

3.10 DEGENERATE BOND EIGENFUNCTIONS: BENZENE

At this point, we shall use the bond eigenfunctions to carry out a calculation for H_6 or, in a sense, benzene (see the discussion centering around Fig. 3.1). The treatment will be restricted to the functions which correspond to the Kekulé structures. The interaction operator is

$$-B(\mathcal{R}_{ab} + \mathcal{R}_{bc} + \mathcal{R}_{cd} + \mathcal{R}_{de} + \mathcal{R}_{ef} + \mathcal{R}_{fa})$$

and the bond eigenfunctions are (p. 132)

$$|1\rangle = N(1 - \mathcal{R}_{ab})(1 - \mathcal{R}_{cd})(1 - \mathcal{R}_{ef})\,|s\rangle$$

$$|2\rangle = N(1 - \mathcal{R}_{bc})(1 - \mathcal{R}_{de})(1 - \mathcal{R}_{fa})\,|s\rangle$$

where the N's are equal by symmetry. The first diagonal matrix element is

$$-B\,\langle 1|\,(\mathcal{R}_{bc} + \mathcal{R}_{de} + \mathcal{R}_{fa})\,|1\rangle + 3B$$

—relations of the form $\mathcal{R}_{ab}\,(1 - \mathcal{R}_{ab}) = -\,(1 - \mathcal{R}_{ab})$ having been used—and each term remaining, for example,

$$-B\,\langle 1\,|\,\mathcal{R}_{bc}\,|\,1\rangle = -\frac{B}{2}$$

by an argument analogous to the one given for $\mathcal{R}_{bc}$ in the previous case of four atoms. The element is therefore $3B - 3B/2 = 3B/2$. The other diagonal element has the same value. The off-diagonal element is

$$N^2\,\langle 1|\,(1 - \mathcal{R}_{ab})(1 - \mathcal{R}_{cd})(1 - \mathcal{R}_{ef})\,[-B(\mathcal{R}_{ab} + \mathcal{R}_{bc} + \mathcal{R}_{cd} + \mathcal{R}_{de} + \mathcal{R}_{ef} + \mathcal{R}_{fa})](1 - \mathcal{R}_{bc})(1 - \mathcal{R}_{de})(1 - \mathcal{R}_{fa})\,|2\rangle$$

which reduces immediately to

$$6B\,\langle 1\,|\,2\rangle$$

The non-orthogonality integral is evaluated by noting that two interchanges of the orbitals will convert $|1\rangle$ into $|2\rangle$

$$R_{bf}\,R_{ce}\,|1\rangle = |2\rangle$$

(the operations carried out on the standard function $|s\rangle$ result in two column interchanges and the projection operator is converted into the one for $|2\rangle$). Thus we have

$$\langle 1\,|\,2\rangle = \langle 1\,|\,R_{bf}\,R_{ce}\,|\,1\rangle = \langle 1\,|\,\mathcal{R}_{bf}\,\mathcal{R}_{ce}\,|\,1\rangle$$

This integral may be evaluated in a manner analogous to the one used in the case of four atoms—by making up a sum which commutes with the projection operator for $|1\rangle$ and then letting the terms of the sum work individually on $|s\rangle$. There are 16 terms in the sum only four of which give a result different from zero, so we have $\langle 1\,|\,2\rangle = 4/16$. Rules for computing matrix elements quickly are given in Section 3.15 of the Appendix.

The operation $C_2' \mid s\rangle$ involves switching a into $-a$, b into $-f$, c into $-e$, and d into $-d$ (it should be remembered that the orbitals are π orbitals)

$$C_2' \mid s\rangle = R_{bf}\, R_{ce} \mid s\rangle = \mathcal{R}_{bf}\, \mathcal{R}_{ce} \mid s\rangle = \mathcal{R}_{bf}\, \mathcal{R}_{ce}\, \hat{A}\alpha^a\, \beta^b\, \alpha^c\, \beta^d\, \alpha^e\, \beta^f = |s\rangle$$

Thus

$$C_2' \mid 1\rangle = |2\rangle$$

If we go on in this fashion, we find

	E	$2C_6$	$2C_3$	C_2	$3C_2'$	$3C_2''$	i	$2S_3$	$2S_6$	σ_h	$3\sigma_d$	$3\sigma_v$
$R \mid 1\rangle$	$\|1\rangle$	$\|2\rangle$	$\|1\rangle$	$\|2\rangle$	$\|2\rangle$	$\|1\rangle$	$\|2\rangle$	$\|1\rangle$	$\|2\rangle$	$\|1\rangle$	$\|1\rangle$	$\|2\rangle$
$\chi(B_{2u})$	1	−1	1	−1	−1	1	−1	1	−1	1	1	−1

The signs in the character operator for B_{2u} are shown in the table, and it may be seen that the function for B_{2u} is non-vanishing.

$$\sum_R \chi(R)\, R \mid 1\rangle = 12 \mid 1\rangle - 12 \mid 2\rangle$$

Before we leave the subject of benzene, a word about the comparison with the molecular orbital calculation and with experiment is in order. The bond eigenfunction and molecular orbital calculations each give the result that the first singlet excited state is B_{2u}, and this agrees with experiment. Just as semiempirical methods may be employed with the orbital scheme (where for example it was seen from a comparison with the benzene spectrum how to estimate β) so also may they be used in the present instance.* If we use the energy going along with the absorption for the $A_{1g} \rightarrow B_{2u}$ transition at 2600 Å (110 kcal/mole or 4.75 e.v.) we can evaluate B; in fact, $-2.4B$ is the calculated energy difference. This gives $B \approx -46$ kcal/mole or -2 e.v. The vertical resonance energy obtained above of $-0.9B$ is thus predicted to be 41 kcal/mole, which is in the range expected.

3.11 BOND EIGENFUNCTIONS FOR DOUBLETS AND TRIPLETS

The problem of an odd number of atoms, $n - 1$, is similar to the corresponding n atom problem, in that the number of linearly independent functions is the same (see Fig. 3.2, the branching diagram). The standard Slater determinant is taken as having α's alternating with β's, starting with α, though of course not with equal numbers of α's and β's.

* We are now applying a theory which is correct when B is infinitesimal, there are no inner shells, and so on, to a case for which these conditions are not fulfilled. Under the circumstances, it is a matter of personal taste how seriously these methods are to be regarded.

We shall study the case of three atoms. The bond eigenfunctions are

$$|1\rangle = N(1 - \mathcal{R}_{ab})\hat{A}\ \alpha^a\,\beta^b\,\alpha^c$$
$$|2\rangle = N(1 - \mathcal{R}_{bc})\hat{A}\ \alpha^a\,\beta^b\,\alpha^c \tag{3.15}$$

Theorem 3.1 about selecting k's from the spin-only case is not restricted to the case of equal numbers of α's and β's; and indeed we shall see by using P_{op} (Section 3.7) that the above functions are doublets

$$\begin{aligned}(P_{12} + P_{13} + P_{23})(1 - P_{12})\ \alpha_1\,\beta_2\,\alpha_3 &\\ &= (1 - P_{12})(P_{12} + P_{13} + P_{23})\ \alpha_1\,\beta_2\,\alpha_3\\ &= (-1 + 1)(1 - P_{12})\ \alpha_1\,\beta_2\,\alpha_3 + (1 - P_{12})\ P_{23}\,\alpha_1\,\beta_2\,\alpha_3\\ &= 0 + 0\end{aligned}$$

Thus substitution of $\pi = 0$ and $n = 3$ into Eq. (3.11) gives $S(S + 1) = \frac{3}{4}$ and $S = \frac{1}{2}$; so that the multiplicity, $2S + 1$, is two (doublet).

Assuming the atoms to be colinear, we have a model substance resembling the π electrons in allyl radical

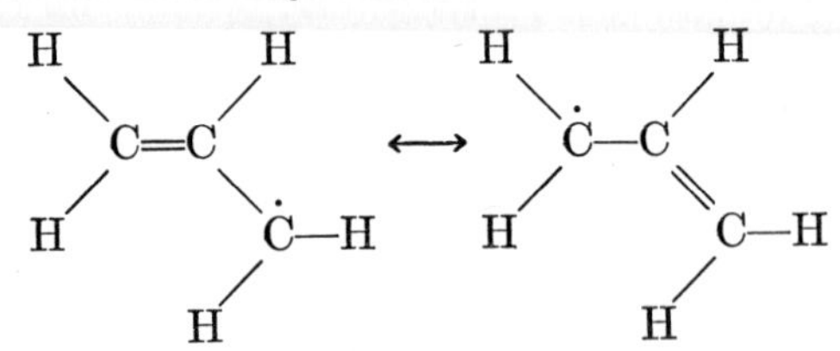

There is no $\mathcal{R}_{ac}$ term in the interaction operator

$$H_{\text{int}} = -B(\mathcal{R}_{ab} + \mathcal{R}_{bc})$$

and

$$\begin{aligned}\langle 1 \mid H_{\text{int}} \mid 1\rangle &= -BN^2\,\langle s|\ (1 - \mathcal{R}_{ab})(\mathcal{R}_{ab} + \mathcal{R}_{bc})(1 - \mathcal{R}_{ab})\ |s\rangle\\ &= B - B\,N^2\,\langle s|\ (1 - \mathcal{R}_{ab})\ \mathcal{R}_{bc}\ (1 - \mathcal{R}_{ab})\ |s\rangle\end{aligned}$$

The remaining integral is evaluated by noting that it is the same as

$$\begin{aligned}-N^2\,B\,\langle s|\ (1 - \mathcal{R}_{ab})\ \tfrac{1}{2}\ (\mathcal{R}_{bc} + \mathcal{R}_{ab}\,\mathcal{R}_{bc}\,\mathcal{R}_{ab})(1 - \mathcal{R}_{ab})\ |s\rangle &\\ &= -N^2\,B\,\langle s|\ (1 - \mathcal{R}_{ab})(1 - \mathcal{R}_{ab})\ \tfrac{1}{2}\ (\mathcal{R}_{bc} + \mathcal{R}_{ac})\ \hat{A}\alpha^a\,\beta^b\,\alpha^c\\ &= -\frac{B}{2}\end{aligned}$$

or combining

$$\langle 1 \mid H_{\text{int}} \mid 1\rangle = \frac{B}{2}$$

The other diagonal element has the same value, and the off-diagonal element is

$$\langle 1 \mid H_{\text{int}} \mid 2 \rangle = -BN^2 \langle s| (1 - \mathcal{R}_{ab})(\mathcal{R}_{ab} + \mathcal{R}_{bc})(1 - \mathcal{R}_{bc}) |s\rangle$$
$$= 2B \langle 1 \mid 2 \rangle$$

The non-orthogonality integral may be worked out by noting that

$$R_{ac} \mid 1 \rangle = NR_{ac} [(1 - \mathcal{R}_{ab})] R_{ac} \hat{A} \alpha^a \beta^b \alpha^c$$
$$= N(1 - \mathcal{R}_{bc}) (-\mathcal{R}_{ac}) \hat{A} \alpha^a \beta^b \alpha^c \qquad (3.16)$$
$$= - |2\rangle$$

so that

$$\mathcal{R}_{ac} \mid 1 \rangle = |2\rangle$$

and

$$\langle 1 \mid 2 \rangle = \langle 1 \mid \mathcal{R}_{ac} \mid 1 \rangle = \tfrac{1}{2}$$

(The last step is essentially equivalent to $\langle 1 \mid \mathcal{R}_{bc} \mid 1 \rangle = \frac{1}{2}$, as found above.) The secular equation is thus

$$\begin{vmatrix} \dfrac{B}{2} - \lambda & B - \dfrac{\lambda}{2} \\ B - \dfrac{\lambda}{2} & \dfrac{B}{2} - \lambda \end{vmatrix} = 0$$

with

$$\lambda = \pm B$$

The pairing situation is degenerate, but one can talk hypothetically about the energy of a structure (diagonal matrix element) as with benzene. The lowest root $\lambda = +B$ thus lies $-B/2$ below the energy of either of the structures. The wave function corresponding to the lowest root $\lambda = +B$ turns out to be

$$|1\rangle + |2\rangle \quad \text{(not normalized)}$$

In order to see how this transforms under the operation of reflection across the long direction of the molecule, we go back to the action of R_{ac} Eq. (3.16)

$$R_{ac} \mid 1 \rangle = - |2\rangle$$

similarly

$$R_{ac} \mid 2 \rangle = - \mid 1 \rangle$$

whence

$$R_{ac} (|1\rangle + |2\rangle) = - (|1\rangle + |2\rangle)$$

and the wave function is antisymmetric. This result is the same as the one obtained using the Hückel theory to describe three electrons in the field of three colinear protons. According to the Hückel theory, the ground

All together the secular equation is

$$\begin{vmatrix} \frac{3B}{2} - \lambda & \frac{3B}{2} - \frac{\lambda}{4} \\ \frac{3B}{2} - \frac{\lambda}{4} & \frac{3B}{2} - \lambda \end{vmatrix} = 0$$

with roots $\lambda = 2.4B$ and 0. The energy of one structure is of course $1.5B$ so the resonance energy in this approximation is $-0.9B$.* The wave functions are

$$|1\rangle \pm |2\rangle$$

(apart from normalization), where the plus sign belongs to the more stable state; and we shall see that these functions belong to A_{1g} (lower state) and B_{2u} (upper state) of the group D_{6h}, if the AO's are π orbitals.

To see how the functions transform, we may operate on one bond eigenfunction with the various character operators. These all require our knowing the action of the group operations (see Table 2.1 for the definition of the operations of D_{6h} and a tabulation of the characters).

Instead of considering every operation in detail, here we pick several examples and go to the final result. We shall work on $|1\rangle$ and first consider one of the operations C_6, namely $C_6 = R_{ab}\, R_{fb}\, R_{eb}\, R_{db}\, R_{cb}$

$$\begin{aligned} C_6 \mid 1\rangle &= N[C_6\,(1 - \mathcal{R}_{ab})(1 - \mathcal{R}_{cd})(1 - \mathcal{R}_{ef})]\; C_6 \mid s\rangle \\ &= N(1 - \mathcal{R}_{bc})(1 - \mathcal{R}_{de})(1 - \mathcal{R}_{fa})\; C_6\, |s\rangle \\ &= N(1 - \mathcal{R}_{bc})(1 - \mathcal{R}_{de})(1 - \mathcal{R}_{fa})[-\mathcal{R}_{ab}\, \mathcal{R}_{fb}\, \mathcal{R}_{eb}\, \mathcal{R}_{db}\, \mathcal{R}_{cb}]|s\rangle \\ &= -N(1 - \mathcal{R}_{bc})(1 - \mathcal{R}_{de})(1 - \mathcal{R}_{fa})\; |\bar{s}\rangle \end{aligned}$$

(where, compared with $|s\rangle$, $|\bar{s}\rangle$ has α's and β's reversed). Then

$$\begin{aligned} C_6 \mid 1\rangle &= -N(1 - \mathcal{R}_{bc})(1 - \mathcal{R}_{de})(1 - \mathcal{R}_{fa})(\mathcal{R}_{bc}\, \mathcal{R}_{de}\, \mathcal{R}_{fa})[\mathcal{R}_{bc}\, \mathcal{R}_{de}\, \mathcal{R}_{fa}\; |\bar{s}\rangle] \\ &= N(1 - \mathcal{R}_{bc})(1 - \mathcal{R}_{de})(1 - \mathcal{R}_{fa})\; |s\rangle \\ &= |2\rangle \end{aligned}$$

Next we look at the effect of C_2', a rotation about the points occupied by atoms a and d

$$C_2' \mid 1\rangle = N(1 - \mathcal{R}_{af})(1 - \mathcal{R}_{de})(1 - \mathcal{R}_{bc})\; C_2' \mid s\rangle$$

* Note that H_6 comes out to be energetically unstable with respect to $3H_2$ (with energy $3B$). With the atoms forced to remain at the corners of a hexagon, however, the variational energy is lower ($2.4B$) than what would be computed under the assumption of perfect pairing ($1.5B$).

configuration has the first (symmetric) molecular orbital doubly filled, and the next (antisymmetric) molecular orbital half filled. The occurrence of the antisymmetric orbital an odd number of times leads to an over-all antisymmetric symmetry classification.

We now look at the question of the distribution of α and β spins. Using Eq. (3.15), we observe that the ground state wave function, $|1\rangle + |2\rangle$, is proportional to

$$\hat{A}[(1 - \mathcal{R}_{ab})\,\alpha^a\,\beta^b\,\alpha^c + (1 - \mathcal{R}_{bc})\,\alpha^a\,\beta^b\,\alpha^c] = \hat{A}(2\alpha^a\,\beta^b\,\alpha^c - \beta^a\,\alpha^b\,\alpha^c - \alpha^a\,\alpha^b\,\beta^c)$$

Disregarding the non-orthogonality, and regarding operation with $\hat{A}$ as producing a normalized function when it works on a single product of spinorbital symbols, we find therefore that

$$\hat{A}(\sqrt{\tfrac{2}{3}}\,\alpha^a\,\beta^b\,\alpha^c - \sqrt{\tfrac{1}{6}}\,\beta^a\,\alpha^b\,\alpha^c - \sqrt{\tfrac{1}{6}}\,\alpha^a\,\alpha^b\,\beta^c)$$

may be considered as normalized. After normalization the contributions of the spin states are the coefficients squared

$$\begin{aligned} \alpha^a\,\beta^b\,\alpha^c &: \tfrac{2}{3} \\ \beta^a\,\alpha^b\,\alpha^c &: \tfrac{1}{6} \\ \alpha^a\,\alpha^b\,\beta^c &: \tfrac{1}{6} \end{aligned}$$

Counting a spin of α as $+1/2$ and β as $-1/2$, this gives spins on a, b, and c, respectively, of $+1/3$, $-1/6$, $+1/3$, adding up to $+1/2$, which is what one expects from an excess of a single α.

As recognized by McConnell, it is interesting to compare this result with what is predicted by Hückel theory. According to Hückel theory, the lowest orbital has coefficients-squared at a, b, and c of 1/4, 1/2, 1/4, respectively. It is doubly filled, which results in no net contribution to the spin because β cancels α. If the spin of the third electron is taken as α there results a spin on each of the end atoms, a and c, of 1/4, because the orbital coefficients-squared for a, b, c are respectively 1/2, 0, 1/2. The molecular orbital method puts no net spin in the center. It has been possible to measure the spin on atom b experimentally with electron spin resonance techniques, with a result which is consistent with the prediction of negative spin density given by the valence bond calculation.*

We turn now to the consideration of molecular triplets (first detected by Lewis, Kasha, and Calvin).† We shall again use four atoms in a line as

* R. Fessenden; also, T. Cole and C. Heller, forthcoming publications.

† See, for example, G. N. Lewis, M. Calvin, and M. Kasha, *J. Chem. Phys.*, **17** (1949), 804.

an example. In Section 3.7, a general method for dealing with any multiplicity was outlined. Here we shall not use this general method, but instead shall see how the bond eigenfunction method can be extended to cover this case. The idea is to use unequal numbers of α's and β's so that having as many spins paired as possible the function will still have some total spin. Let us investigate first the spin-only case. We start from a standard

$$\alpha_1 \beta_2 \alpha_3 \alpha_4$$

where even if electron two is paired with another there will be two α's left over, making a total spin of one. To see formally that having one "bond" gives a triplet, we use

$$P_{op} = P_{12} + P_{13} + P_{14} + P_{23} + P_{24} + P_{34}$$

on, for example,

$$(1 - P_{12})\, \alpha_1 \beta_2 \alpha_3 \alpha_4$$

The term P_{12} gives a -1 and leaves

$$(1 - P_{12})(P_{13} + P_{14} + P_{23} + P_{24} + P_{34})\, \alpha_1 \beta_2 \alpha_3 \alpha_4$$

Of the P's remaining, P_{13}, P_{14}, and P_{34} give $+1$ apiece, whereas the other two give zero after the action of $(1 - P_{12})$. The eigenvalue is $+2$ and we may therefore substitute $\pi = +2$ and $n = 4$ into Eq. (3.11), getting $S = 1$, or a multiplicity of three.

Referring now to the branching diagram (Fig. 3.2), we see that there is the number three at $n = 4$ and $S = 1$, so that we need three linearly independent functions. We shall choose the functions as indicated by the diagrams*

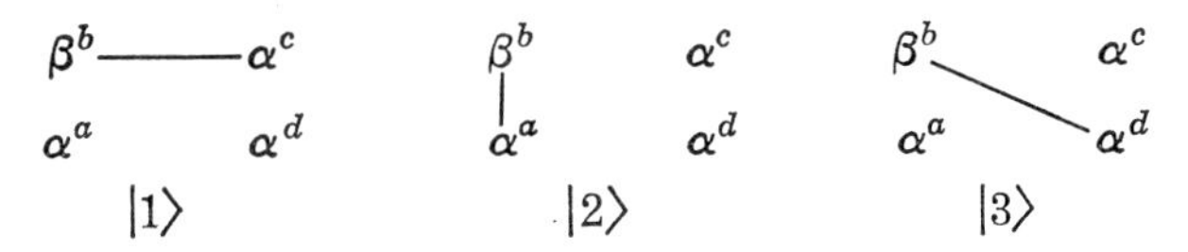

One finds that the energy of the first triplet function is $\langle 1 \mid H_{\text{int}} \mid 1 \rangle = 0$, the same as for

* When $n > 4$ the procedure is analogous. That is, one starts with alternating α's and β's arranged in a circle and changes a single one of the β's to an α. He then connects each β to some α making sure that no lines cross, and uses a factor $1 - \mathcal{R}$ in the projection operator for each connecting line. There are as many diagrams as there are linearly independent triplets (as determined by reference to the branching diagram). This relationship between the number of diagrams and the number of triplets was discovered by Dr. Reid Kellogg. See also A. D. McLachlan, *J. Chem. Phys.*, **33** (1960), 663; M. A. Kovner and L. M. Sverdlov, *Doklady Akad. Nauk. S.S.S.R.*, **59** (1948), 1129.

$$\beta^b \text{———} \alpha^c$$
$$\alpha^a \text{———} \beta^d$$

the corresponding function used in the singlet calculation (Section 3.9). Now $-B\mathcal{R}_{ad}\,\alpha^a\,\alpha^d = -B\alpha^a\,\alpha^d$, so with $B < 0$ there would be an antibond between a and d. It makes no difference energetically, however, whether centers a and d are bonded or antibonded, provided that a and d are on opposite ends of the molecule and $-B\mathcal{R}_{ad}$ fails to appear in the interaction operator. In fact, the singlet and triplet diagrams each correspond to the same structural formula

$$\dot{a}\ b - c\ \dot{d}$$

Consideration of the interaction over full blocks changes the picture considerably, however, because the singlet is at the top of its block of two, energywise, and is pushed up by the interaction, whereas the triplet is at the bottom of its block of three and is pushed down. Thus the singlet upper state energy finally becomes $-\sqrt{3}\,B$, whereas the triplet lower state comes out to be $0.41B$.

We shall compute several of the matrix elements in detail, beginning with the first

$$\begin{aligned}\langle 1 \mid H_{\text{int}} \mid 1\rangle &= \\ &-N^2\,B\langle s|\,(1 - \mathcal{R}_{bc})(\mathcal{R}_{ab} + \mathcal{R}_{bc} + \mathcal{R}_{cd})(1 - \mathcal{R}_{bc})\,|s\rangle \\ &= B - N^2\,B\langle s|\,(1 - \mathcal{R}_{bc})(\mathcal{R}_{ab} + \mathcal{R}_{cd})(1 - \mathcal{R}_{bc})\,|s\rangle\end{aligned}$$

The matrix element of $\mathcal{R}_{ab}$ is the same as that of $\mathcal{R}_{bc}\,\mathcal{R}_{ab}\,\mathcal{R}_{bc} = \mathcal{R}_{ac}$, and similarly, for $\mathcal{R}_{cd}$, we can substitute $\mathcal{R}_{bd}$, giving for the integral yet to be evaluated

$$\begin{aligned}&-N^2\,B\langle s|\,(1 - \mathcal{R}_{bc})(1 - \mathcal{R}_{bc}) \\ &\qquad \tfrac{1}{2}\,(\mathcal{R}_{ab} + \mathcal{R}_{cd} + \mathcal{R}_{ac} + \mathcal{R}_{bd})\,\hat{A}\alpha^a\,\beta^b\,\alpha^c\,\alpha^d\end{aligned}$$

The operators $\mathcal{R}_{cd}$ and $\mathcal{R}_{ac}$ each give unity, and the others are canceled out, so that the integral is $-B$ and the matrix element

$$\langle 1 \mid H_{\text{int}} \mid 1\rangle = 0$$

To pick another example, the third diagonal element is

$$\begin{aligned}&-N^2\,B\langle s|\,(1 - \mathcal{R}_{bd})(\mathcal{R}_{ab} + \mathcal{R}_{bc} + \mathcal{R}_{cd})(1 - \mathcal{R}_{bd})\,|s\rangle \\ &\qquad = -N^2\,B\langle s|\,(1 - \mathcal{R}_{bd})(1 - \mathcal{R}_{bd}) \\ &\qquad \tfrac{1}{2}\,(\mathcal{R}_{ab} + \mathcal{R}_{ad} + \mathcal{R}_{bc} + \mathcal{R}_{cd} + \mathcal{R}_{cd} + \mathcal{R}_{bc})\,\hat{A}\alpha^a\,\beta^b\,\alpha^c\,\alpha^d \\ &\qquad = -\frac{3B}{2}\end{aligned}$$

The various others are evaluated similarly, leading to

$$\begin{vmatrix} -\lambda & \frac{B}{2}-\frac{\lambda}{2} & -\frac{B}{2}-\frac{\lambda}{2} \\ \frac{B}{2}-\frac{\lambda}{2} & -\frac{B}{2}-\lambda & -\frac{\lambda}{2} \\ -\frac{B}{2}-\frac{\lambda}{2} & -\frac{\lambda}{2} & -\frac{3B}{2}-\lambda \end{vmatrix} = 0$$

with roots

$$0.41B, \quad -1.00B, \quad \text{and} \quad -2.41B$$

Remembering that the lowest singlet has an energy of $1.73B$, we see that the first singlet-triplet transition has an energy $-1.32B$. This may be compared with the first singlet-singlet energy for the case of six atoms at the corners of a hexagon ($-2.40B$ using the Kekulé structures, or $-2.60B$ using all five structures). The transition energy is quite low by comparison; in fact, it might be expected that the singlet-triplet absorption for butadiene should come at around twice the wave length of the first singlet-singlet absorption for benzene at 2600 Å.* This would make butadiene red in extremely high concentrations and no doubt accounts for the low activation energy in the Diels-Alder reaction.

The method of bond eigenfunctions can be adapted to the study of ions and the last part of the chapter is devoted to some aspects of this subject.

3.12 CHARGE MIGRATION

The physical system to be studied is a fairly large number of hydrogen atoms, regularly arranged in a line and interrupted at some point by a bare proton. To begin, we shall consider for definiteness five protons, equally spaced, and four electrons. If the centers are so widely separated as to be effectively an infinite distance apart, the energy will be $4E_0$, where E_0 is the ground state energy of a single atom. The *permutation degeneracy* introduces nothing more than a meaningless exchange of labels amongst the physical electrons, and may be disregarded if desired (Chapter 4). There is in addition a *spatial degeneracy*, which has to be considered no matter how widely separated the atoms may be. For example, the electrons may be on centers a, b, d, e,

* The zero-zero band is observed to come at 4800 Å—D. F. Evans, *J. Chem. Soc.*, 347 (1960), 1735. This compares favorably with the calculated value based on the benzene zero-zero band at 2660 Å: $2660 \times (2.60/1.32) = 5280$ Å.

leaving center c as the bare proton. In this case, we should have for the wave function

$$a_1 \, b_2 \, d_3 \, e_4$$

where a_1 means electron one in a $1s$ orbital based on the center a, and so on. The wave function is a pure single-configuration function. Analogous wave functions having some center other than c bare may be constructed, and have the same energy. When we bring the centers together so that they may not quite be regarded as infinitely separated, we have a typical perturbation. The zero-order functions are degenerate; hence we may not attach physical significance to the expectation value of the Hamiltonian over one of the unperturbed functions (as giving the energy of a stationary state). Rather, we are obligated to interact the various unperturbed functions, so that we are immediately faced with zero-order configuration interaction. Also, when the centers are brought together the neutral atoms start to interact because of the permutation degeneracy. For example, we might have to consider the wave function, still keeping c as the bare proton,

$$a_2 \, b_1 \, d_3 \, e_4$$

which, together with the one above, can give a bond between centers a and b. We therefore must weigh the permutation degeneracy against the spatial degeneracy to see which might be predominant. If the bringing together of the atoms is carried out so delicately that the perturbation is infinitesimal, the permutation degeneracy effect comes out to be the smaller; this because the probability distribution modulating term associated with permutation degeneracy, typically

$$a_1 \, b_2 \, a_2 \, b_1 = (ab)_1 \, (ab)_2$$

is the product of two overlap distributions, each one of which is in a sense infinitesimal. From this standpoint, the permutation degeneracy is a second-order effect. The corresponding energy quantity for the permutation degeneracy, moreover, is the exchange integral, which again is higher order. Let us therefore set up a secular equation for just the spatial degeneracy, among functions, for example,

$$|c\rangle = N \sum_P k_P \, P \, a_1 \, b_2 \, d_3 \, e_4$$

Here N is the normalizing factor. The label of the many-electron function stands for the bare proton, and the coefficients k_P are fixed up so that the orbital part can be combined with a spin part giving all together a function which satisfies the Pauli principle. If all the spins are the same, k_P has to be $(-1)^P$ so that the functions are orbitally antisymmetric. We shall assume this is the case, which has the consequence that there is only one many-electron function for each vacant center. The form of the secular equation is then quite simple, in that a function, for example, $|c\rangle$, overlaps and interacts with adjacent functions only, for example, $|b\rangle$ and $|d\rangle$. To see this consider the overlap between $|c\rangle$ and

$$|e\rangle = \sum_P (-1)^P \, P a_1 \, b_2 \, c_3 \, d_4$$

It is sufficiently general to consider only one term of $|c\rangle$ provided that we use all terms of $|e\rangle$. Let us list all centers, and then fill in electron numbers

a	b	c	d	e
1	2		3	4
1	2	3	4	
1	2	4	3	

The first row represents the one term of $|c\rangle$, whereas the second and third rows are terms of $|e\rangle$ which might overlap with the $|c\rangle$ term. The second row would bring in the product of the two overlaps

$$(cd)_3 \, (de)_4$$

which, considering infinitesimal overlapping of the orbitals, is an infinitesimal of higher order and is therefore neglected. The third row would bring in the overlap of orbitals not on adjacent centers

$$(ce)_4$$

so it too is regarded as zero. No other terms in $|e\rangle$ change the situation. Moreover, the Hamiltonian operating on terms of $|e\rangle$ cannot succeed in moving probability amplitudes around enough to vitiate the corresponding conclusions for the energy matrix elements. In summary, we have therefore

$$\langle c \mid H \mid e \rangle = \langle c \mid e \rangle = 0$$

The diagonal matrix element is essentially $4E_0$ (except perhaps as modified by the electrostatic effect of the proton). The non-vanishing off-diagonal matrix elements will be set equal, which is ignoring end effects

$$\langle a \mid H \mid b \rangle = \langle b \mid H \mid c \rangle = \ldots = \beta$$
$$\langle a \mid b \rangle = \langle b \mid c \rangle = \ldots = s$$

This gives a 5×5 secular equation

$$\begin{vmatrix} 4E_0 - \lambda'' & \beta - s\lambda'' & 0 & \cdots \\ \beta - s\lambda'' & 4E_0 - \lambda'' & \beta - s\lambda'' & \cdots \\ 0 & \beta - s\lambda'' & 4E_0 - \lambda'' & \cdots \\ \vdots & \vdots & \vdots & \end{vmatrix} = 0$$

As an approximation we set

$$\lambda'' = 4E_0$$

when it occurs in off-diagonal positions, and then

$$\beta - s(4E_0) = \gamma$$

Following this substitution, we use a new λ

$$4E_0 - \lambda'' = -\lambda'$$

which amounts to measuring the energy from $4E_0$, an arbitrary zero. The resulting secular equation is

$$\begin{vmatrix} -\lambda' & \gamma & 0 & \cdots \\ \gamma & -\lambda' & \gamma & \cdots \\ 0 & \gamma & -\lambda' & \cdots \\ \vdots & \vdots & \vdots & \end{vmatrix} = 0$$

A final simplification comes from dividing each row by $|\gamma|$. The phases of the functions may be so selected that $\gamma < 0$, representing attraction, so that the off-diagonal elements become -1. For convenience, we adopt again a new λ for which energy is in units of $|\gamma|$. This gives (after further division of the rows by -1)

$$\begin{vmatrix} \lambda & 1 & 0 & 0 & 0 \\ 1 & \lambda & 1 & 0 & 0 \\ 0 & 1 & \lambda & 1 & 0 \\ 0 & 0 & 1 & \lambda & 1 \\ 0 & 0 & 0 & 1 & \lambda \end{vmatrix} = 0 \tag{3.17}$$

The first wave function will have the plus charge distributed according to a simple cos-squared loop, with no alternations. The Hückel theory, which is able to handle the same ion, gives a similar prediction (remember that all spins are the same) because in this case each Hückel orbital for the neutral H_5 molecule is half filled (giving an even distribution of charge) and going over to H_5^+ means taking an electron from the highest-energy orbital, which has coefficients squared exactly the same as found from the solution of Eq. (3.17).

The singlet state according to Hückel theory is derived from the neutral molecule doublet with the first two orbitals doubly filled and the third half filled. The third is non-bonding, having a node on atoms b and d; and considering all orbitals the charge distribution is uniform. Going over to the ion, one removes the electron from the third orbital, which results in an alternating distribution of charge

$$\overset{\delta+}{a} \quad b \quad \overset{\delta+}{c} \quad d \quad \overset{\delta+}{e}$$

A similar result is obtained for the singlet using the bond eigenfunction approach, as will become apparent.*

We shall now consider the case in which the permutation degeneracy gives an effect which is much larger than the charge-transfer energy going with the spatial degeneracy. This might occur when the atoms are much closer to one another than for the treatment above, but under such conditions we are forced to make some guesses about the matrix elements.

Going back to the functions, for example,

$$|a\rangle = N \sum k_P \, P b_1 \, c_2 \, d_3 \, e_4$$

we now specify that the spin function has equal numbers of α's and β's, and that also the spins are all paired. There is more than one linearly independent function which can be constructed according to this specification. These functions correspond to the following valence bond structures:

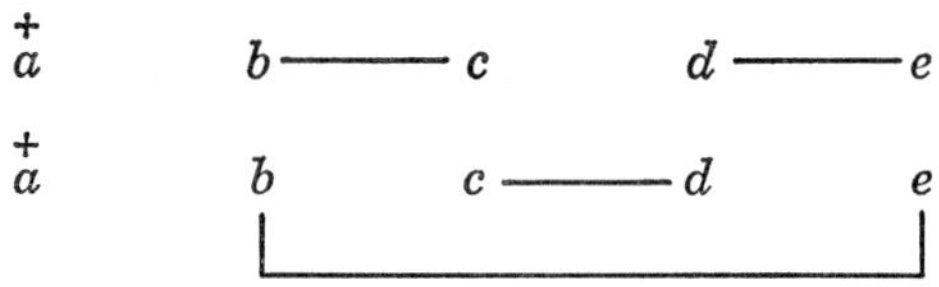

$$\overset{+}{a} \quad b \text{——} c \quad d \text{——} e$$

$$\overset{+}{a} \quad b \quad c \text{——} d \quad e \quad (b \text{ bonded to } e)$$

There is only one structure with two, the maximum number of bonds, namely, the first of the above structures. It is this function which will be called $|a\rangle$.† Similarly, we can define a unique $|c\rangle$ and $|e\rangle$

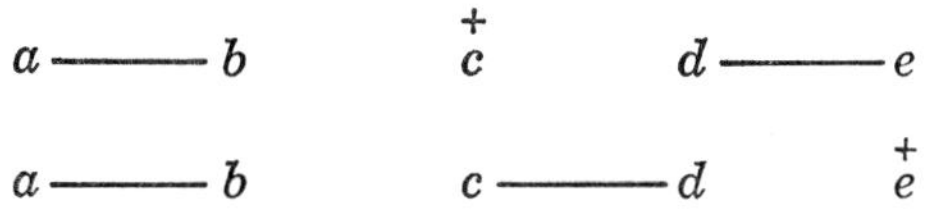

$$a \text{——} b \quad \overset{+}{c} \quad d \text{——} e$$

$$a \text{——} b \quad c \text{——} d \quad \overset{+}{e}$$

but no $|b\rangle$ or $|d\rangle$. Because of the assumed strength of the chemical bonds, we are led to group $|a\rangle$, $|c\rangle$ and $|e\rangle$ together as having the same "unperturbed energy" (unperturbed with respect to the subsequent calculation of the spatial degeneracy effect). This energy is below $4E_0$, because of the stabilization coming from the bonding. Ignoring end effects, we have

$$\langle a \mid H \mid a\rangle = \langle c \mid H \mid c\rangle = \langle e \mid H \mid e\rangle$$

* Hückel theory and the bond eigenfunction approach are compared by H. C. Longuet-Higgins, *J. Chem. Phys.*, **18** (1950), 265.

† We are using the approximation of perfect pairing.

The off-diagonal elements involve the product of two overlap distributions, but then so do the characteristic quantities occurring in the Heitler-London type calculation for the bonding. By analogy with the calculation leading to the 5×5 secular determinant, we consider as higher order such terms as

$$\langle a \mid H \mid e \rangle = \langle a \mid e \rangle = 0, \quad \text{and so on}$$

where the charge is transferred over not two, but four interatomic distances. We are thus led to a secular equation where energy is measured from the diagonal matrix element and where the off-diagonal elements are abbreviated as before.

$$\begin{vmatrix} \lambda & 1 & 0 \\ 1 & \lambda & 1 \\ 0 & 1 & \lambda \end{vmatrix} = 0 \tag{3.18}$$

Note that here the unit of energy must have a very different value than for the first treatment, the formal similarity notwithstanding. The first wave function puts the positive charge on a, c, and e with coefficients following a simple sin loop, a result which, as noted above, is also given by the Hückel theory.

As recognized by Pauling and by Herzfeld and Sklar there are classes of compounds which may be described by a theory like the foregoing. One example is the family of dyelike substances related to formate ion

$$\mathrm{O{=}CH{-}\overset{\ominus}{O}}, \quad \mathrm{\overset{\ominus}{O}{-}CH{=}O}$$

as, for example, the five-carbon ion with structures

$$\mathrm{\overset{\ominus}{O}{-}CH{=}CH{-}CH{=}CH{-}CH{=}O}$$

$$\mathrm{\overset{\ominus}{O}{-}CH{=}CH{-}CH{=}CH{-}\overset{\oplus}{C}H{-}\overset{\ominus}{O}}$$

$$\mathrm{\overset{\ominus}{O}{-}CH{=}CH{-}\overset{\oplus}{C}H{-}CH{=}CH{-}\overset{\ominus}{O}}$$

$$\mathrm{\overset{\ominus}{O}{-}\overset{\oplus}{C}H{-}CH{=}CH{-}CH{=}CH{-}\overset{\ominus}{O}}$$

$$\mathrm{O{=}CH{-}CH{=}CH{-}CH{=}CH{-}\overset{\ominus}{O}}$$

If we proceed, hopefully, by neglecting the monopolar in favor of the tripolar structures because of the electronegativity of oxygen, the analogy with the preceding treatment is close, even though here π electrons are involved. With three tripolar structures, the secular equation is the 3×3 given above. The roots are $-\sqrt{2}$, 0, $+\sqrt{2}$ so that the first transition energy is $\sqrt{2}$. The secular equation for the three-carbon substance is 2×2, with roots ± 1, the difference between which is 2. Generalizing, the transition energy is predicted to decrease as the chain length increases, an effect which has been found universally by Brooker* for dyes resembling the simple ions we are considering here. For the particular substances related to formate ion, the first ultraviolet absorptions are strong, with intensities which correspond to a movement of charge over a path length covering the entire molecule. The transition comes at 268 mμ for the molecule with three carbons and 362 mμ for the molecule with five carbons, with ratio 1.35 to be compared with the calculated ratio $\sqrt{2}$. It is quite common to find low-lying excited states which can be classified as growing out of the ambiguity about the location of charge and the associated spatial degeneracy—in fact, this is almost always the cause of color in dyes.

In Section 3.13 there is described a model for dealing with secular equations of the type found in connection with the spatial degeneracy (and, incidentally, likewise of the type found in connection with the J matrix in Section 2.5).

Appendix to Chapter 3

3.13 EFFECTIVE MASS MODEL

We shall first develop an approximate treatment for the calculation of the energy of a particle in a one-dimensional box of length l. The energy eigenvalues are

$$\frac{n^2 \pi^2 \hbar^2}{2ml^2} \quad n = 1, 2, 3, \ldots \tag{3.19}$$

corresponding to the Hamiltonian

$$\frac{-\hbar^2}{2m} \frac{\partial^2}{\partial x^2} + V$$

where V is zero inside the box (0 to l) and infinity outside. The effect of V is to make the wave function go to zero outside the box. Inside, we shall represent the coordinate axis by a string of finite points and shall take four interior points for definiteness:

* See for example L. G. S. Brooker, *Revs. Mod. Phys.*, **14** (1942), 275.

The wave function may be conceived as a collection of bars at the lattice points (parts of a "bar graph") and the heights of the bars used as elements of a column vector. The value of the wave function at the ith point will be described as h_i, and the distance between points taken as Δ. In this notation the finite difference analog of the derivative at $i + \frac{1}{2}$ is $(h_{i+1} - h_i)/\Delta$. Similarly the derivative at $i - \frac{1}{2}$ is $(h_i - h_{i-1})/\Delta$ so that the second derivative at i is

$$\frac{h_{i+1} - 2h_i + h_{i-1}}{\Delta^2}$$

The finite difference Hamiltonian (inside the box) operating on the column vector is

$$\frac{\hbar^2}{2m\Delta^2}(h_{i-1} - 2h_i + h_{i+1}) \qquad i = 1, 2, 3, 4$$

and the eigenvalue equation $H \mid \psi\rangle = E \mid \psi\rangle$ goes over into the simultaneous equations

$$\frac{\hbar^2}{2m\Delta^2}(h_0 - 2h_1 + h_2) = Eh_1, \quad \text{and so on}$$

or with

$$\frac{2mE\Delta^2}{\hbar^2} = \mu$$

$$h_0 + (\mu - 2)\, h_1 + h_2 = 0$$

$$h_1 + (\mu - 2)\, h_2 + h_3 = 0$$

$$h_2 + (\mu - 2)\, h_3 + h_4 = 0$$

$$h_3 + (\mu - 2)\, h_4 + h_5 = 0$$

This is a set of homogeneous linear equations and can have a non-trivial solution only if the determinant of the coefficients vanishes. Remembering that $h_0 = h_5 = 0$ and setting

$$\mu - 2 = \lambda$$

we are led to the secular equation

$$\begin{vmatrix} \lambda & 1 & 0 & 0 \\ 1 & \lambda & 1 & 0 \\ 0 & 1 & \lambda & 1 \\ 0 & 0 & 1 & \lambda \end{vmatrix} = 0$$

The lowest root is called λ_1. Corresponding to this, we have

$$\mu_1 = \lambda_1 + 2$$

$$E_1 = \frac{\hbar^2}{2m\Delta^2}\mu_1 = \frac{\hbar^2}{2m\Delta^2}(\lambda_1 + 2)$$

or, with $5\Delta = l$ in the present case

$$E_1 = \frac{25\hbar^2}{2ml^2}(\lambda_1 + 2)$$

The lowest root is -1.618, which gives

$$\frac{0.382 \cdot 25}{\pi^2}\frac{\pi^2\hbar^2}{2ml^2} = 0.98\frac{\pi^2\hbar^2}{2ml^2}$$

as an approximation to the true lowest root (compare Eq. (3.19)).

We are not so much interested in how good an approximation this might be as in the possibility of turning the argument around. That is, we may use the differential equation as an approximation to the finite difference problem, or secular equation. This implies that the quantum mechanical model of a particle in a one-dimensional box may be used whenever the secular equation may be brought into the form where the only off-diagonal matrix elements are immediately adjacent to the diagonal and nearly equal—see Eq. (3.17) and Eq. (3.18). It should be possible to relate the interaction matrix element to physical consonants of the model, l or m. For the examples considered in the previous section, it seems most natural to take l from the actual molecule, so that m in the model remains to be adjusted to fit the value of the interaction matrix element.

In order to illustrate this idea, we shall consider the second example in Section 3.12. In this example, the permutation degeneracy was assumed to dominate, giving three positions for the plus charge and a corresponding 3×3 secular equation (3.18). The molecular species and potential box may be correlated as in Fig. 3.3

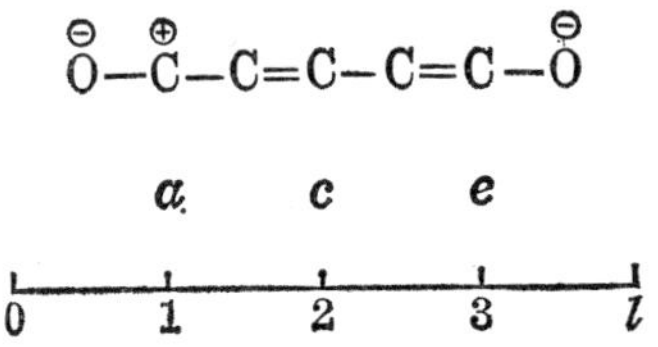

$$\overset{\ominus}{\text{O}}-\overset{\oplus}{\text{C}}-\text{C}=\text{C}-\text{C}=\text{C}-\overset{\ominus}{\text{O}}$$

	a		c		e	
0	1		2		3	l

giving the relation

$$4\Delta = l \tag{3.20}$$

where now Δ is two interatomic distances.

The unit of energy is

$$\gamma = \langle a \mid H \mid c\rangle - \langle a \mid c\rangle\langle a \mid H \mid a\rangle$$

For the box model, putting aside any question about the zero of energy, the unit of energy is

$$\frac{\hbar^2}{2m\Delta^2} = \frac{16\hbar^2}{2ml^2}$$

Observing that $\gamma < 0$ we therefore find

$$m = -\frac{\hbar^2}{2\Delta^2}\left(\frac{1}{\gamma}\right)$$

One way the effective mass model may be used in practice is to employ the simple energy eigenvalue expression, Eq. (3.19), as obtained from the differential form of the kinetic energy operator. For example, one might equate the observed transition energy to

$$(2^2 - 1^2)\,\frac{\pi^2\hbar^2}{2ml^2}$$

in order to find a value for m, the effective mass, and use this to make predictions about related compounds, thus completely bypassing the calculation of γ. In this connection, we may look once more at the dyelike ion

$$\overset{\ominus}{\text{O}}\text{—}\overset{\oplus}{\text{CH}}\text{—CH=CH—CH=CH—}\overset{\ominus}{\text{O}}$$

The strong absorption at 362 $m\mu$ gives a transition energy which we may equate to the particle-in-a-box first transition energy

$$\frac{2\pi\hbar c}{3.62 \times 10^{-5}} = \frac{3\pi^2\hbar^2}{32m\,\Delta^2}$$

where we have incorporated Eq. (3.20) and Δ is two interatomic distances. With the interatomic distance 1.4 Å, this gives an effective mass governing the motion of the positive charge of about 0.24×10^{-27} g (the mass of an electron is 0.9×10^{-27} g).

3.14 MODIFICATION RESULTING FROM NON-ORTHOGONALITY

In the text, we found a Hamiltonian for the 1s block Eq. (3.6)

$$\sum_t \langle t \mid H \mid 0 \rangle R_t$$

by applying a unitary transformation to the Hamiltonian in the Schrödinger representation. Actually, the unitarity condition on the many-electron functions

$$\langle r \mid s \rangle = \delta_{rs}$$

does not hold. For example, for two electrons in adjacent orbitals we have

$$\langle a_1\, b_2 \mid a_2\, b_1 \rangle = \left[\int a_\nu\, b_\nu\, d\tau_\nu \right]^2 \neq 0$$

That the orbital overlap is non-zero is well known to be an essential factor in giving binding. There are various schemes which can be used to more-or-less straighten out the difficulty.

One plan is to use orthogonal many-electron functions in carrying out the unitary transformation. The reader will verify that, for just two orbitals, the following are orthogonal to the first order (we neglect the square of the non-orthogonality integral $\langle a_1\, b_2 \mid a_2\, b_1 \rangle$):

$$\begin{aligned} |0\rangle &= |\, a_1\, b_2 \rangle - \tfrac{1}{2} \langle a_1\, b_2 \mid a_2\, b_1 \rangle \mid a_2\, b_1 \rangle \\ |1\rangle &= |\, a_2\, b_1 \rangle - \tfrac{1}{2} \langle a_1\, b_2 \mid a_2\, b_1 \rangle \mid a_1\, b_2 \rangle \end{aligned} \tag{3.21}$$

The analog of Eq. (3.6) is then

$$H = \langle 0 \mid H \mid 0 \rangle R_0 + \langle 1 \mid H \mid 0 \rangle R_1$$

where Eq. (3.21) is used. Thus, for example, to the first order

$$\langle 1 \mid H \mid 0 \rangle = \langle a_2\, b_1 \mid H \mid a_1\, b_2 \rangle - \langle a_1\, b_2 \mid a_2\, b_1 \rangle \langle a_1\, b_2 \mid H \mid a_1\, b_2 \rangle$$

and this becomes

$$B = \langle a_2\, b_1 \mid V \mid a_1\, b_2 \rangle - \langle a_1\, b_2 \mid a_2\, b_1 \rangle \langle a_1\, b_2 \mid V \mid a_2\, b_1 \rangle$$

(the terms $+\langle a_1\, b_2 \mid H^0 \mid a_2\, b_1 \rangle$ and $-\langle a_1\, b_2 \mid a_2\, b_1 \rangle \langle a_1\, b_2 \mid H^0 \mid a_1\, b_2 \rangle$ having canceled). The first-order diagonal matrix element is unaffected by using orthogonalized functions* so that the Hamiltonian becomes

$$2E_o + \langle a_1\, b_2 \mid V \mid a_1\, b_2 \rangle + BR_1$$

like Eq. (3.6a), and the interaction operator correspondingly becomes BR_1, like Eq. (3.7a). We have therefore found Eq. (3.7c) for the special case $n = 2$. The general case is similar, and the first-order result, Eq. (3.7c), can be obtained, provided that all the adjacent free orbitals are equivalent. That is, we can proceed by neglecting the non-orthogonality, provided that we use B in place of K.

To treat the general case here we shall not use orthogonalized many-electron functions, though this is possible. We go back to the derivation of Eq. (3.6), now abandoning the notion of a unitary transformation on the Schrödinger Hamiltonian. Instead we employ the linear variation method and proceed to set up a secular equation for the 1s block. Using the notation and method of the text but recognizing that $|r\rangle$ and $|s\rangle$ are

* We neglect the product of an exchange integral times a non-orthogonality integral.

not orthogonal, we find—compare with the eigenvalue expression for the matrix form of Eq. (3.6)—

$$\left| \sum_t (\langle t \mid H \mid 0 \rangle \mathbf{R}_t - \langle t \mid 0 \rangle \mathbf{R}_t W) \right| = 0 \tag{3.22}$$

The **R** matrices are the same as matrices in the text calculated under the assumption that unitarity holds. Now we assume that $\langle t \mid 0 \rangle$ is zero if the atoms joined by the permutation are non-adjacent; also if $\langle t|$ is connected to $|0\rangle$ through a multiple permutation. This last is tantamount to the assumption that the non-vanishing $\langle t \mid 0 \rangle$ value (t different from zero) is small. The typical non-zero value for $\langle t \mid 0 \rangle$ will be called s^2

$$s = \int a_\nu \, b_\nu \, d\tau_\nu$$

The secular equation (3.22) may be simplified in a manner analogous to that employed in going from Eq. (3.6) to Eq. (3.7c). The interaction energy eigenvalue is called λ

$$\langle 0 \mid H \mid 0 \rangle - W = -\lambda$$

The diagonal of the secular equation thus contains entries $-\lambda$. The off-diagonal part has, in positions where R_t connects adjacent atoms,

$$\begin{aligned} \langle t \mid H \mid 0 \rangle - s^2 W &= \langle t \mid H \mid 0 \rangle - s^2 \langle 0 \mid H \mid 0 \rangle + s^2 \langle 0 \mid H \mid 0 \rangle - s^2 W \\ &= B - s^2 \lambda \end{aligned}$$

Here $B = \langle t \mid H \mid 0 \rangle - s^2 \langle 0 \mid H \mid 0 \rangle$, but this reduces to the prior definition where V replaces H. We now have a secular equation

$$| (B - s^2 \lambda) \boldsymbol{\Delta} - \mathbf{I}\lambda | = 0 \tag{3.23}$$

where $\boldsymbol{\Delta}$ is the matrix having ones covering all the positions referring to adjacent atoms—see Eq. (3.7b)

$$\boldsymbol{\Delta} = \sum_j{}'' \mathbf{R}_j \tag{3.24}$$

To solve Eq. (3.23) we have primarily to find the eigenvalues of μ of $\boldsymbol{\Delta}$. These values are obtained from

$$| \boldsymbol{\Delta} - \mu \mathbf{I} | = 0$$

or equivalently from

$$| B \boldsymbol{\Delta} - B\mu \mathbf{I} | = 0$$

This last is seen essentially to be Eq. (3.23) with s^2 set equal to zero, and represents our goal: proof that Eq. (3.7c) with B can be used for Eq. (3.7b), with K. The λ's, not the μ's, however, are the interaction energies. The eigenvectors of $\boldsymbol{\Delta}$ are obviously the same as the eigenvectors of $B\boldsymbol{\Delta}$

and form the basis for a unitary transformation S. The columns of $\mathsf{S}^\dagger = \mathsf{S}^{-1}$ are the normalized eigenvectors. Then according to an algebraic theorem

$$\mathsf{S}\,\boldsymbol{\Delta}\mathsf{S}^\dagger = \boldsymbol{\mu}$$

where $\boldsymbol{\mu}$ is the diagonal matrix of eigenvalues of $\boldsymbol{\Delta}$.

Going now to Eq. (3.23), we use the theorem that the determinant of the product of matrices is the product of the determinants, and compute

$$\begin{aligned}
|\,(B - s^2\lambda)\,\boldsymbol{\Delta} - \mathbf{I}\lambda\,| &= |\,(B - s^2\lambda)\,\boldsymbol{\Delta} - \mathbf{I}\lambda\,||\,\mathsf{S}\,||\,\mathsf{S}^\dagger\,| \\
&= |\,\mathsf{S}\,||\,(B - s^2\lambda)\,\boldsymbol{\Delta} - \mathbf{I}\lambda\,||\,\mathsf{S}^\dagger\,| \\
&= |\,(B - s^2\lambda)\mathsf{S}\boldsymbol{\Delta} - \mathsf{S}\mathbf{I}\lambda\,||\,\mathsf{S}^\dagger\,| \\
&= |\,(B - s^2\lambda)\mathsf{S}\boldsymbol{\Delta}\mathsf{S}^\dagger - \mathsf{S}\mathbf{I}\mathsf{S}^\dagger\lambda\,| \\
&= |\,(B - s^2\lambda)\boldsymbol{\mu} - \mathbf{I}\lambda\,| \\
&= 0
\end{aligned}$$

This last is the determinant of a diagonal matrix, and considered as a polynomial equation, is already factored. Taking any diagonal element of $\boldsymbol{\mu}$, say the ith, we obtain

$$(B - s^2\lambda)\mu_{ii} - \lambda = 0$$

or*

$$\lambda = \frac{\mu_{ii}B}{1 + s^2\mu_{ii}} \tag{3.25}$$

The λ's are very nearly eigenvalues of $B\,\boldsymbol{\Delta}$ and our goal is very nearly achieved. In fact, if $s^4 \ll s^2$, we have

$$\frac{\mu_{ii}B}{1 + s^2\mu_{ii}}\,\frac{1 - s^2\mu_{ii}}{1 - s^2\mu_{ii}} = \mu_{ii}B - s^2B\mu_{ii}$$

but also s^2B is a small quantity of the second order (having the dimensions of energy) because B is already in a sense a first-order small quantity. Equation (3.25) is thus equivalent, to the first order, to

$$\lambda = \mu_{ii}B$$

so that, keeping in mind Eq. (3.24), we have derived Eq. (3.7c) in the text.

The further work with spin tends to mask the fact that we are always looking for eigenvalues of the spinless 1s block of H, in effect, the μ's. Bringing in the spin accomplishes a factoring and, at the same time, tells

* Professor John Coope, University of British Columbia, has informed the author that he has independently obtained this result.

one which spinless eigenstates are unphysical (cannot be put together with spin functions so as to be totally antisymmetric).

Finally, it is a moot point whether the correction $(1 + s^2 \mu_{ii})^{-1}$ in Eq. (3.25) should be used. There is a corresponding quantity often used with Hückel theory which, however, has s rather than s^2. Also, it is used with a wider range of μ's, so on both counts it has a bigger effect. In the present case, if we were to use the correction, we might be fooled into thinking our procedure is satisfactory for finite s^2, whereas actually we used the fact that s^2 is small in ignoring multiple permutations. Going back to the explanation in the text given in conjunction with Fig. 3.1, one now sees the reason for the insistence that rigorously the calculations apply and only apply to the shaded portion.

3.15 MATRIX ELEMENTS INVOLVING UNCOUPLED SPINS

In the more complicated cases, the job of evaluating bond eigenfunction matrix elements using the techniques illustrated in the text is unnecessarily tedious. In such cases, it is better to fall back on a set of rules. Sets of rules were discovered independently by Eyring and Kimball and by Pauling. Pauling's rules* are chiefly used, and are called "The Method of Islands." We shall study an equivalent set of rules for use with the projection operator formalism.†

The first and main rule is to be invoked after all the $\mathcal{R}$'s possible have been collapsed onto the projection operators. With certain exceptions, the remaining $\mathcal{R}$'s connect uncoupled spins. The rule states: *The diagonal matrix element of a product of n $\mathcal{R}$'s referring to uncoupled spins is* $(\frac{1}{2})^n$. Rule one applies, of course, only to bond eigenfunctions, and holds only for $\mathcal{R}$'s not involved in "cycles" (see below).

The calculation of the non-orthogonality integral between the Kekulé structures in benzene affords a prime illustration of the main rule. The bond eigenfunctions are based on the diagrams

* L. Pauling, *J. Chem. Phys.*, **1** (1933), 280.

† The present rules were formulated with the help of Dr. E. E. Barnes.

and as shown in Section 3.10

$$\langle 1 \mid 2 \rangle = \langle 1 \mid \mathcal{R}_{bf}\, \mathcal{R}_{ce} \mid 1 \rangle$$

We observe that b and f are uncoupled* in $|1\rangle$ as are also c and e. Moreover there are no cycles. This is established by drawing lines connecting b to f and c to e on the Rümer diagram for $|1\rangle$ and noting that there is no closed path.

```
     a
f-------b
|
e-------c
    d
```

(This new kind of diagram is called a *test diagram*; it is used to test for the presence or absence of cycles.) Applying rule one, we therefore find that the matrix element is $(\frac{1}{2})^2 = \frac{1}{4}$.

The rule is not only useful in computing non-orthogonality integrals but also in finding actual matrix elements, as, for example, the element of $\mathcal{R}_{af}$ between $|1\rangle$ and $|3\rangle$.

```
    a
f   |   b
|   |   |
e   |   c
    d
```

$|3\rangle$

We convert $|1\rangle$ to $|3\rangle$ using an R not referring to a or to f so that

$$\begin{aligned} \langle 1 \mid \mathcal{R}_{af} \mid 3 \rangle &= -\langle 1 \mid \mathcal{R}_{af}\, R_{bd} \mid 1 \rangle \\ &= \langle 1 \mid \mathcal{R}_{af}\, \mathcal{R}_{bd} \mid 1 \rangle \\ &= \tfrac{1}{4} \end{aligned}$$

The test diagram is as follows

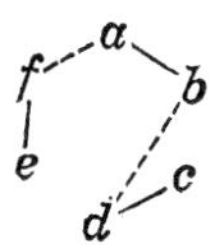

There are no cycles, and our rule applies.

If we attempt to compute the matrix element of $\mathcal{R}_{ad}$ between $|1\rangle$ and

* That is, b is paired elsewhere (to a) and likewise f is paired elsewhere (to e).

$|2\rangle$ as a diagonal matrix element, we might consider, for example,

$$\langle 1 \mid \mathcal{R}_{ad}\, \mathcal{R}_{bf}\, \mathcal{R}_{ce} \mid 1 \rangle$$

which has the following test diagram

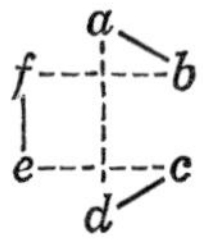

This reveals that $\mathcal{R}_{ad}$ is involved in a cycle. Other ways of writing the matrix element,

$$\langle 1 \mid \mathcal{R}_{ad}\, \mathcal{R}_{ac}\, \mathcal{R}_{df} \mid 1 \rangle$$

$$\langle 2 \mid \mathcal{R}_{bf}\, \mathcal{R}_{ac}\, \mathcal{R}_{ad} \mid 2 \rangle, \quad \text{and so on}$$

inevitably lead to the same conclusion. For this example, our rule does not apply. We shall postpone further consideration of these special cases.

We now go on to obtain an informal proof of rule one, and in so doing shall find out why $\mathcal{R}$'s in cycles must be treated separately. Instead of working with the projection operators, here (reassured by Theorem 3.1) we shall use the algebra of spin states of numbered electrons: the spin-only case. Also we shall use wave function notation. We consider a function, ψ_1, in which electrons one and two are paired, also three and four, and which has reference to still other electrons

$$\psi_1 = 2^{-1/2}\, (\alpha_1\, \beta_2 - \beta_1\, \alpha_2) 2^{-1/2}\, (\alpha_3\, \beta_4 - \beta_3\, \alpha_4) \varphi$$

Here φ is a normalized function referring to electrons five, six, ... The matrix element

$$\int \psi_1\, P_{23}\, \psi_1\, d\tau$$

is analogous to one covered in our rule because electrons two and three are each paired elsewhere. Multiplied out, this matrix element is

$$\tfrac{1}{4} \int \varphi^2\, (\alpha_1\, \beta_2\, \alpha_3\, \beta_4 + \beta_1\, \alpha_2\, \beta_3\, \alpha_4 - \beta_1\, \alpha_2\, \alpha_3\, \beta_4 - \alpha_1\, \beta_2\, \beta_3\, \alpha_4)$$

$$P_{23}\, (\alpha_1\, \beta_2\, \alpha_3\, \beta_4 + \beta_1\, \alpha_2\, \beta_3\, \alpha_4 - \beta_1\, \alpha_2\, \alpha_3\, \beta_4 - \alpha_1\, \beta_2\, \beta_3\, \alpha_4)\, d\tau$$

After integration over electrons one, four, five, six . . . there remains

$$\int \psi_1\, P_{23}\, \psi_1\, d\tau = \tfrac{1}{4} \Big[\int \beta_2\, \alpha_3\, P_{23}\, \beta_2\, \alpha_3\, d\tau_2\, d\tau_3 + \int \alpha_2\, \beta_3\, P_{23}\, \alpha_2\, \beta_3\, d\tau_2\, d\tau_3$$

$$+ \int \alpha_2\, \alpha_3\, P_{23}\, \alpha_2\, \alpha_3\, d\tau_2\, d\tau_3 + \int \beta_2\, \beta_3\, P_{23}\, \beta_2\, \beta_3\, d\tau_2\, d\tau_3 \Big] \qquad (3.26)$$

In the literature, this result is sometimes arrived at intuitively as the ensemble average of P_{23} expectation values. Correspondingly, the fact that the four possibilities $\beta\alpha$, $\alpha\beta$, $\alpha\alpha$, $\beta\beta$ occur with equal weights is described by saying that electrons two and three, each paired elsewhere, must be *unpaired* (neither paired not antipaired).

To formally evaluate the matrix element we may use the expansion of the $\alpha\beta$ and $\beta\alpha$ terms in eigenfunctions of P_{23}

$$P_{23}\, 2^{-1/2}\, (\alpha_2\, \beta_3 \pm \beta_2\, \alpha_3) = \pm 2^{-1/2}\, (\alpha_2\, \beta_3 \pm \beta_2\, \alpha_3)$$

These eigenfunctions are abbreviated

$$\varphi_\pm = 2^{-1/2}\, (\alpha_2\, \beta_3 \pm \beta_2\, \alpha_3)$$

(The minus sign gives the singlet and the plus sign one of the triplets.) Now we can write the first term of Eq. (3.26)

$$\begin{aligned}\int \beta_2\, \alpha_3\, P_{23}\, \beta_2\, \alpha_3\, d\tau_2\, d\tau_3 & \\ &= \int 2^{-1/2}\, (\varphi_+ - \varphi_-) P_{23}\, 2^{-1/2}\, (\varphi_+ - \varphi_-)\, d\tau_2\, d\tau_3 \\ &= \int 2^{-1/2}\, (\varphi_+ - \varphi_-) 2^{-1/2}\, (\varphi_+ + \varphi_-)\, d\tau_2\, d\tau_3 \\ &= 0\end{aligned}$$

(where we have used $P_{23}\, \varphi_\pm = \pm\varphi_\pm$). Similarly, the second term of Eq. (3.26) is zero

$$\begin{aligned}\int 2^{-1/2}\, (\varphi_+ + \varphi_-) P_{23}\, 2^{-1/2}\, (\varphi_+ + \varphi_-)\, d\tau_2\, d\tau_3 & \\ &= \int 2^{-1/2}\, (\varphi_+ + \varphi_-) 2^{-1/2}\, (\varphi_+ - \varphi_-)\, d\tau_2\, d\tau_3 \\ &= 0\end{aligned}$$

The third and fourth terms give 1 apiece so we have

$$\int \psi_1\, P_{23}\, \psi_1\, d\tau = \tfrac{1}{4}[0 + 0 + 1 + 1] = \tfrac{1}{2}$$

Except for a trivial change of basis this is the same as the spin multiplet ensemble average

$$\begin{aligned}\tfrac{1}{4}\Big[\int \varphi_-\, P_{23}\, \varphi_-\, d\tau_2\, d\tau_3 + \int \varphi_+\, P_{23}\, \varphi_+\, d\tau_2\, d\tau_3 & \\ + \int \alpha_2\, \alpha_3\, P_{23}\, \alpha_2\, \alpha_3\, d\tau_2\, d\tau_3 &+ \int \beta_2\, \beta_3\, P_{23}\, \beta_2\, \beta_3\, d\tau_2\, d\tau_3\Big] \\ = \tfrac{1}{4}[-1 + 1 + 1 + 1] = \tfrac{1}{2} &\end{aligned}$$

The correct result, $\frac{1}{2}$, was obtained in Section 3.9 using the projection operator technique with the example of four atoms in a line. The present treatment has this important feature: the manner of derivation especially lends itself to extension. For example, it is obvious that if the wave function were as follows

1——2 3——4 5——6 7——8

the matrix element of $P_{23}\,P_{67}$ would be $\frac{1}{4}$, $\frac{1}{2}$ for each P. In fact, however, the matrix element of $P_{23}\,P_{45}$ is also $\frac{1}{4}$

1——2-----3——4-----5——6 7——8

What is newly required is that the spin of four be α or β, each with the same probability and independent of the spin of five. There is coupling between two and three—P_{23} can be considered as a linear combination of pairing, $(1 - P_{23})$, and antipairing, $(1 + P_{23})$, operators—so that four is coupled all the way back to one. Nevertheless, having no connection between electrons one to four, and five (or the electrons coupled to five) is all that is needed in order that the ensemble average method apply. In fact, according to this way of looking at it, the matrix element of $P_{23}\,P_{25}$ is again $\frac{1}{4}$

We are using test diagrams here, and what is required in every case is the absence of a cycle.

Cycles occur in connection with our attempts to compute off-diagonal matrix elements of a single $\mathcal{R}$. The procedure for converting the problem into computation of an equivalent diagonal matrix element may be shown diagrammatically. Thus for the matrix element $\langle 1 \mid \mathcal{R} \mid 2\rangle$, we first turn $|2\rangle$ into $|1\rangle$ using sets of two R's, always related to $\mathcal{R}$'s which are either $\alpha\alpha$ or $\beta\beta$ interchanges

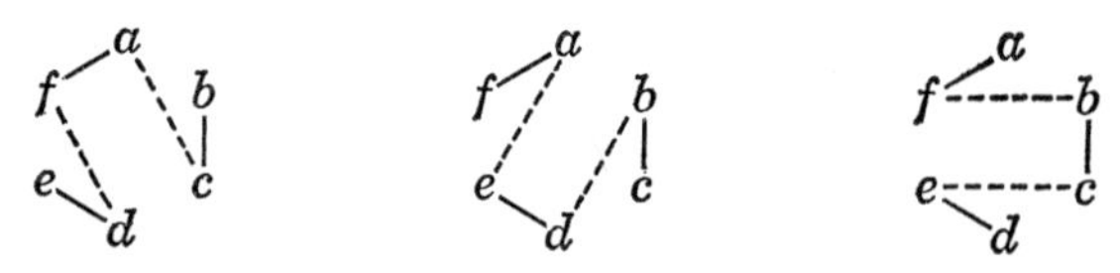

or we turn $|1\rangle$ into $|2\rangle$, again using R's corresponding to $\mathcal{R}$'s which are either $\alpha\alpha$ or $\beta\beta$ interchanges

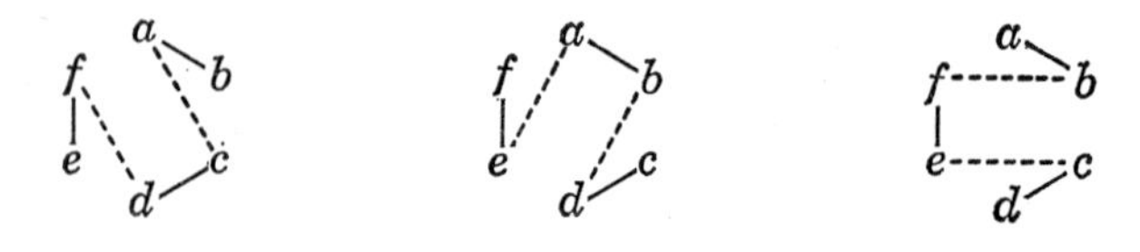

Every case shown has the same characteristic, that the centers turn out to be strung together continuously with only one break in the chain. This is most readily discovered by superimposing the Rümer diagrams for $|1\rangle$ and $|2\rangle$ directly, a process which correspondingly gives an island.

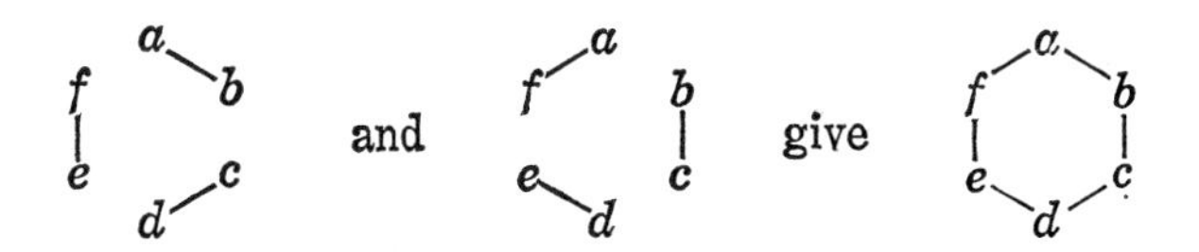

Evidently the matrix element of any $\mathcal{R}_{ij}$ where i and j are members of the continuous string (or in the same island) gives a cycle. For $\mathcal{R}_{ad}$ we already found

At this point, we must recognize two cases: (1) if the $\mathcal{R}_{ij}$ connects centers having the same spin in $|s\rangle$; (2) if the $\mathcal{R}_{ij}$ connects centers having opposite spins in $|s\rangle$. Recalling that the spins alternate in $|s\rangle$ we see that $\langle 1 \mid \mathcal{R}_{ad} \; |2\rangle$ falls in case (2), whereas an example of case (1) would be

$$\langle 1 \mid \mathcal{R}_{ac} \mid 2\rangle$$

The rule for case (1) is direct. As a study of the diagrams above suggests, it is always possible to go from one bond eigenfunction to the other, using an R to match. In the example,

$$\langle 1 \mid \mathcal{R}_{ac} \mid 2\rangle = \langle 1 \mid \mathcal{R}_{ac} \, (\mathcal{R}_{ac} \, \mathcal{R}_{df} \mid 1\rangle)$$

Therefore the matrix element is the same as the non-orthogonality integral

$$\langle 1 \mid 2\rangle = \langle 1 \mid \mathcal{R}_{ac} \, \mathcal{R}_{df} \mid 1\rangle$$

except that one of the $\mathcal{R}$'s is obliterated on account of

$$\mathcal{R}_{ac}^2 = 1$$

and therefore one of the factors $\frac{1}{2}$ occurring after the application of rule one is obliterated. For case (1): *The matrix element is twice the non-orthogonality integral.*

To evaluate the integral in case (2) we switch over temporarily from $\mathcal{R}$'s to R's. The effect of operating with R_{ad} on $|2\rangle$ is to cross bonds

$$R_{ad}|2\rangle \longrightarrow$$

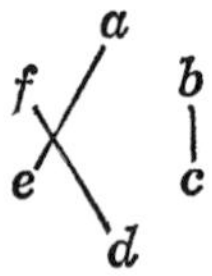

a f b e c d

This same crossing occurs if we use R_{ef}, and $\mathcal{R}_{ef}$ can be collapsed onto a projection operator. Unfortunately, we cannot simply replace R_{ad} by R_{ef} because the R's also change $|s\rangle$. Thus we write

$$R_{ef}\, R_{ad} \mid 2\rangle = \mid \bar{2}\rangle$$

where the standard determinant is replaced in $|\bar{2}\rangle$ by

$$\mid \bar{s}\rangle = R_{ef}\, R_{ad} \mid s\rangle = \mathcal{R}_{ef}\, \mathcal{R}_{ad} \mid s\rangle = \mathcal{R}_{af}\, \mathcal{R}_{ed} \mid s\rangle$$

Going back to $\mathcal{R}$'s, we have

$$\mathcal{R}_{ef}\, \mathcal{R}_{ad} \mid 2\rangle = |\bar{2}\rangle$$

and solving for $\mathcal{R}_{ad} \mid 2\rangle$, we find

$$\mathcal{R}_{ad} \mid 2\rangle = \mathcal{R}_{ef} \mid \bar{2}\rangle$$

Then using $\mathcal{R}_{af}\, \mathcal{R}_{ed} \mid s\rangle$ for $|\bar{s}\rangle$ in $|\bar{2}\rangle$ and collapsing the $\mathcal{R}$'s, we obtain

$$\mathcal{R}_{ad} \mid 2\rangle = \mathcal{R}_{ef} \mid 2\rangle$$

so that

$$\langle 1 \mid \mathcal{R}_{ad} \mid 2\rangle = \langle 1 \mid \mathcal{R}_{ef} \mid 2\rangle = -\langle 1 \mid 2\rangle$$

To replace an $\alpha - \beta$ interchange involving uncoupled spins with one which will collapse into a projection operator is not always this easy. Sometimes several steps are needed. The replacement can, however, always be effected. Thus for case (2): *The matrix element is the negative of the non-orthogonality integral.*

3.16 THE DIRAC SPIN-EXCHANGE IDENTITY

We work in the usual representation for which the spin along the z axis is diagonal. The Pauli matrices are

$$\sigma_z = \begin{pmatrix} 1 & 0 \\ 0 & -1 \end{pmatrix} \qquad \sigma_x = \begin{pmatrix} 0 & 1 \\ 1 & 0 \end{pmatrix} \qquad \sigma_y = \begin{pmatrix} 0 & i \\ -i & 0 \end{pmatrix}$$

Then what we have called α is

$$\begin{pmatrix} 1 \\ 0 \end{pmatrix}$$

(going along with the eigenvalue $+1$ of σ_z) and β is

$$\begin{pmatrix} 0 \\ 1 \end{pmatrix}$$

(going with the eigenvalue -1 of σ_z). We now define subsidiary matrices

$$a^{\pm} = \tfrac{1}{2}(\sigma_x \mp i\sigma_y) \tag{3.27}$$

With this definition

$$a^- = \begin{pmatrix} 0 & 0 \\ 1 & 0 \end{pmatrix}$$

and

$$a^+ = \begin{pmatrix} 0 & 1 \\ 0 & 0 \end{pmatrix}$$

The action of the a's is found by direct computation to be

$$a^- \begin{pmatrix} 0 \\ 1 \end{pmatrix} = 0 \qquad a^- \begin{pmatrix} 1 \\ 0 \end{pmatrix} = \begin{pmatrix} 0 \\ 1 \end{pmatrix}$$

$$a^+ \begin{pmatrix} 0 \\ 1 \end{pmatrix} = \begin{pmatrix} 1 \\ 0 \end{pmatrix} \qquad a^+ \begin{pmatrix} 1 \\ 0 \end{pmatrix} = 0$$

Thus a^+ raises the spin if possible (puts β into α), and a^- lowers it. If we work on the product, for example,

$$\alpha_\mu \, \beta_\nu \quad \text{or} \quad \begin{pmatrix} 1 \\ 0 \end{pmatrix}_\mu \begin{pmatrix} 0 \\ 1 \end{pmatrix}_\nu$$

to lower the spin of the μth electron and raise the spin of the νth

$$a_\mu^- \, a_\nu^+ \begin{pmatrix} 1 \\ 0 \end{pmatrix}_\mu \begin{pmatrix} 0 \\ 1 \end{pmatrix}_\nu = \begin{pmatrix} 0 \\ 1 \end{pmatrix}_\mu \begin{pmatrix} 1 \\ 0 \end{pmatrix}_\nu$$

we have in effect permuted μ and ν. The action of $a_\mu^+ \, a_\nu^-$ on $\alpha_\mu \, \beta_\nu$ gives zero, but accomplishes a similar purpose when working on $\beta_\mu \, \alpha_\nu$. We might, therefore, tentatively try for $P_{\mu\nu}$

$$a_\mu^- \, a_\nu^+ + a_\mu^+ \, a_\nu^- \tag{3.28}$$

To round out the treatment, we need also to get the correct result

$$P_{\mu\nu} \, \alpha_\mu \, \alpha_\nu = \alpha_\mu \, \alpha_\nu$$

and the same for $\beta_\mu \, \beta_\nu$. The tentative form Eq. (3.28) gives zero in these cases, which necessitates our adding extra terms. As the reader may verify, the correct expression turns out to be

$$P_{\mu\nu} \equiv a_\mu^- \, a_\nu^+ + a_\mu^+ \, a_\nu^- + \frac{\sigma_{z\mu} \, \sigma_{z\nu}}{2} + \frac{1}{2}$$

This result is now general for any two-electron spin function, since only $\alpha\beta$, $\beta\alpha$, $\alpha\alpha$, $\beta\beta$ and linear combinations occur. Using the definition Eq. (3.27), we then find

$$P_{\mu\nu} \equiv \frac{\sigma_{z\mu} \, \sigma_{z\nu} + \sigma_{x\mu} \, \sigma_{x\nu} + \sigma_{y\mu} \, \sigma_{y\nu}}{2} + \frac{1}{2}$$

or

$$2P_{\mu\nu} \equiv \boldsymbol{\sigma}_\mu \cdot \boldsymbol{\sigma}_\nu + 1$$

the required identity.

In the literature of solid state physics, frequently a formalism is used in which quantities like the $a^+ a^-$ products appear in place of the $\mathcal{R}$'s—both in the interaction operator and in the projection operators.

CHAPTER 4

The Independent Systems Approach

When molecules are considered as collections of atoms brought up to one another until the outer orbitals begin to mesh, there is, as we have seen in Chapter 3, still a considerable complication from the permutation degeneracy. A simple electrostatic perturbation exists even when the atoms are so far apart as to make the exchange interactions amongst outer orbitals negligible. The energy shift of the *ground state* for separations large enough to rule out exchange is the integral over the London or dispersion force. A stronger effect comes from the resonance force, as, for example, in the slightly artificial case of a system of two hydrogen atoms, one in a $1s$ state, and the other in a $2p_z$ state. The level is spatially degenerate, and the wave functions which are obtained in a degenerate perturbation calculation are

$$| 1sa\mu) \, | 2p_z \, b\nu) \pm | 2p_z \, a\mu) \, | 1sb\nu) \qquad (4.1)$$

where electron μ is on a and ν is on b. Use of an abbreviated form which emphasizes the location of the excitation $1 \rightarrow 2$ shows most clearly the type of spatial degeneracy

$$| 1a) \, | 2b) \pm | 2a) \, | 1b)$$

The energies come on either side of $E_{1s} + E_{2p}$; the splitting governed by the expectation value of the coulomb potential connecting the charged particles at a with the charged particles at b.

This exemplifies what is called the *independent systems approach,* the essence of which is that the exchange is ignored. This simplification underlies the quantal theory of dispersion forces and in addition is satisfactory for electronic states of molecular crystals. It is even applicable to certain molecules, in that sometimes parts of a molecule appear to be isolated from other parts of the same molecule, as regards exchange.

Let us (following Tolman*) look more carefully into the question of ignoring exchange. Fundamentally, we would have to use Slater determinants. This involves assigning spins to centers. For the first term in Eq. (4.1), we might assign α to a and β to b, in which case we should use

$$2^{-1/2} \sum_P (-1)^P P \, | 1sa\alpha\mu) \, | 2pb\beta\nu)$$

in place of the simplified function

$$| 1sa\mu) \, | 2pb\nu)$$

Either of these, however, plays the same part in a degenerate perturbation calculation when the atoms are well separated. To see this let us investigate, for example, the off-diagonal element

$$2^{-1} \sum_P (-1)^P P(1sa\alpha\mu \, | \, (2pb\beta\nu \, | \, V \sum_P (-1)^P P \, | 2pa\alpha\mu) \, | 1sb\beta\nu)$$

Using the equivalence of μ and ν, and spin orthogonality, this becomes

$$(1sa\mu \, | \, (2pb\nu \, | \, V \, | 2pa\mu) \, | 1sb\nu)$$

Observe, now, that the parts of the simplified function Eq. (4.1) interact so as to give the same off-diagonal element. Also, starting with β on a and α on b

* R. C. Tolman, *The Principles of Statistical Mechanics* (Oxford: Oxford University Press, 1938), p. 312.

$$2^{-1/2} \sum_P (-1)^P P \mid 1sa\beta\mu) \mid 2pb\alpha\nu)$$

still one obtains the same thing, provided that the function which is allowed to interact has the same assignment of spins to centers. What is more, matrix elements between functions each having a different assignment of spins to centers are negligible. For example,

$$2^{-1} \sum_P (-1)^P P(1sa\alpha\mu \mid (2pb\beta\nu \mid V \sum_P (-1)^P P \mid 1sa\beta\mu) \mid 2pb\alpha\nu)$$
$$= -(1sa\mu \mid (2pb\nu \mid V \mid 1sa\nu) \mid 2pb\mu) \approx 0$$

Considering the relation to time-dependent perturbation theory, this result implies that a spin α on nucleus a will effectively remain on a, provided that the atoms are far enough apart to reduce the overlap to zero. Physically, it is the spins which label the electrons, not the electron numbers (like μ and ν), so when the overlap is negligible the exchange of electron numbers in, for example,

$$2^{-1/2} \sum_P (-1)^P P \mid 1sa\alpha\mu) \mid 2pb\beta\nu)$$

does not mean that the electrons are exchanging.

The wave functions which it is natural to use (for example, the one directly above) are not necessarily eigenfunctions of S^2 for the combined system. It is, of course, natural to use spin multiplet functions locally, when there is more than one electron on a given center distant from other centers. We might say that the correct procedure from a physical standpoint is then to assign spin arrangements to centers. A typical example is a valence bond function based on perfect pairing

H—H H—H
a b

where the centers are considered to be the molecules labeled a and b and the spin arrangements are electrons paired in a and also in b. The valence bond function in this case happens to be a proper spin multiplet function for the combined system and might seem to be not a natural function from the independent systems point of view. Further study of the question reveals that here having the electrons unpaired as between molecules a and b (perfect pairing in a and b) is just the physically correct function to consider as epitomizing the independent systems approximation. If the molecules a and b are isolated as regards exchange we may treat the particles on a as distinguishable from those on b by modifying the valence bond function—omitting the terms in the antisymmetrizer which bring in unwanted permutations.

As a practical matter, we may use numbers or letters to denote hypothetical distinguishable particles, as in a function such as

$$\mid 1sa\mu) \mid 2pb\nu)$$

because assigning μ to a and ν to b as if particles μ and ν were distinguishable leads to the same result as the more rigorous procedure of assigning spins to centers.

The independent systems approach will now be further explored, as we take up the model problem of two weakly interacting distinguishable harmonic oscillators, where the interaction is specifically coulombic. The model will subsequently be applied to molecular crystals, and will even be developed to include a discussion of non-stationary states. Parenthetically, this last is shown to provide a way of understanding the interaction between molecules and the radiation field. Finally, the model will be used to describe actual "molecules in molecules," in which case a form of interaction more general than the coulomb one must be postulated. To begin, we shall look at the standard form for the coulomb interaction.

4.1 THE POTENTIAL

Collections of positive and negative charge (called *charge complexes*) exhibit a static interaction with one another even though neutral. For example let us consider two simple charge complexes, a and b, with two unit charges in each complex (as in Fig. 4.1). We shall consider the locations of the positive charges as defining

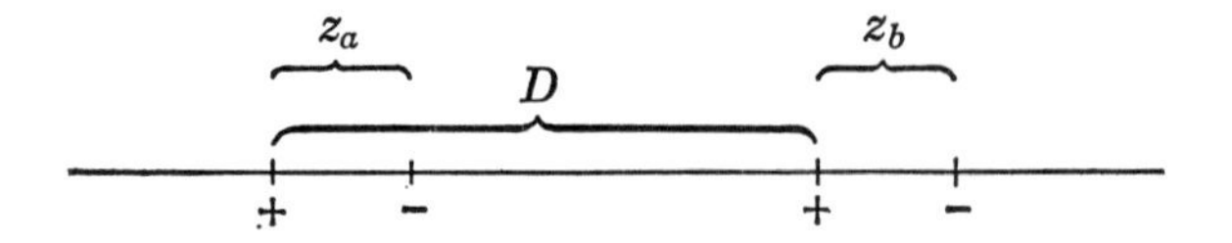

Figure 4.1

the positions of the complexes, so that the distance apart is D. Also the distances z_a and z_b are the distances of the negative charges in local coordinate systems. The electrostatic potential in this case is

$$V = \frac{1}{D} + \frac{1}{D + z_b - z_a} - \frac{1}{D - z_a} - \frac{1}{D + z_b}$$

If $z \ll D$, we can write, for example,

$$\frac{1}{D - z_a} = \frac{1}{D}\frac{1}{1 - (z_a/D)}$$

$$= \frac{1}{D}\left[1 + \left(\frac{z_a}{D}\right) + \left(\frac{z_a}{D}\right)^2 + \dots\right]$$

This gives

$$V = \frac{1}{D}\left\{1 - \left[1 + \left(\frac{z_a}{D}\right) + \left(\frac{z_a}{D}\right)^2 + \ldots\right] - \left[1 - \left(\frac{z_b}{D}\right) + \left(\frac{z_b}{D}\right)^2 - \ldots\right]\right.$$
$$\left. + \left[1 - \left(\frac{z_b - z_a}{D}\right) + \left(\frac{z_b - z_a}{D}\right)^2 - \ldots\right]\right\}$$
$$= -2\frac{z_a z_b}{D^3} + \ldots \tag{4.2a}$$

To get some idea of the effectiveness of the approximation, we consider as an example that $D = 10$ and $z_a = z_b = +1$, in which case a direct determination of the potential is

$$\frac{1}{10} + \frac{1}{10} - \frac{1}{9} - \frac{1}{11} = -\frac{2}{990}$$

whereas Eq. (4.2a) gives

$$V = -\frac{2}{1000} + \ldots$$

When each negative charge is permitted to move in three dimensions around its central positive charge, it can be shown that the potential is

$$V = \frac{1}{D^3}(-2z_a z_b + x_a x_b + y_a y_b) \tag{4.2b}$$

When there are several negative charges moving around the positive center, as in an atom, the formula includes all pairwise interactions

$$\frac{1}{D^3}\left(-2\sum_{\nu \text{ on } a} z_a(\nu) \sum_{\mu \text{ on } b} z_b(\mu) + \ldots\right) \tag{4.2c}$$

As a first example of the use of this potential, we shall study two 2-dimensional oscillators lying in the same plane.

4.2 TWO HARMONIC OSCILLATORS

The oscillators will be taken parallel, with orientation as given in Fig. 4.2. The force constants are unequal, one much higher than the other, with the low force constant permitting oscillation in the direction of the $\bar{z}$ axes, and the high going with $\bar{x}$. Each oscillator is assumed to be negatively charged and attached to a fixed center which is itself positively charged. The springs holding the oscillators may be supposed to be slightly anharmonic so that the local coulomb attractions between the positive and negative charges (at a and

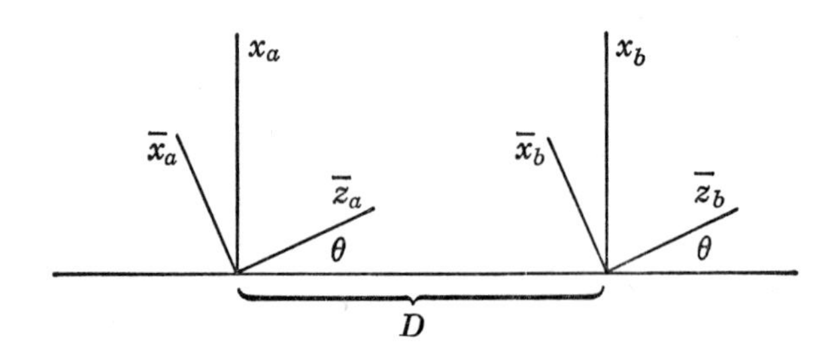

Figure 4.2

also at b) together with the springs give harmonic binding. The wave function for a single oscillator in the ground state at a is $|0a)$, represented by

$$N_0\, e^{-\alpha\bar{x}_a^2/2}\, e^{-\beta\bar{z}_a^2/2}$$

The lower of the two classical frequencies is related to β

$$\beta = \frac{m\omega_\beta}{\hbar}$$

with a similar expression for α. If there were no electrostatic interaction between the left and right oscillators the Hamiltonian would be

$$H^0 = H_a^0 + H_b^0$$

where, for example,

$$H_a^0 = T_a + \tfrac{1}{2}k_\alpha\, \bar{x}_a^2 + \tfrac{1}{2}k_\beta\, \bar{z}_a^2$$

The degree of independence of the a and b oscillators can be made as high as desired by making D large. Thus a perturbation treatment based on eigenfunctions of H^0 is appropriate. When the Hamiltonian is a sum, the wave functions are products referring to the independent systems, so that the ground state wave function for the combined system is

$$|\,0\rangle = |\,0a)\,|\,0b)$$

where again $|0a)$ depicts the oscillator at a in its ground state. Other wave functions for the combined system are obtained by introducing excitation in the separate oscillators systematically. We shall assume that only excitation in the $\bar{z}$ direction gives excited states which are low enough in energy to be of importance dynamically, so we have representing the ith state of a single oscillator, or $|i)$

$$N_i\, e^{-\alpha\bar{x}^2/2}\, e^{-\beta\bar{z}^2/2}\, h_i\,(\bar{z}) \tag{4.3}$$

where h_i is the ith Hermite polynomial. A list of states for the combined system in order of increasing unperturbed energy may now be constructed

$$
\begin{array}{ll}
|0\rangle = |0a)\,|0b) & |3\rangle = |2a)\,|0b) \\
|1\rangle = |1a)\,|0b) & |4\rangle = |1a)\,|1b) \\
|2\rangle = |0a)\,|1b) & |5\rangle = |0a)\,|2b) \\
 & \text{and so on}
\end{array} \tag{4.4}
$$

The unperturbed energies are $\frac{1}{2}\hbar\,(\omega_\alpha + \omega_\beta)$ for each oscillator, to which is added

$$E^0 = \hbar\omega_\beta\,(n_a + n_b)$$

where n is the appropriate quantum number—and which is called i in (4.3). There is degeneracy: $|1\rangle$ and $|2\rangle$ form a pair, $|3\rangle$, $|4\rangle$, and $|5\rangle$ a triad, and so on. The calculation of the effect of the perturbation requires that we know the transformation between the natural molecule-fixed system $(\bar{x}, \bar{z})$ and the system corresponding to the description of the perturbation (x, z)

$$
\begin{aligned}
x &= \cos\theta\bar{x} + \sin\theta\bar{z} \\
z &= -\sin\theta\bar{x} + \cos\theta\bar{z}
\end{aligned} \tag{4.5}
$$

The Hamiltonian, correct to terms in D^{-3}, is

$$H = H^0 + V$$

where, see Eq. (4.2b)

$$V = \frac{1}{D^3}\,[-2z_a\,z_b + x_a\,x_b]$$

Introducing Eq. (4.5)

$$
\begin{aligned}
V = \frac{1}{D^3}\,\{-2[\sin^2\theta\bar{x}_a\,\bar{x}_b &- \sin\theta\cos\theta(\bar{x}_a\,\bar{z}_b + \bar{x}_b\,\bar{z}_a) \\
&+ \cos^2\theta\bar{z}_a\,\bar{z}_b] + \cos^2\theta\bar{x}_a\,\bar{x}_b \\
&+ \sin\theta\cos\theta(\bar{x}_a\,\bar{z}_b + \bar{x}_b\,\bar{z}_a) + \sin^2\theta\bar{z}_a\,\bar{z}_b\}
\end{aligned}
$$

Remembering that the $|i)$'s never involve excitation of the high-frequency mode, we shall always find—see Eq. (4.3)

$$(i\,|\,\bar{x}\,|\,j) = N_i\,N_j \int e^{-\alpha\bar{x}^2/2}\,e^{-\beta\bar{z}^2/2}\,h_i\,(\bar{z})\bar{x}e^{-\alpha\bar{x}^2/2}\,e^{-\beta\bar{z}^2/2}\,h_j\,(\bar{z})\,d\bar{x}\,d\bar{z} = 0$$

so that we can disregard the terms in $\bar{x}_a$ and $\bar{x}_b$ and find in this case

$$V = \frac{1}{D^3}\,(1 - 3\cos^2\theta)\,\bar{z}_a\,\bar{z}_b \tag{4.6}$$

Using Eq. (4.6), we find that the first-order correction to the energy of the ground state is

$$\langle 0\,|\,V\,|\,0\rangle = \frac{1}{D^3}\,(1 - 3\cos^2\theta)\,(0a|\,(0b\,|\,\bar{z}_a\,\bar{z}_b\,|\,0a)\,|0b)$$

The integration variables can be measured each from the appropriate molecule-fixed origin; moreover, one can just as well use the barred coordinates, because the transformation has a Jacobian of one. This then gives zero for the first-order energy correction because

$$(0 \mid \bar{z} \mid 0) = 0$$

The first-order correction for the degenerate pair $|1\rangle$ and $|2\rangle$ under the perturbation, Eq. (4.6), comes from a secular equation. The roots are given by

$$\lambda^2 = [\langle 1 \mid V \mid 2\rangle]^2$$

and the off-diagonal matrix element is

$$\langle 1 \mid V \mid 2\rangle = \frac{1}{D^3} (1 - 3\cos^2\theta)\, (1a|\, (0b \mid \bar{z}_a \bar{z}_b \mid 0a)\, |1b) \tag{4.7}$$

The $\bar{x}$ integration gives unity from the normalization of the wave function for the $\bar{x}$ modes and the $\bar{z}$ integration brings in the square of the local $\bar{z}$ matrix element

$$(0 \mid \bar{z} \mid 1) = N_0 N_1 \int e^{-\beta \bar{z}^2/2}\, \bar{z} h_1(\bar{z})\, e^{-\beta \bar{z}^2/2}\, d\bar{z}$$

$$= \frac{1}{\sqrt{2\beta}}$$

The sign of the matrix element in the secular equation depends on the phases of $|1a)$ and $|1b)$, but if these are chosen symmetrically, we have

$$(1a|\, (0b \mid \bar{z}_a \bar{z}_b \mid 0a)\, |1b) = \frac{1}{2\beta} > 0 \tag{4.8}$$

To summarize, to the first order $|0\rangle$ is unaffected by the perturbation; whereas the first degenerate manifold, $|1\rangle$, $|2\rangle$, is split by $\pm\langle 1 \mid V \mid 2\rangle$ (Eq. (4.7) with Eq. (4.8)).

4.3 PROBABILITY DISTRIBUTION

The correct zero-order state vectors are found by the usual secular equation technique to be

$$|+\rangle = 2^{-1/2}\, (|1\rangle + |2\rangle)$$

going with $\lambda = +\langle 1 \mid V \mid 2\rangle$ and

$$|-\rangle = 2^{-1/2}\, (|1\rangle - |2\rangle)$$

going with $\lambda = -\langle 1 \mid V \mid 2\rangle$—compare Eq. (4.1). Recalling (Chapter 2) that the probability density is the diagonal of the density matrix, we shall be looking at, for example,

$$|+\rangle\langle+| = \tfrac{1}{2}(|1\rangle\langle 1| + 2\,|\,1\rangle\langle 2| + |2\rangle\langle 2|)$$

This expression contains the average of what would be expected if the excitation were on a: $|1\rangle\langle 1|$ and on b: $|2\rangle\langle 2|$; but also (and this is crucial) a cross term

$$|1\rangle\langle 2| = |1a)\,|0b)\,(0a|\,(1b| = [|1a)\,(0a|]\,[|0b)\,(1b|]$$

We digress here in order to introduce a simplified notation. The single-particle density matrix for the particle at a in the Schrödinger representation is

$$(\bar{z}_a \mid 1a)\,(0a \mid \bar{z}'_a)$$

with diagonal elements ($\bar{z}_a = \bar{z}'_a$) equal to the product of the wave functions. These functions of $\bar{z}_a$ will be called a_0 and a_1 for the two states, for example, for the first excited state

$$a_1 \equiv (\bar{z}_a \mid 1a) = N_1\, e^{-\beta\bar{z}_a^2/2}\, h_1(\bar{z}_a)$$

Let us now specialize to the case where the oscillators are end for end ($\theta = 0$, $\bar{z} = z$), and the phases are as depicted in Fig. 4.3. Then from Eq. (4.7) and Eq.(4.8)

$$\langle 1 \mid V \mid 2\rangle < 0$$

The energy of $|+\rangle$, $\hbar\omega_a + 2\hbar\omega^\beta + \langle 1 \mid V \mid 2\rangle$, is therefore the lower. The functions of $\bar{z}_a$ and $\bar{z}_b$ are as shown in Fig. 4.3. The Roman numerals refer

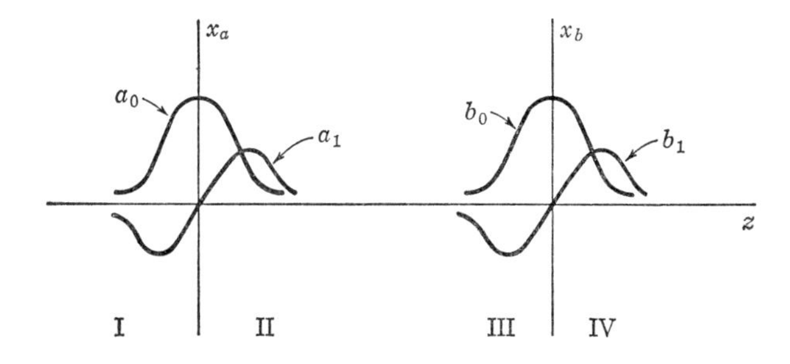

Figure 4.3

to regions of space, and will be used as we now proceed to examine the effect of the cross term. The diagonal of the cross term is the product of four wave functions

$$a_0\, a_1\, b_0\, b_1$$

This product is a modulating term which adds to the probability of some relative orientations of the two oscillators and subtracts from the probability of some other orientations. The term comes in with a positive sign for $|+\rangle\langle+|$. Suppose the a oscillator is in region I and the b oscillator is in region III. Then the product functions of $\bar{z}_a$ and $\bar{z}_b$, $a_0\, a_1$ and $b_0\, b_1$ respectively, will each be negative, so that the cross term will add probability to the independent systems part (which, incidentally, is $\frac{1}{2}(a_1^2\, b_0^2 + a_0^2\, b_1^2)$). Whatever chance the a and b oscillators have of simultaneously being on the left is enhanced. By a similar argument, the configuration in which the oscillators are respectively in II and IV is enhanced, and in contrast, configurations I, IV and II, III occur with less probability than is implied by the independent-systems term. This result provides a particularly direct example of correlation (compare Section 1.4 where, by the way, the word "configuration" is used in a different sense than in the foregoing).

The connection between the energy and the probability can be seen when one remembers that the oscillators are negatively charged, while the centers are positively charged. The configurations which gain in probability through the modulating term are the low-energy ones (see Fig. 4.4), whereas the high-energy ones lose in probability correspondingly.

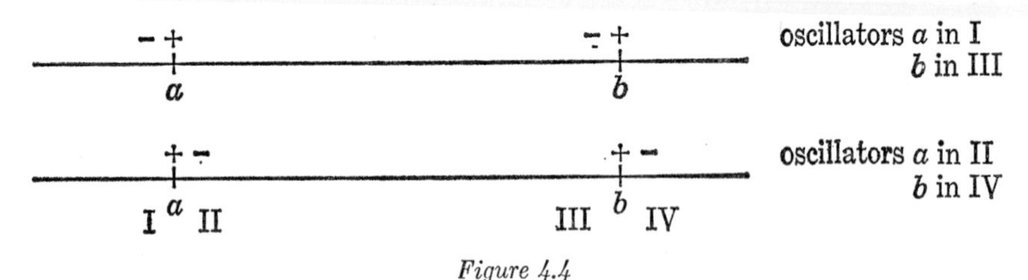

Figure 4.4

The higher-energy state, with function $|-\rangle$, has the opposite correlation effect, the higher-energy configurations being the ones enhanced, because the cross term comes in with a negative sign.

When $\theta = 90°$, the argument is along the same lines. The low-energy function gives enhanced contributions from

$$\pm a \qquad \mp b$$

as well as from

$$\mp a \qquad \pm b$$

Correspondingly, there are diminished contributions from

$$\pm \qquad \pm$$

and

$$\mp \qquad \mp$$

The opposite of all this is true for the high-energy state.

If the wave function is not that for a stationary state but, for example, is known to be $|1a)\,|0b)$, it will change to $|0a)\,|1b)$ and back in a time

$$\nu^{-1} = \left(\frac{E_{-} - E_{+}}{h}\right)^{-1}$$

as will be shown in Section 4.6. Having the initial state $|1a)\,|0b)$ is like observing that the left-hand pendulum in a system of two identical coupled pendula is swinging. After a time $\nu^{-1}/2$, it will be observed that the swinging motion has passed over completely to the pendulum on the right—like $|0a)\,|1b)$—where ν, the classical resonance frequency, is also the difference in frequency between the normal modes (like $\Delta E/h$). Drawing on this analogy, we say that $|1\rangle$ and $|2\rangle$ can "resonate" because the main frequencies are compatible (that is, the unperturbed energies are equal).

The transition-moment lengths are $\langle 0|\,(z_a + z_b)\,|\pm\rangle$ and $\langle 0|\,(x_a + x_b)\,|\pm\rangle$. The two cases of particular interest $\theta = 0$ and $90°$, will be examined separately. For $\theta = 0$ (oscillators end to end), we have $\bar{z} = z$ and $\bar{x} = x$, with the result

$$\begin{aligned}\langle 0|\,(z_a + z_b)\,|\,\pm\rangle\\ &= 2^{-1/2}\,(0a|\,(0b|\,(\bar{z}_a + \bar{z}_b)\,[|1a)\,|0b) \pm |0a)\,|1b)]\\ &= 2^{-1/2}\,[(0\,|\,\bar{z}\,|\,1) \pm (0\,|\,\bar{z}\,|\,1)]\end{aligned}$$

use having been made, for example, of

$$(0a|\,(0b\,|\,\bar{z}_a\,|\,0a)\,|1b) = 0$$

For the case with the minus sign, the result is zero. Moreover, it is readily found that $\langle 0|\,(x_a + x_b)\,|\pm\rangle = 0$. Thus, the only intensity will be in the transition

$$|0\rangle \rightarrow |+\rangle$$

which is allowed polarized in the $\bar{z} = z$ direction; the intensity is proportional to

$$\langle 0|\,(z_a + z_b)\,|+\rangle^2 = [2^{-1/2}\cdot 2(0\,|\,\bar{z}\,|\,1)]^2 = 2(0\,|\,\bar{z}\,|\,1)^2$$

We see that the intensity is the same as if the oscillators were independent, but it is all concentrated in the low-energy transition.

Turning now to the case where $\theta = 90°$ (oscillators side by side), we need to define the phases. This will be as in Fig. 4.5. The lower-energy state vector is now

$$|-\rangle = 2^{-1/2}\,[|1a)\,|0b) - |0a)\,|1b)]$$

The transition-moment length expressions are all zero except for

$$\begin{aligned}\langle 0|\,(x_a + x_b)\,|+\rangle = 2^{\ 1/2}\,&(0a|\,(0b|\,(x_a + x_b)\\ &\times [|1a)\,|0b) + |0a)\,|1b)]\end{aligned}$$

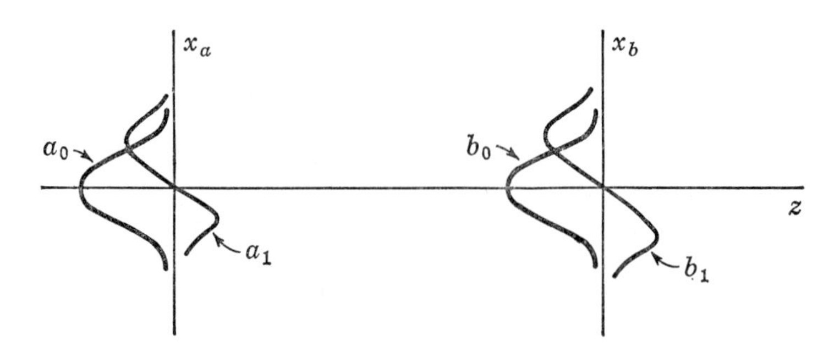

Figure 4.5

This time we have $\bar{z} = x$, so the result is

$$\langle 0|\ (x_a + x_b)\ |+\rangle = 2^{-1/2}\cdot 2(0 \mid \bar{z} \mid 1)$$

and the intensity is the same as before, namely, proportional to $2(0 \mid \bar{z} \mid 1)^2$. Here, however, all the intensity is in the high-energy transition.

It is convenient in thinking about these results intuitively to use arrows to represent the dipoles lined up according to the type of correlation that is enhanced. Thus for $\theta = 0$ we have corresponding to $|+\rangle$

$$\longrightarrow \quad \longrightarrow$$

and to $|-\rangle$

$$\longrightarrow \quad \longleftarrow$$

whereas for $\theta = 90°$ we have

$$|+\rangle \uparrow \uparrow; \quad |-\rangle \uparrow \downarrow$$

The transition moment calculation is now visualized as involving vector addition. The zero value for the intensity for $|-\rangle$ is readily seen. For example, the intuitive interpretation for $|-\rangle$ ($\theta = 90°$) would be that in the non-stationary state formed from $|0\rangle$ and $|-\rangle$ the left and right dipoles move out of phase, so that while one absorbs radiation the other is emitting. The energy corresponding to a given function is also indicated, because the arrows are equivalent to the charge distributions represented above (as in Fig. 4.4) by $+\ -$.

4.4 DISPERSION FORCES

The second order correction to the energy of the ground state will be called $V(D)$. It is

$$V(D) = -\sum_i \frac{\langle 0 \mid V \mid i\rangle^2}{E_i^0 - E_0^0}$$

This reduces to just a single term because the only non-zero matrix element connecting the unperturbed ground state function with the others is —recall Eq. (4.4) and Eq. (4.6)

$$\langle 0 \mid V \mid 4 \rangle = \frac{1}{D_3} (1 - 3 \cos^2 \theta) (0a| (0b \mid \bar{z}_a \bar{z}_b \mid 1a) |1b)$$

$$= \frac{1}{D_3} (1 - 3 \cos^2 \theta) (0 \mid \bar{z} \mid 1)^2$$

Here we use the fact that for a harmonic oscillator $(i \mid \bar{z} \mid j \pm 1) = \text{const.}\ \delta_{ij}$. [Also we find that $\langle 0 \mid V \mid 4 \rangle = \langle 1 \mid V \mid 2 \rangle$—see Eq. (4.7).] The potential associated with the dispersion force is thus found to be

$$V(D) = -\frac{1}{2\hbar\omega_\beta} \frac{1}{D^6} (1 - 3 \cos^2 \theta)^2 (0| \bar{z} \mid 1)^4 \tag{4.9}$$

The wave function corresponding to the second-order energy correction is the first order

$$|0\rangle - \frac{\langle 0 \mid V \mid 4 \rangle}{2\hbar\omega_\beta} |4\rangle$$

or, serving to define ϵ,

$$= |0\rangle - \epsilon \mid 4\rangle$$

The probability distribution to the first order in ϵ is given by

$$|0\rangle \langle 0 \mid -2\epsilon \mid 0\rangle \langle 4|$$

We see again the presence of a modulating term which, moreover, proves to be the same as before

$$|0\rangle \langle 4| = |1\rangle \langle 2|$$

In the present instance, however, the modulation itself is infinitesimal instead of essential owing to the presence of the factor ϵ. Going over to $\theta = 0$ we have $\langle 1 \mid V \mid 2 \rangle = \langle 0 \mid V \mid 4 \rangle < 0$ so that the modifications introduced come in with a positive sign just as for $|+\rangle$ $(\theta = 0)$ as illustrated in Fig. 4.4. The low-energy mutual orientations are in preponderance, which is the reason why it is said that dispersion forces result because "instantaneous dipoles jitter together in phase."

The typical energy parameter appearing in these calculations is $\langle 1 \mid V \mid 2 \rangle$, or in the case of the dispersion forces, $\langle 1 \mid V \mid 2 \rangle^2/2\hbar\omega_\beta$. Since $\langle 1 \mid V \mid 2 \rangle$ contains the transition moment length, one can see how to make use of the various formulas empirically, namely, to select a representative transition moment length, from experiment, for what is considered to be the single subsystem or isolated oscillator. One can then calculate, for example, the energy split for a double molecule, judged to resemble two oscillators.

In the case of dispersion forces, an alternate plan is to introduce the polarizability, which brings in the resonance denominator $2\hbar\omega$ along with the transition moment.

The polarizability is the moment per unit electric field. The effect of a field $\mathcal{E}_z$ on a single oscillator having unit charge, and lined up along the z axis is given by

$$V = \mathcal{E}_z z$$

so that the first-order wave function becomes

$$|0) - \frac{(0 \mid V \mid 1)}{\hbar\omega} |1) = |0) - \frac{\mathcal{E}_z}{\hbar\omega} (0 \mid \bar{z} \mid 1) \, |1)$$

The electric moment is the expectation value

$$\left\{ -(1| \frac{\mathcal{E}_z}{\hbar\omega} (0 \mid \bar{z} \mid 1) + (0| \right\} \bar{z} \left\{ |0) - \left[\frac{\mathcal{E}_z}{\hbar\omega} (0 \mid \bar{z} \mid 1) \right] |1) \right\}$$

which to the first order in small quantities is

$$-2 \frac{\mathcal{E}_z}{\hbar\omega} (0 \mid \bar{z} \mid 1)^2$$

(recall that $(0 \mid \bar{z} \mid 0) = 0$). The polarizability, α, is found after division by $\mathcal{E}_z$

$$\alpha = -\frac{2}{\hbar\omega} (0 \mid \bar{z} \mid 1)^2$$

Substituting this in the potential, Eq. (4.9), and using $\theta = 0$ one obtains

$$V(D) = -\frac{\alpha^2}{D^6} \frac{\hbar\omega}{2}$$

This formula can be used empirically for suitably oriented molecules when the polarizability arises mainly from one direction of charge oscillation. When the analogous derivation is carried out for an isotropic three-dimensional oscillator, one obtains the London formula

$$V(D) = -\frac{3}{2} \frac{\alpha^2}{D^6} \frac{\hbar\omega}{2}$$

In either case, to use the formula empirically requires the employment of a characteristic frequency.

A treatment of polarizability for time dependent perturbations is given in the Appendix.

4.5 SPECTRUM OF MOLECULAR CRYSTALS

The theory in the preceding sections will next be adapted to the calculation of the electrostatic contribution to the electronic frequencies, in crystals composed of parts not interacting through exchange. Before we consider how this is to be done, we shall briefly consider several complications.

In the first place, one observes two separate forms of behavior in molecular crystals, depending on what happens to the electronic excitation after it is considered as first appearing on a given molecule. If the excitation stays too long on a molecule, it will no longer be pure electronic but will be converted in part to Lissajous-figure motion of the atomic nuclei—this because the force constants change between ground and excited states. When a fraction of the electronic excitation has turned into nuclear vibration, the excitation is no longer able to resonate in the direct sense discussed in Section 4.3. A weaker resonance (among degenerate vibronic levels) still obtains, and the situation is then said to be characterized by *weak coupling*. When the electronic excitation jumps to a neighboring molecule before the Lissajous-figure motion can get started, strong resonance is possible, and the coupling is called *strong*. The criterion for deciding which type of coupling will be encountered is the comparison of the halfwidth of the single-molecule electronic band (consisting of vibronic transitions), Δ, with the so-called exciton bandwidth, $\omega_p^2/2\omega_0$. Force constant variation between ground and excited states is measured by Δ, whereas resonant transfer of excitation to a nearby molecule is measured by $\omega_p^2/2\omega_0$. Here ω_p^2, the plasma frequency squared, is $4\pi Nfe^2/m$, and f is the oscillator strength, a quantity related to the transition moment.* (An approximation to the exciton bandwidth is double the matrix element of the electrostatic perturbation for dimers, or $2\langle 1 \mid V \mid 2 \rangle$). When we have the inequality:

$$\frac{\omega_p^2}{2\omega_0} > \Delta$$

strong coupling occurs, and the single-molecule vibrational energy levels become a comparatively unimportant factor.

Another complication which occurs in the theory of the spectrum of molecular crystals is the need for recognizing the internal field. The matrix element of the electrostatic perturbation considered as a field acting on a given molecule has contributions from neighboring molecules which are analogous to the contributions occurring in the classical theory of a

* Refer to Section 4.9 for oscillator strength and Section 4.10 for plasma frequency.

polarized dielectric. In summing all these contributions (as is well known in the classical treatment), one runs into convergence difficulties in the three-dimensional case, in that the D^{-3} fall-off is not quite abrupt enough to make up for the large numbers of "neighbors" at great distances. This calls for an approach which is out of the ordinary, according to which it is found that the average effect of the distant molecules (in this case, when all the instantaneous dipoles point in the same direction) may be treated as a surface charge on a spherical cavity having a volume of many molecular volumes. The surface charge produces a field at a representative molecule which may not be neglected, equal to $4\pi P/3$ where P is analogous to polarization. The sense of the field is so as to produce a red shift, and this red shift is maintained even when the instantaneous dipoles are not all lined up the same way, provided that the phase reversals do not occur spaced too closely. As a rule of thumb, the internal field probably has its full effect when the wave function governing the excitation in the crystal keeps the dipoles in phase over a distance of about fifty molecular diameters, D.

Still another complication occurs; along with the electrostatic interaction there is also an effect which comes from the concerted action of the energy radiated by many distant molecules.* The radiation from a single molecule is weak, but a radiation field falls off only slowly, as D^{-1}, so that summing over the many distant molecules produces an appreciable effect. The strength of the *static* contribution may be assessed by thinking about the field strength at a bound electron, caused by a dipole a (nearest neighbor) distance D away

$$|\mathcal{E}_S| \sim \frac{ez}{D^3}$$

where z is a characteristic amplitude and e is the electronic charge. The field caused by many dipoles is of the same order, even considering the internal field. The *radiation* field acting on a bound electron is

$$|\mathcal{E}_R| = \frac{e\mathbf{r} \times [\mathbf{r} \times \dot{\mathbf{v}}]}{c^2 r^3}$$

$$\sim \frac{e\dot{v}}{c^2 r}$$

where $\dot{v}$ is the acceleration taking place at the distance r. For harmonic oscillation, this acceleration is $\omega^2 z$ where ω is the frequency. Let us also put

* J. J. Hopfield, *Phys. Rev.*, **112** (1958), 1555. See also V. M. Agranovich, *J. Exptl. Theoret. Phys.* (U.S.S.R.), **37** (1959), 430.

$r \sim \lambda$, a wavelength associated with this frequency according to $c = \omega\lambda$. This gives

$$|\mathcal{E}_R| \sim \frac{ez}{\lambda^3}$$

If this is to be comparable to the static part (as asserted), we need to have

$$\frac{ez}{\lambda^3} \sim \frac{ez}{D^3}$$

Thus the integrated effect of all the radiating molecules must bring in the factor $(\lambda/D)^3$, which is the number of molecules in a cube λ on a side. It is found that, for molecular crystals large with respect to λ, there is indeed a radiation contribution, limited by retardation effectively to all the molecules in a cube of wavelength equal to the wavelength in vacuum—provided, however, that the crystal wave function makes the accelerations in this block go with the same phase. The field has a sense so as to give a blue shift, and this blue shift is much more strongly dependent on having all the instantaneous dipoles in phase than for the static part. Thus if the wavelength governing the distribution of excitation in the crystal is fifty or so molecular diameters, this effectively means that the radiation contributions from the molecules in the λ^3 block will be self-canceling. Experiments which confirm this picture have been carried out through measurements of the reflection spectrum*; however, considerable experimental and theoretical work remains to be done.

We return to the project at hand, which is to treat the static interaction in a large sample in a way analogous to our treatment of just two oscillators. (This was first done by Davydov.)† For this purpose we shall consider a two-dimensional crystal, a slab of material normal to the propagation direction of the light. We shall assume strong coupling. At least for the slab itself there is no internal field correction, and it will be shown that the sums converge. Besides, there is no radiation correction because there are not sufficient molecules to contribute (it takes a three-dimensional collection). A portion of the two-dimensional crystal may be pictured for definiteness as in Fig. 4.6. The directions of oscillation in the local $\mathfrak{z}$ direction are given by the lines, and the oscillators are assumed located at the dots.

The potential is the sum of all pairwise interactions, and assuming a

* B. G. Anex and W. T. Simpson, *Revs. Mod. Phys.*, **32** (1960), 466.

† A. S. Davydov, *Theory of Molecular Excitations* (New York: McGraw-Hill Book Company, Inc. 1962), translated by M. Kasha and M. Oppenheimer, Jr. (Note supplementary references on p. 165 including references to key papers by H. Winston and D. P. Craig).

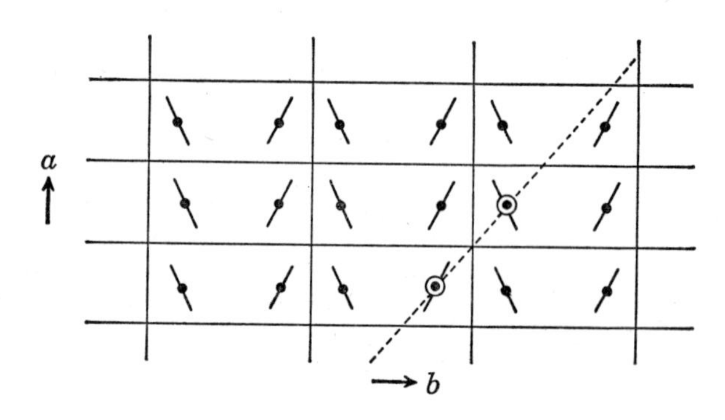

Figure 4.6

single oscillator in each molecule, we have a typical term from the molecules joined by the dashed line, as in Fig. 4.7. This is almost like the example of two parallel oscillators, already considered. In order to include this and even more general examples, we treat the three-dimensional case. As before, we simplify by assuming the local $\bar{x}$ and $\bar{y}$ oscillators will not come in. The angles are similar to the conventional ones used with spherical polar coordinates, and the r of spherical polar coordinates becomes $\bar{z}$. This gives

$$z = \bar{z} \cos \theta$$

$$y = \bar{z} \sin \theta \sin \varphi$$

$$x = \bar{z} \sin \theta \cos \varphi$$

for the i and also for the j oscillator, to be substituted in Eq. (4.2b)

$$\frac{-2z_i z_j + y_i y_j + x_i x_j}{D^3}$$

The result is

$$V_{ij} = (-2 \cos \theta_i \cos \theta_j + \sin \theta_i \sin \varphi_i \sin \theta_j \sin \varphi_j + \sin \theta_i \cos \varphi_i \sin \theta_j \cos \varphi_j)\, \bar{z}_i \bar{z}_j / D^3 \tag{4.10}$$

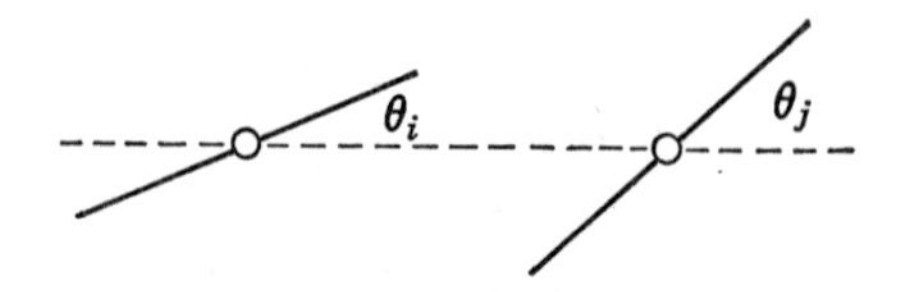

Figure 4.7

Going now to the case of oscillators in the xz plane ($\varphi = 0$), we have the required generalization of Eq. (4.6)

$$V_{ij} = \frac{(-2 \cos \theta_i \cos \theta_j + \sin \theta_i \sin \theta_j)\, \bar{z}_i \bar{z}_j}{D^3} \tag{4.10a}$$

also

$$V = \sum_{i<j} V_{ij} \tag{4.11}$$

The unperturbed first excited state is N-fold degenerate, where N is the number of oscillators. Instead of setting up a very large secular equation, we shall calculate the energy of the particular state in this degenerate manifold which is reached in an allowed transition, polarized a (Fig. 4.6). With this limited objective, we can just as well take $N \rightarrow \infty$, as will become apparent.

The correct wave function must have the phases of the oscillations reinforcing (like $|+\rangle$ for two oscillators), this because the propagation direction of the light is normal to the slab with the electric vector lying in the plane. For example, we should have as a picture of the wave function

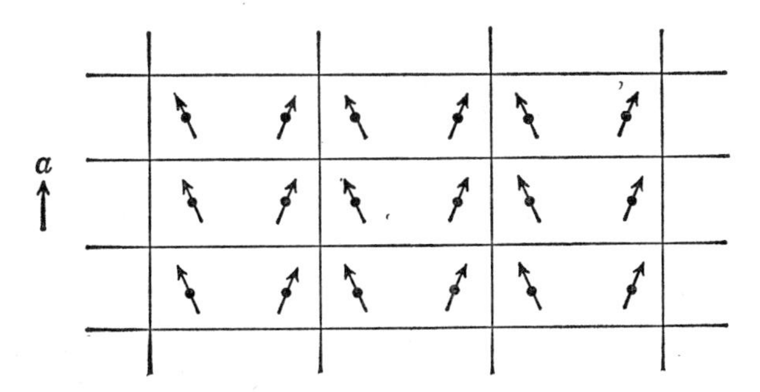

Figure 4.8

for the state reached in the a transition that given in Fig. 4.8. The function is a sum of products, a typical product being

$$|j\rangle = |00)\,|01) \cdots |0i)\,|1j)\,|0k) \cdots |0N)$$

where $|1j)$ signifies that the excitation is at the jth position. The correct many-particle function for a-polarized light is

$$|+a\rangle = N^{-1/2} \sum_{j=0}^{N} |j\rangle$$

Since all oscillators are equivalent, in the limit of an infinite crystal, the coefficients of the individual terms are all the same.

The correction to the energy is the expectation value of V, (4.11),

$$\langle +a \mid V \mid +a \rangle = \frac{1}{N} \sum_{i=0}^{N} \langle i \mid V \sum_{s=0}^{N} \mid s \rangle$$

which may be simplified (if boundary effects are ignored) by using only one term on the left and multiplying by N

$$= \frac{N}{N} (00| \, (01| \ldots (0i| \, (1j| \, (0k| \ldots (0N| \, V \sum_{s=0}^{N} |s\rangle$$

This is our main result, according to which we can calculate the energy correction by assuming that the excitation is localized on an interior oscillator, here called the jth. We then have to evaluate the lattice sum over all s, a typical term of which is

$$(01| \, (02| \ldots (0i| \, (1j| \, (0k| \ldots (0N \mid V \mid 01) \, |02) \ldots |0r) \, |1s) \, |0t) \ldots |0N)$$
$$= (1j| \, (0s \mid V_{js} \mid 0j) \, |1s)$$

In this term, we have only V_{js} Eq. (4.10a) giving anything because $(0 \mid \bar{z} \mid 0) = 0$ for the other $\bar{z}_i$'s. After integration we therefore find that each term contains the local transition moment length $(0 \mid \bar{z} \mid 1)$ (squared) together with functions of the angles and the distance from the jth to the molecule being considered. Naturally, many terms in the lattice sum will be identical, which simplifies things (without any formal group theory being required).

The calculation for the b-allowed transition is entirely analogous. Of course for this transition, the phases of the various product functions $|j\rangle$ will be different. If the local phases have already been defined so that for the a transition the signs are all positive in $|+a\rangle$, then there will be negative signs for half the functions in $|+b\rangle$ corresponding to the picture of the instantaneous dipoles given in Fig. 4.9.

The lattice sum for the two-dimensional case converges, as can be seen going to the extreme of considering that all pairwise interactions of the various oscillators contribute to lower the energy. The sum is then, roughly speaking,

$$\text{const} \int_{1}^{\infty} \frac{n}{D^3} D dD$$

where n is the number of oscillators per unit area. The same type of argument in the three-dimensional case leads to the conclusion that the sum diverges logarithmically. Even when the signs are considered, a convergent result for the lattice sum in this case is not easy to obtain owing to the appearance of "surface" contributions (on summation or integration outward from a molecule in question). As noted above, the correct treat-

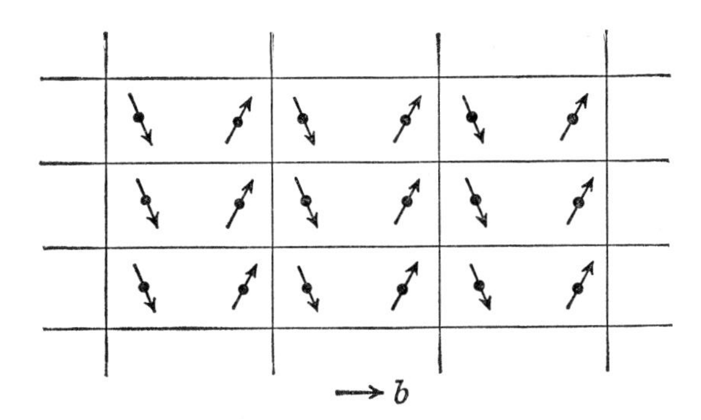

Figure 4.9

ment of these effects leads to an extra term in the energy coming from the internal field.

The lattice sums in the three-dimensional case require the computation of pairwise interactions in three-space Eq. (4.10), but this is completely analogous to the computation in two-space. The interaction matrix elements are functions of the distance, and mutual orientation of the dipoles, and bring in the constant $(0 \mid \bar{z} \mid 1)$.

In closing this section on the electrostatic contribution to molecular electronic energies, it should be declared that the examples we have been using are far from general. Note that in Fig. 4.9 as well as in Fig. 4.8 all moments for molecules which are translationally equivalent have the same phase. If there are n molecules per unit cell there are n ways of combining the several all-in-phase functions, although not always to give an allowed transition. If all the molecules are equivalent, the proper combinations are obtainable by symmetry, and that is what was done in the example above (Fig. 4.8 and Fig. 4.9) in order to get the a- and b-axis allowed transitions. If the oscillators are not equivalent, one cannot use symmetry but must solve a secular equation. Consider the example in Fig. 4.10. The unit cell is represented on the left, and the all-in-phase functions are

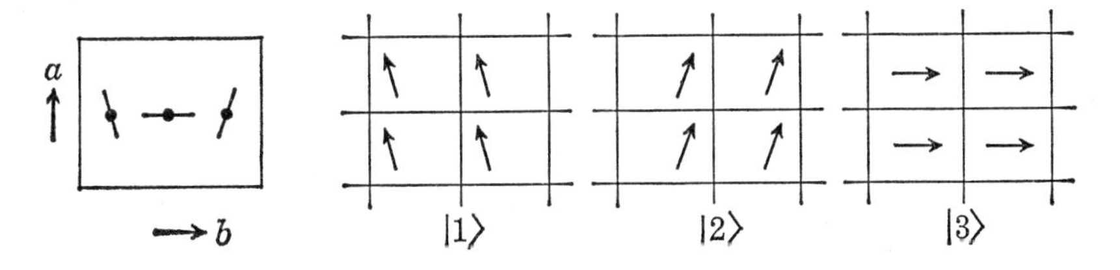

Figure 4.10

depicted on the right. We should have $|1\rangle - |2\rangle$ (determined by symmetry, as in Fig. 4.9) mixing with $|3\rangle$ to give two b-axis transitions.

4.6 TIME-DEPENDENT PROCESSES

We now return to the consideration of two parallel oscillators lined up along the z axis end to end (Fig. 4.2, $\theta = 0$). This time, however, we shall examine the non-stationary states. As we have seen, the correct zero-order functions in a perturbation calculation for the first degenerate level are

$$|\pm\rangle = 2^{-1/2}\,[|1a)\,|0b) \pm |0a)\,|1b)] \qquad (4.12)$$

The corresponding time-dependent functions are

$$|\pm, t\rangle = |\pm\rangle\, e^{-2\pi i E_{\pm} t/h} \qquad (4.12a)$$

where the E_+ and E_- are the first-order total energies. The difference, $E_- - E_+$, is positive when the oscillators are end for end ($\langle 1 \mid V \mid 2\rangle < 0$). In any case, the unperturbed energy cancels, giving,

$$\Delta E = E_- - E_+ = -2\,\langle 1 \mid V \mid 2\rangle \qquad (4.13)$$

Suppose we start with an unexcited oscillator, b, and shoot an excited oscillator, a, at it. It is then reasonable to take for the wave function—notation of Eq. (4.4)

$$|1\rangle = |1a)\,|0b)$$

This is not a stationary state and so the probability amplitude will change with time. To see how, we must write $|1a)\,|0b)$ as a solution at a particular time of the Schrödinger equation

$$i\frac{h}{2\pi}\frac{d}{dt} = H$$

The general solution of this equation—not in the notation of Eq. (4.4) is

$$\sum_j c_j \mid j, t\rangle = \sum_j c_j \mid j\rangle\, e^{-2\pi i E_j t/h}$$

where the $|j\rangle$ are energy eigenfunctions and the c's are independent of time. In the limit of a very small perturbation, we treat $|+\rangle$ and $|-\rangle$ as exact energy eigenfunctions. Then the following, see Eq. (4.12a)

$$|1, t\rangle = 2^{-1/2}\,[|+, t\rangle + |-, t\rangle] \qquad (4.14)$$

is a solution of the Schrödinger equation. Moreover, at $t = 0$ it goes over into

$$2^{-1/2}\,[|+\rangle + |-\rangle]$$

which, on application of Eq. (4.12), becomes

$$|1a)\,|0b) = |1\rangle$$

We now have the means to see how the non-stationary state in question changes with time.

Let us multiply $|1, t\rangle$ by an arbitrary complex number

$$e^{2\pi i E_+ t_1/h}$$

This cannot cause any physical change, though now the function becomes

$$2^{-1/2} \left[|+\rangle\, e^{-2\pi i E_+ t/h}\, e^{2\pi i E_+ t_1/h} + |-\rangle\, e^{-2\pi i E_- t/h}\, e^{2\pi i E_+ t_1/h}\right]$$

When the time, t, reaches the parameter, t_1, this is

$$2^{-1/2} \left[|+\rangle + |-\rangle\, e^{-2\pi i \Delta E t_1/h}\right]$$

where ΔE is as in Eq. (4.13). If t_1 is selected so that

$$\frac{\Delta E t_1}{h} = \frac{1}{2} \tag{4.15}$$

we find that the function $|-\rangle$ comes in with a minus sign

$$e^{2\pi i E_+ t_1/h}\, |1, h/2\Delta E\rangle = 2^{-1/2} \left[|+\rangle - |-\rangle\right]$$

and using Eq. (4.12) we find this is $|2\rangle$ in the notation of Eq. (4.4). That is,

$$|1, 0\rangle = |1\rangle = |1a)\,|0b)$$

$$|1, h/2\Delta E\rangle = |2\rangle = |0a)\,|1b)$$

—the excitation travels over onto b in a time $h/2\Delta E$. Arguing similarly, we find the frequency for motion of the excitation to be given by the full ΔE:

$$\nu = \frac{\Delta E}{h}$$

We can avoid having to introduce the phase factor by working with probability density rather than probability amplitude. Let us therefore compute $|1, t\rangle\,\langle 1, t|$ and observe the same cyclic variation. Again using Eq. (4.12a) we find*

$$\begin{aligned} |1, t\rangle\,\langle 1, t| &= \tfrac{1}{2} \left[|+, t\rangle\,\langle +, t| + |+, t\rangle\,\langle -, t| + |-, t\rangle\,\langle +, t| + |-, t\rangle\langle -, t|\right] \\ &= \tfrac{1}{2} \left[|+\rangle\,\langle +| + (e^{2\pi i \Delta E t/h} + e^{-2\pi i \Delta E t/h})\, |+\rangle\,\langle -| + |-\rangle\,\langle -|\right] \\ &= \frac{1}{2} \left[|+\rangle\,\langle +| + |-\rangle\,\langle -|\right] + \cos 2\pi \frac{\Delta E t}{h}\, |+\rangle\,\langle -| \end{aligned}$$

This expression is familiar in that it contains an independent systems part and a modulating term, only now the modulating term depends on the time. At $t = 0$, we have

* We put $|+\rangle\,\langle -| = |-\rangle\,\langle +|$ because we are using only the part on the diagonal.

$$\tfrac{1}{2}\,[|+\rangle\langle+| + 2|+\rangle\langle-| + |-\rangle\langle-|] = 2^{-1/2}\,[|+\rangle + |-\rangle]\,2^{-1/2}\,[\langle+| + \langle-|] = [|1a)\,(1a|]\,[|0b)\,(0b|]$$

(density matrix for the excitation initially on a). At a time t such that the cross term comes in with a minus sign, this is

$$2^{-1/2}\,[|+\rangle - |-\rangle]\,2^{-1/2}\,[\langle+| - \langle-|] = [|0a)\,(0a|]\,[|1b)\,(1b|]$$

(density matrix for the excitation over on b). The earliest time this happens after $t = 0$ is again given by Eq. (4.15).

A somewhat different mathematical analysis becomes necessary when ΔE is so small that the transfer takes place with a probability comparable to the probability for dissipative effects. In this case, we calculate the coefficient (see Eq. 4.14)

$$k(t) = |0a)\,|1b)\,\langle 1, t|$$

expressing the infinitesimal probability that the b oscillator has picked up the excitation when very little time has elapsed after one knows the excitation is on a. Carrying out the integration we find for the amplitude

$$k(t) = 2^{-1/2}\,(e^{2\pi i E_{+}t/h} - e^{2\pi i E_{-}t/h})$$

so that the probability is

$$w(t) = k^*k = \frac{1 - \cos 2\pi\,\Delta E t}{h}$$

Expanding about $t = 0$ we have

$$w(t) = \frac{2\pi^2(\Delta E)^2 t^2}{h^2} + \ldots \tag{4.16}$$

The first appearance of excitation on the b oscillator (which we visualize as standing to the right of the a oscillator) is described by a probability proportional to the square of the split of the degenerate pair Eq. (4.13). This split (oscillators end for end) is

$$\Delta E = \frac{4(1a|\,(0b\,|\,\bar{z}_a\,\bar{z}_b\,|\,0a)\,|1b)}{D^3}$$

so we see that the probability of the right-hand oscillator's picking up the excitation is proportional to

$$(0b\,|\,\bar{z}_b\,|\,1b)^2$$

the square of the "transition moment length." This calculation shows most of the features of the interaction of a quantum mechanical system (like b) with light (like a). The non-stationary state $|1\rangle$ is created when the light is turned on.

To explore the analogy a little further, we note that if we had started with n units of excitation on the left, the degenerate manifold would be different but still a splitting would occur

$$4(n, a|\ (0b\ |\ \bar{z}_a\ \bar{z}_b\ |\ n - 1, a)\ |1b)$$

In its dependence on conditions on the left, the probability Eq. (4.16) then depends on the square of the $\bar{z}_a$ matrix element, namely,

$$(n, a\ |\ \bar{z}_a\ |\ n - 1, a)^2$$

This matrix element, for a harmonic vibration (as for the radiation field), is

$$\text{const}\ \sqrt{n}$$

so the probability, $w(t)$, is proportional to n, the square, or equivalently, to the energy of the radiation oscillator. This, in turn, for large n is proportional to the square of the field strength, $(\mathcal{E}_z)^2$.

Going back to the right-hand oscillator, b, there is nothing about the theory which says that the wave functions must be harmonic oscillator functions or that there has to be just one particle involved. This gives the general result for the probability of "absorption of light"

$$w_{ij}\ (t) = \text{const}\ (\mathcal{E}_z)^2\ \langle i|\ \sum_{\nu} z_\nu\ |\ j\rangle^2\ t^2 \qquad (4.17)$$

The unperturbed energy interval between the ith and j^{th} states has to be the same as between two adjacent states of the radiation oscillator, because the whole treatment is based on degenerate perturbation theory. Since the light is harmonic, we have, independent of n, the energy interval

$$E_i^0 - E_j^0 = h\nu_{\text{light}}$$

which is the Bohr frequency condition.

The occurrence of t^2 in Eq. (4.17) is out of line with what is found experimentally. This occurs because during the time for which the expansion used with Eq. (4.16) is valid, and considering excitation with a broad band of frequencies, the number of radiation oscillators effectively equal in energy to $E_i^0 - E_j^0$ actually changes with time. A detailed treatment* leads to the result that the range of frequencies, $\Delta\nu$, about $(E_i^0 - E_j^0)/h$ narrows according to the uncertainty principle

$$(h\Delta\nu)t \sim h$$

* L. I. Schiff, *Quantum Mechanics* (New York: McGraw-Hill Book Company, Inc., 1949), sec. 29.

so that

$$\Delta\nu \sim \frac{1}{t}$$

As time goes on having the range of frequencies narrow means that the number of oscillators that are effectively degenerate with the mechanical system decrease the same way. So, considering not just one radiation oscillator, we have the average result, modifying Eq. (4.17)

$$\overline{w}(t) = \frac{1}{t} \text{ const } w(t) = \text{const } t$$

The foregoing treatment carries through in much the same way in the case of spontaneous emission. In this case, the starting point is $|0a)\,|1b)$.

4.7 MOLECULES IN MOLECULES

In the treatment of the stationary states of two oscillators and also of molecular crystals we have used two main notions, which are only indirectly related. One is the idea of employing product functions (the independent systems approximation) as a basis for the perturbation treatment. The other is the adoption of coulombic interaction, albeit expressed as a power series. In this section, we shall apply the first idea without necessarily using the second.

It is a matter of common experience in chemistry that some groupings are much more polarizable than others, and it is also well known that some groups are insulating, in that charge transfer across them occurs with difficulty. For example, the succinic acid anion

```
   -O  H  H
    |  | /
    C—C       O
   //   \    //
  O      C—C
        /  \  \
       H    H  O-
```

may be considered as containing two polarizable carboxylate groups separated by the insulating $—CH_2–$ groups. The first strong ultraviolet absorption of carboxylate would come in about the same place (1730 Å) and have about the same intensity (transition moment length 0.7 A–0.8 Å) for all carboxylic acids. In consequence, one can quite reasonably think about an electronically excited carboxylate group, even though it might be extremely difficult to write down a wave function for it.

We can bring this together with the prior work on independent systems by writing wave functions for succinate in the pattern of Eq. (4.4)

$$
\begin{aligned}
|0\rangle &= |0a)\,|0b)\,|0c) \\
|1\rangle &= |1a)\,|0b)\,|0c) \\
|2\rangle &= |0a)\,|0b)\,|1c) \\
|3\rangle &= |0a)\,|1b)\,|0c)
\end{aligned}
$$

and so on

Thus, the ground and certain of the excited state functions are depicted as products referring to parts labeled a and c, the carboxylate groups, and a b part, the insulating methylene groups. Just where the left and right merge with the center is not specified. This is not unsatisfactory, because the matrix elements are obtained from experiment. We may imagine a Hamiltonian

$$H_a^0 + H_b^0 + H_c^0 + V$$

so that we have the unperturbed energy, for example,

$$
\begin{aligned}
\langle 1 \mid H_a^0 + H_b^0 + H_c^0 \mid 1\rangle \\
&= (1a \mid (0b \mid (0c \mid H_a^0 \mid 1a) \mid 0b) \mid 0c) + \text{and so on} \\
&= E_a^1 + E_b^0 + E_c^0
\end{aligned}
$$

This lies above the ground state unperturbed energy by an amount

$$E_a^1 - E_a^0 \equiv \alpha$$

This quantity can be equated to the observed transition energy for carboxylate as, for example, measured from the spectrum of acetate

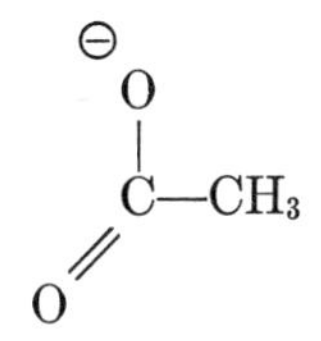

At this stage, we see that the off-diagonal matrix elements, as for example

$$\langle 1 \mid V \mid 2\rangle \equiv \beta$$

must be left undetermined. Nevertheless, consideration of the unperturbed energy allows us to classify the functions $|1\rangle$ and $|2\rangle$ as different from $|0\rangle$ and the high-energy $|\rangle$'s (like $|3\rangle$) and indeed as belonging to a degenerate manifold. The secular equation for this manifold is

$$\begin{vmatrix} \alpha - \lambda & \beta \\ \beta & \alpha - \lambda \end{vmatrix} = 0$$

showing that the carboxylate transition would be expected to split, giving a level diagram similar to the one for the two weakly interacting harmonic oscillators.

If the interaction is in fact too weak, we may not infer a value of β from the observed succinate ion spectrum, because the splitting is then only one of a number of small effects, all cooperating to make the carboxylate band different from that of acetate. Also, if the parts are too closely juxtaposed, the independent systems approach is no longer applicable owing to modifications brought in by the exchange. As a matter of fact, the interaction may be too weak for the example we have been using. (This particular example was selected as a sort of *reductio ad absurdum* to show the plausibility of an independent systems approach to parts of the same molecule.)

When the interaction is about the right strength, as it is, for example, in the polyenes, like butadiene

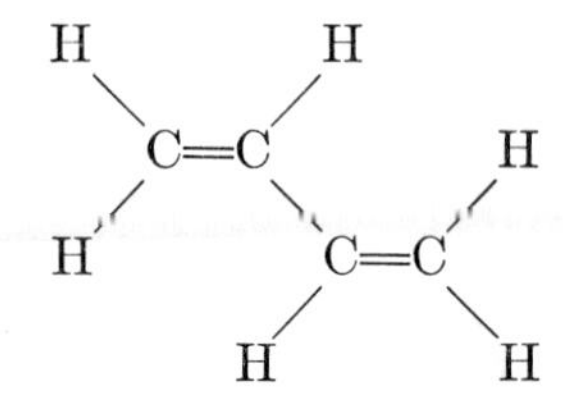

then it is possible to calculate β empirically by going to the spectrum of one compound and using this to calculate the spectrum of others. For hexatriene,

```
H         H
 \       /
  C==C        H
 /     \     /
H       C==C        H
       /     \     /
      H       C==C
             /     \
            H       H
```

we expect a secular equation describing the degenerate manifold to be as follows:

$$\begin{vmatrix} \alpha - \lambda & \beta & 0 \\ \beta & \alpha - \lambda & \beta \\ 0 & \beta & \alpha - \lambda \end{vmatrix} = 0$$

This has roots $\lambda - \alpha = \sqrt{2}\,\beta, 0, -\sqrt{2}\,\beta$. We may assume the phases have been chosen so as to make $\beta < 0$, so we have the energy level patterns for butadiene and hexatriene shown in Fig. 4.11. Using the first strong ultraviolet transition in say butene-1

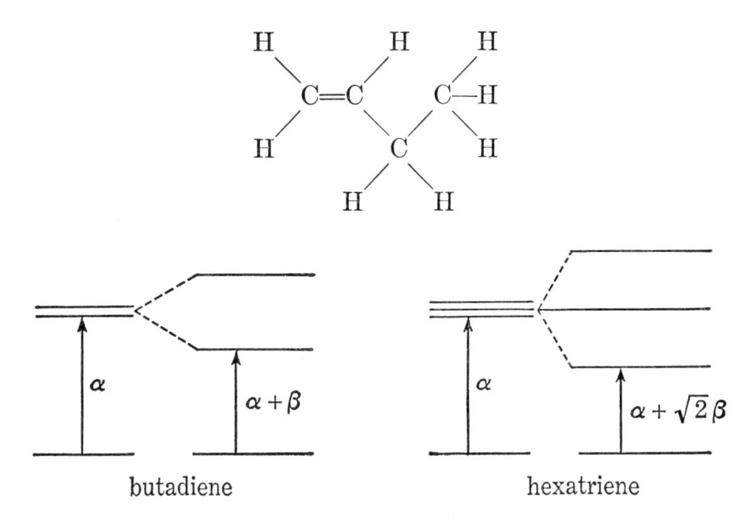

Figure 4.11

to find α, we can then evaluate β from either the butadiene or hexatriene spectrum and use it to "predict" where the related transition will come for the other compound.

There is a strong transition at 2500 Å–2600 Å for hexatriene which can in all probability be assigned as related in the foregoing sense to the transition for just one double bond (1700 Å–1750 Å for substituted ethylenes). Thus (using $\text{cm}^{-1} \times 10^4$), we take $\alpha = 5.8$ and $\alpha + \sqrt{2}\,\beta = 3.9$, which gives $\beta = -1.3$. Accordingly, the first transition energy for butadiene is predicted to be 4.5, a value which corresponds quite well with what is observed: absorption at around 210 mμ with a corresponding energy of 4.8.

All this has required our setting long-range interaction (the 1,3 matrix element in the secular equation for hexatriene) equal to zero. This is reasonable if we think the interaction is largely electrostatic, and it turns out to be all the more reasonable if the interaction involves local exchange effects (which if they involve only adjacent subsystems can be incorporated into an independent systems treatment).

To employ the independent systems model in the way previously illustrated requires no elaborate mathematics. But testing whether the model is truly applicable is a problem of considerable difficulty. Enlarging on this, let us recall that we have used four hydrogen atoms in a line or a closely related system (the π-electrons in butadiene) to help illustrate in succession the molecular orbital method, the valence bond method, and the independent systems model. If we compare theory with experiment within a narrow range of compounds and observed electronic energies, we can achieve a modest agreement for each approach, yet the approaches give wave functions and patterns of levels which are in many ways dissimilar.

We could, of course, decide which of the approaches is better in a given instance if we could compare with the results of a true quantum mechanical calculation. Lacking this, we must use as complete an experimental study as possible: frequencies, intensities, polarizations, multiplicities, calorimetric measurements on the ground state, and all this extended to whole families of molecules. In the comparison with experiment for the manifestly approximate theories, a perfect match is not to be expected. When an approximate match is obtained with more than one theoretical approach, then the problem is to compare the theories. Thus it might turn out, for example, that the molecular orbital wave function describing a given electronic state is actually quite similar to the valence bond function or the independent systems function. Such a comparison is easily made for the molecular orbital and valence bond state functions whenever each one involves the same atomic orbitals, because the amplitude for the "amount" of one function in another is the overlap integral. In order to calculate overlaps involving independent systems wave functions, one must write down an explicit function for each local state, whether excited or unexcited, using one of the other approaches.

When this is done for butadiene, it is found that the valence bond and independent systems functions are almost the same for the ground state, and not radically different from the molecular orbital function.* The latter appears not to describe the ground state as well, however, according to a consideration of much empirical evidence. For the excited states, the situation is less clear, in a large measure because the experimental situation itself is not at the present time sufficiently resolved. It appears that the first few strong transitions should not be associated with any of the valence bond excited functions we have found, because transitions to the excited states represented by these functions would be low in intensity. (Charge transfer states are not to be found in the permutation degeneracy block.) The excited state reached in the first strong transition may turn out to be fairly well described by a function intermediate between the first excited singlet found by the molecular orbital method and the one found by the independent systems method. These functions have the same symmetry, and are not as different as might be supposed even though extreme delocalization is present with the former.

Getting back to the subject of molecules in molecules, a few remarks are in order about our not using explicit wave functions. In this Spartan cir-

* For a comparison of these methods in which higher approximations are brought in see R. S. Berry, *J. Chem. Phys.*, **30** (1959), 937.

cumstance, it is more appropriate to use the Heisenberg representation, where the matrices themselves are the fundamental operator quantities and the representatives of the unperturbed states are simply unit vectors. For example, the preceding calculation for hexatriene would be considered as diagonalizing a block of a perturbed energy matrix

$$\begin{pmatrix} \alpha & \beta & 0 \\ \beta & \alpha & \beta \\ 0 & \beta & \alpha \end{pmatrix}$$

Generalizing, the technique we have been considering is a procedure for working up spectroscopic data using a pattern which is suggested by, and not inconsistent with, quantum mechanics. We have used essentially similar techniques before; in Chapter 3 in connection with the spatial degeneracy occurring with the ions H_n^+, and in connection with the Kekulé resonance in benzene. In each of these cases, what is being done is essentially a matrix diagonalization where the form of the matrix is inferred from a model and the values of the matrix elements are adapted from spectroscopic or related measurements.

If we cannot make accurate calculations for complex molecules, we can still assign transitions in accordance with this or that model. To be able to make such classifications of energy levels often requires only the crude forms of calculation which are at present possible. For example, one can tell whether or not exchange should be ruled out by making an order of magnitude calculation of an exchange integral. To be able to say that one model is applicable and another is not is a reasonable if restricted goal.

Appendix to Chapter 4

4.8 FORMULAS USED IN SPECTROPHOTOMETRY

The transition probability per unit time for absorption and emission of light can be calculated using a form of quantum electrodynamics in which all orders of perturbation theory higher than the first are neglected. This is not rigorous because the higher orders apparently make an infinite contribution. It turns out that the calculated first-order result is the same as obtained using a theory modified so as properly to handle the infinities. In order to apply the crude theory consistently, one must use the experimental mass and charge of an electron, which is convenient, although not obviously correct when considered in the light of the many ramifications of the full theory.

The results may be expressed in terms of the Einstein coefficients A and

B. The probability per unit time for absorption when the sample is randomly oriented* is

$$B\rho(\omega) = \frac{1}{3} | \langle 0 | \mu | 1 \rangle |^2 \frac{4\pi^2\rho(\omega)}{\hbar^2} \tag{4.18a}$$

and for emission is

$$B\rho(\omega) + A = B\rho(\omega) + \frac{1}{3} | \langle 0 | \mu | 1 \rangle |^2 \frac{4\omega^3}{\hbar c^3} \tag{4.18b}$$ †

The quantity $\rho(\omega)$ is the energy density of radiation, and has to be multiplied by both dv and $d\omega$ to give an energy. It is related to the average $\mathcal{E}$-field per unit frequency in that

$$\rho(\omega)\, d\omega = \frac{1}{4\pi} \bar{\mathcal{E}}^2 (\omega)\, d\omega$$

We shall now see how the formula for absorption may be used in connection with practical measurements on a spectrophotometer. Consider an element of a gas or a solution of length dx and surface ds intercepting the light beam as follows

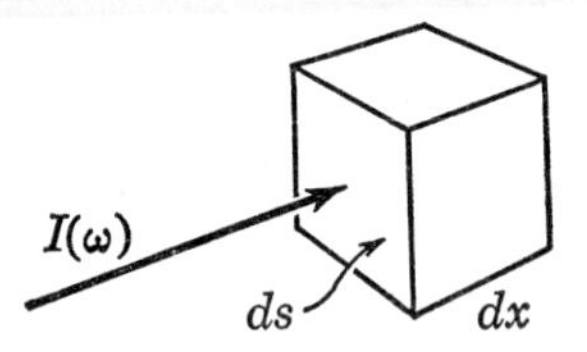

The energy passing across ds in time t is

$$I(\omega)\, d\omega\, ds\, t$$

which amounts to the definition of the intensity per unit frequency range, $I(\omega)$. The velocity is c, so in a time

$$t = \frac{dx}{c}$$

energy starting at the front surface would have just reached the back but not yet emerged. Therefore, the energy in the volume element of volume $ds\, dx$ is

$$\frac{1}{c} I(\omega)\, d\omega\, ds\, dx$$

so the energy density is

$$\rho(\omega) = \frac{I(\omega)}{c}$$

* When the transition moment of the molecule is parallel to the electric vector of the light, the factor, $\frac{1}{3}$, is omitted.

† L. Pauling and E. B. Wilson, Jr., *Introduction to Quantum Mechicans* (New York: McGraw-Hill Book Company, Inc., 1935), sec. 40.

Now for absorption, the transition probability is $B\rho(\omega)$, Eq. (4.18a), or for a broad electronic band with probability varying with the individual vibronic levels,

$$B(\omega)\,d\omega\,\rho(\omega) = \frac{B(\omega)\,d\omega\,I(\omega)}{c}$$

where $B(\omega)$ is an Einstein coefficient frequency density. In a time t, the number of molecules which have undergone transition is

$$\frac{n_0\,B(\omega)\,d\omega\,I(\omega)t}{c}$$

where n_0 is the number of molecules in the volume element

$$n_0 = \frac{ds\,dx\,Lk}{1000}$$

Here L is Avogadro's number and k is the concentration in moles per liter. The energy absorbed in the volume element is found by multiplying by $\hbar\omega$

$$dE = \frac{B(\omega)\,d\omega\,I(\omega)t}{c} \cdot \frac{ds\,dx\,Lk}{1000} \cdot \hbar\omega$$

The energy change per unit time for the light beam is equal to the change in flux from the front surface to the back surface so that also

$$dE = -d[I(\omega)\,d\omega]t\,ds$$

and these equations can be combined. The situation is changed in a succeeding volume element, in that the intensity of the light has diminished owing to the absorption. We therefore prepare to integrate the changes of intensity

$$\frac{dI(\omega)}{dx} = -\frac{B(\omega)I(\omega)\hbar\omega Lk}{1000c}$$

Note that no allowance is made for a change in concentration of the absorbing species. This is all right in most cases because the occasional molecule which absorbs light is returned to the ground state by dissipative processes in a time which is short with respect to the reciprocal of the transition probability for absorption.

Integrating from the front to the back of the absorption cell, we obtain

$$\ln\frac{I(\omega)^a}{I(\omega)^b} = \frac{B(\omega)\hbar\omega Lk(b-a)}{1000c}$$

With $b - a = l$, the cell thickness, and using the base 10,

$$D = \log\frac{I^0}{I} = \frac{B(\omega)\hbar\omega Lkl}{2.303 \cdot 1000c} \qquad (4.19)$$

In spectrophotometry, one has the Beer-Lambert law

$$D = \epsilon k l \quad (l \text{ in cm, } k \text{ in moles/liter})$$

Comparing with Eq. (4.19), one finds

$$\epsilon = \frac{B(\omega)\hbar\omega L}{2.303 \cdot 1000c}$$

This leads further to

$$\frac{1}{2.303}\int \frac{\epsilon\, d\omega}{\omega} = \int \epsilon d \log \omega = \frac{\hbar L}{2.303^2 \cdot 1000c}\int B(\omega)\, d\omega$$

Going back to Eq. (4.18a) for B or equivalently for $\int B(\omega)\, d\omega$ (say, the sum of all vibronic transition probabilities for a single electronic transition, as studied in Section 2.13), we obtain

$$\int \epsilon d \log \omega = \frac{\hbar L}{2.303^2 \cdot 1000c}\,\frac{1}{3}\,|\langle 0 \,|\, \boldsymbol{\mu} \,|\, 1\rangle|^2\,\frac{4\pi^2}{\hbar^2} \qquad (4.20a)$$

Note that $d \log \omega = d \log \nu = -d \log \lambda$, and so on. If we take the electronic charge into the constant part, in cgs units this becomes

$$\int \epsilon d \log \lambda = -1.090 \times 10^{19}\,|\langle 0 \,|\, \mathbf{q} \,|\, 1\rangle|^2 \qquad (4.20b)$$

where $\langle 0 \,|\, \mathbf{q} \,|\, 1\rangle$, the vector transition moment length, is

$$\langle 0 \,|\, \mathbf{q} \,|\, 1\rangle = \int \psi_0 \sum_\nu (\mathbf{i}x_\nu + \mathbf{j}y_\nu + \mathbf{k}z_\nu)\,\psi_1\, d\tau$$

Here ψ_0 and ψ_1 are electronic wave functions for some representative value of the nuclear coordinates, as explained in the Appendix to Chapter 2.

In the absence of incident radiation, the chance of a single molecule emitting is A. It is possible, using the integrated intensity of an electronic transition and Eq. (4.20b), to obtain an "observed" transition moment length and thus, using Eq. (4.18b), to find A*

$$A = \frac{4\pi^3}{\hbar c^3}\,\frac{e^2}{3}\,|\langle 0 \,|\, \mathbf{q} \,|\, 1\rangle|^2 \qquad (4.21a)$$

$$= 1.083 \times 10^{-23}\,\omega^3\,|\langle 0 \,|\, \mathbf{q} \,|\, 1\rangle|^2 \qquad (4.21b)$$

To get at the experimental significance of A, we first recall that, in a typical experiment, electronically excited molecules are in a quasi-thermal equilibrium in that the vibrational energy is distributed according to the Boltzmann distribution law. Except at very high temperatures, we can

* For visible light $\omega \sim 3 \times 10^{15}$ and $\langle 0 \,|\, q \,|\, 1\rangle \sim 10^{-8}$, giving $A \sim 3 \times 10^{7}\ \text{sec}^{-1}$.

assume that a representative molecule is in the ground vibrational level of the excited electronic state. Transitions will occur into the sea of vibrational levels of the ground electronic state, but by an argument similar to the one for absorption, the integrated transition probability is obtained from the pure electronic transition moment (as discussed in Section 2.13). The number of molecules emitting radiation per second is nA if n is the total number of excited molecules, hence

$$-\frac{dn}{dt} = nA \qquad n = n_0 \, e^{-At}$$

The A^{-1} value is thus a fluorescence lifetime, obtainable from the decay characteristic. Fluorescence measurements therefore provide an independent possibility for obtaining an experimental transition moment length.

4.9 OSCILLATOR STRENGTH

All the transition probability for the quantum jump of a harmonically bound electron is to an adjacent level. Anharmonicity in effect spreads the probability so that jumps to non-adjacent levels have appreciable strengths, but at the expense of the intensity for the jump to the adjacent level. Thus it is informative to compare observed absorption intensity, represented by the transition moment length squared, with what would be a bigger number, the same quantity calculated for harmonic binding. The transition moment length squared for an electron, harmonically bound, is the "ideal"

$$\frac{(n+1)\hbar}{2M\omega} \tag{4.22}$$

where M is the mass of the electron, n is the quantum number of the originating level, and $n + 1$ is the quantum number of the final level. (For an isotropically bound electron, one must take three times this amount, but this is inappropriate in applications to molecules, for which excitation almost invariably involves a change in but a single electronic mode of motion.) For transitions from an unexcited orbital, the ratio of actual to ideal, (using Eq. (4.22) with $n = 0$), is

$$f_{0i} \equiv |\,(0\,|\,\mathfrak{z}_\nu\,|\,i)\,|^2\, 2M\frac{\omega}{\hbar} = |\,(0\,|\,\mathfrak{z}_\nu\,|\,i)\,|^2 \frac{2M}{\hbar^2}(E_i - E_0) \tag{4.23}$$

where f_{0i} is called the *one-dimensional oscillator strength*—here $\mathfrak{z}$ is taken as having the same direction as $\mathbf{q}$ in Eq. (4.20b).

We now prove* that the sum over all transitions from the first orbital can only equal the value for the first transition for an electron harmonically bound; that is,

$$\sum_i f_{0i} = 1 \qquad (4.24)$$

We shall use the notation of wave functions. There is a general relation between the matrix elements of two operators, $\partial/\partial z$ and z, which we have to prove first. The starting point is two solutions of the energy eigenvalue expression

$$\nabla^2 \psi_0 + \frac{2M}{\hbar^2}(E_0 - V)\psi_0 = 0$$

$$\nabla^2 \psi_i^* + \frac{2M}{\hbar^2}(E_i - V)\psi_i^* = 0$$

Multiplying the first equation by $\psi_i^* z$ and the second by $\psi_0 z$, and integrating, gives

$$\int \psi_i^* z \nabla^2 \psi_0 \, d\tau + \frac{2M}{\hbar^2} E_0 \int \psi_i^* z \psi_0 \, d\tau - \frac{2M}{\hbar^2} \int \psi_i^* z V \psi_0 \, d\tau = 0$$

$$\int \psi_0 z \nabla^2 \psi_i^* \, d\tau + \frac{2M}{\hbar^2} E_i \int \psi_0 z \psi_i^* \, d\tau - \frac{2M}{\hbar^2} \int \psi_0 z V \psi_i^* \, d\tau = 0$$

Subtracting, we obtain

$$\int [\psi_i^* z \nabla^2 \psi_0 - \psi_0 z \nabla^2 \psi_i^*] \, d\tau = \frac{2M}{\hbar^2}(E_i - E_0) z_{0i}$$

However,

$$\psi_i^* \nabla^2 (z\psi_0) = \psi_i^* z \nabla^2 \psi_0 + 2\psi_i^* \frac{\partial}{\partial z} \psi_0$$

so that the expression on the left-hand side becomes

$$\int \left[\psi_i^* \nabla^2 (z\psi_0) - 2\psi_i^* \frac{\partial}{\partial z} \psi_0 - \psi_0 z \nabla^2 \psi_i^*\right] d\tau$$

It can be shown by Green's theorem that the volume integral of the terms containing ∇^2 is equal to a surface integral, and assuming the ψ_i^* and ψ_0 to vanish at infinity, the surface integral itself is zero. This gives the general relation (which, incidentally, is sometimes used in connection with the computation of z_{0i}),

$$-2\left(\frac{\partial}{\partial z}\right)_{0i} = \frac{2M}{\hbar^2}(E_i - E_0) z_{0i}$$

We can now prove the sum rule. First, we combine with Eq. (4.23), obtaining

$$f_{0i} = -2\left(\frac{\partial}{\partial z}\right)_{0i} z_{0i}$$

* This follows the treatment given by N. F. Mott and I. N. Sneddon, *Wave Mechanics and Its Application* (New York: Oxford University Press, 1948), chap. 7.

so that the sum becomes

$$\sum_i f_{0i} = -2 \sum_i z_{0i} \left(\frac{\partial}{\partial z}\right)_{0i}$$

The summation is then equivalent to the computation of the matrix element of the product dynamical variable in the 0,0 position, so we have

$$\sum_i f_{0i} = -2 \int \psi_0 \, z \frac{\partial}{\partial z} \psi_0 \, d\tau$$

Integrating by parts gives

$$\int \psi_0 \, z \frac{\partial}{\partial z} \psi_0 \, d\tau = \psi_0 \, z \psi_0 \Big]_{-\infty}^{+\infty} - \int \psi_0 \psi_0 \, d\tau - \int \psi_0 \, z \frac{\partial}{\partial z} \psi_0 \, d\tau$$

so that the integral is $-\frac{1}{2}$ and the sum rule, Eq. (4.24), is proved.

As shown in Section 2.10, the transition moment for a transition from a doubly-filled orbital has a factor $2^{1/2}$, so that the intensity doubles. In the light of the foregoing theorem, it is seen that a one-dimensional oscillator strength of two is then a theoretical limit.

It is tempting to conclude that one-dimensional oscillator strengths greater than 2 show that more than two electrons must be involved, indicating the breakdown of the orbital approximation. This conclusion is mistaken, because the intensity for a harmonically bound electron Eq. (4.22) has the additional factor $n + 1$ where n is the quantum number of the originating orbital. For a simple dyelike molecule, the highest filled molecular orbital has already several nodes in the direction of oscillation, hence the potentiality for the development of higher intensity than the theoretical maximum based on an electron, harmonically bound, but in its ground state. In any event, oscillator strength is the ratio defined above with $n = 0$, Eq. (4.23).

For a practical calculation of the one-dimensional oscillator strength, we start from Eq. (4.20a) except with an average frequency outside the integral sign

$$|\langle 0 \,|\, \mathfrak{q} \,|\, 1\rangle|^2 \approx \frac{1}{\omega} \int \epsilon \, d\omega \, \frac{3 \cdot 2.303 \cdot 1000c}{L} \, \frac{\hbar}{4\pi^2 e^2}$$

Dividing by the theoretical maximum $\hbar/2M\omega$ gives the oscillator strength. After rearrangement, this is

$$f \approx \frac{3 \cdot 2.303 \cdot 1000c^2 M}{L\pi e^2} \int \epsilon \, d\bar{\nu} \tag{4.25}$$

where $\bar{\nu}$ is in cm^{-1}. The constant is 1.296×10^{-8}. A formula which frequently finds use in the literature is that for the three-dimensional oscillator strength, in which case the constant is 0.432×10^{-8}.*

* R. S. Mulliken, *J. Chem. Phys.*, 7 (1939), 14.

The area under the absorption curve (also the fluorescence lifetime) is related to the index of refraction, conveniently through the oscillator strength. This relationship will be explored in the following section.

4.10 TIME-DEPENDENT POLARIZABILITY

If H^0 is independent of the time, with time-dependent energy eigenvectors $|j, t\rangle$, and H' is time dependent, it is readily shown that the Schrödinger equation takes the form

$$i\hbar \frac{dc_j}{dt} = \sum_k c_k \langle j, t \mid H' \mid k, t\rangle \tag{4.26}$$

Solution of Eq. 4.26 for the c's then allows one to write down state vectors with the correct time dependence

$$\sum_j c_j(t) \mid j, t\rangle \tag{4.27}$$

where the coefficients change with time.

Now we assume

$$H' = -\sum_\nu e_\nu z_\nu \mathcal{E}_z \cos \omega t$$

where $\mathcal{E}_z \cos \omega t$ is the time-dependent effective field polarized along the molecule (compare with the treatment in Section 4.4). We shall use $c_0 = 1$ all other $c_k = 0$ on the right-hand side of Eq. (4.26), which is a form of perturbation theory.* Moreover, we shall consider only the first transition as pertinent, so we are concerned with how the excited state $|1, t\rangle$ comes in. Thus we obtain for the coefficient

$$\frac{dc_1}{dt} = \frac{i}{\hbar} e\mathcal{E}_z \langle 1 \mid z \mid 0\rangle e^{+i\omega_1 t} e^{-i\omega_0 t} \frac{1}{2} [e^{i\omega t} + e^{-i\omega t}]$$

where the matrix element over the electric moment is computed from the time independent wave functions

$$e\langle 1 \mid z \mid 0\rangle = e \int \psi_1^* \sum_\nu z_\nu \psi_0 \, d\tau$$

Let us further abbreviate $\omega_1 - \omega_0$ to ω_1, giving

$$\frac{dc_1}{dt} = ie\mathcal{E}_z \frac{\langle 1 \mid z \mid 0\rangle}{2\hbar} [e^{i(\omega_1+\omega)t} + e^{i(\omega_1-\omega)t}]$$

This may be immediately integrated

$$c_1 = e\mathcal{E}_z \frac{\langle 1 \mid z \mid 0\rangle}{2\hbar} \left[\frac{e^{i(\omega_1+\omega)t}}{\omega_1+\omega} + \frac{e^{i(\omega_1-\omega)t}}{\omega_1-\omega}\right] + \text{const}$$

* The time dependence of the c's is assumed not to produce much change away from the initial conditions.

The solution, Eq. (4.27), is now determined in the sense of perturbation theory. The electric moment expectation value is computed to be

$$e\langle z(t)\rangle = \int (\psi_0^* \, e^{+i\omega_0 t} + c_1^* \, \psi_1^* \, e^{+i\omega_1 t}) \, e \sum_\nu z_\nu$$

$$(\psi_0 \, e^{-i\omega_0 t} + c_1 \, \psi_1 \, e^{-i\omega_1 t}) \, d\tau$$

or, with $\omega_1 - \omega_0$ called ω_1 and neglecting both the static moment and $| c_1 |^2$,

$$= e\langle 1 \mid z \mid 0\rangle \, [c_1^* \, e^{+i\omega_1 t} + c_1 \, e^{-i\omega_1 t}]$$

Substituting the part of c_1 and c_1^* that is not constant (which substitution gives the part of $e\langle z(t)\rangle$ resulting from the applied frequency, ω)

$$= e^2 \mathcal{E}_z \frac{\langle 1 \mid z \mid 0\rangle^2}{2\hbar} \left[\frac{e^{-i\omega t}}{\omega_1 + \omega} + \frac{e^{-i\omega t}}{\omega_1 - \omega} + \frac{e^{i\omega t}}{\omega_1 + \omega} + \frac{e^{i\omega t}}{\omega_1 - \omega} \right]$$

$$= e^2 \mathcal{E}_z \frac{\langle 1 \mid z \mid 0\rangle^2}{\hbar} \cos \omega t \left[\frac{1}{\omega_1 - \omega} + \frac{1}{\omega_1 + \omega} \right]$$

whence (dividing by the effective field) the polarizability is

$$\alpha = 2e^2 \frac{\langle 1 \mid z \mid 0\rangle^2}{\hbar} \frac{\omega_1}{\omega_1^2 - \omega^2}$$

The formula for the one-dimensional oscillator strength, Eq. (4.23), is

$$f_{0i} = \frac{2\langle 1 \mid z \mid 0\rangle^2 M\omega_1}{\hbar}$$

in terms of which the polarizability becomes

$$\alpha = \frac{e^2}{M} \frac{f_{0i}}{\omega_1^2 - \omega^2}$$

The classical expression is $(e^2/M)(1/\omega_1^2 - \omega^2)$ for the case in which the oscillator with frequency ω_1 is harmonic. Since for quantal harmonic oscillators also $f_{0i} = 1$, the quantum mechanical result matches the classical result. With several transitions having to be considered, the contributions are additive, giving the final result

$$\alpha = \frac{e^2}{M} \sum_i \frac{f_{0i}}{\omega_i^2 - \omega^2} \qquad (4.28)$$

Maxwell's equations in macroscopic form allow one directly to derive an expression for n, the index of refraction

$$n^2 - 1 = \frac{4\pi P}{\mathcal{E}}$$

where $P/\mathcal{E}$ is the polarization per unit average field in the medium, and P itself is the dipole per unit volume or bulk polarization. It is straightforward to compute the bulk polarization from the molecular polarizability

$$P = \mathcal{E}_{\text{eff}}\, \alpha N$$

where N is the number of molecules per unit volume and $\mathcal{E}_{\text{eff}}$ is the field acting on a molecule. As a rough approximation, the effective field is also the macroscopic Maxwell $\mathcal{E}$ field inside the dielectric, an assumption which, in conjunction with Eq. (4.28), leads directly to the Sellmeier formula

$$n^2 - 1 = \frac{4\pi N e^2}{M} \sum_i \frac{f_{0i}}{\omega_i^2 - \omega^2} = \sum_i \frac{(\omega_p)_i^2}{\omega_i^2 - \omega^2}$$

where ω_p is called a *plasma frequency*. A more comprehensive treatment leads to the Clausius-Mosotti equation

$$\frac{n^2 - 1}{n^2 + 2} = \frac{1}{3} \frac{4\pi N e^2}{M} \sum_i \frac{f_{0i}}{\omega_i^2 - \omega^2}$$

but here, as well, uncertainty about $\mathcal{E}_{\text{eff}}$ intrudes. It is probably correct to use the Clausius-Mosotti equation if the ω_i's are taken as frequencies for fairly large spherical collections of single molecules. These frequencies are calculable from the actual single-molecule frequency modified by the electrostatic perturbation, using the methods of this chapter and the assumption of strong coupling.

Index

Boldface numbers refer to sections.